MATHEMATICS IN YOUR WORLD

MATHEMATICS

Translated by P. S. MORRELL, B.A. (Dunelm)
and J. E. BLAMEY, B.A. (Dunelm)

Illustrated by WOLFGANG MENNINGER

IN YOUR WORLD

by K. W. MENNINGER

Published by THE VIKING PRESS · NEW YORK

Published in 1962 by The Viking Press, Inc.
625 Madison Avenue, New York 22, N.Y.

Library of Congress catalog card number: 62-8867

PRINTED IN THE U.S.A.

Contents

Introduction

This book is about the nature of mathematics and mathematical thought. It is not a textbook, from which one would learn how to solve an equation or calculate an integral, but a book to be read. One can dip into it and read any section without having to know what has gone before. At the same time the chapters are arranged in a logical sequence for those who prefer to read the book straight through. It is written for all who like—or dislike—mathematics, and also for a third kind of person, exemplified by a certain clever man who once said to me, "I love mathematics, but it doesn't love me!" The book's approach is thus completely informal; it is written in everyday language, without formulas, and there are numerous examples and little drawings. At times, the would-be calculator, equipped with simple school mathematics (falling short, however, of differential and integral calculus), is given a chance to see some exciting relationships in terms of symbols, but these passages are set in smaller print and can be ignored by the layman.

We encounter mathematics everywhere: we write on quarto- or octavo-size paper, and spot the winners for our football pools; we grind our coffee beans and roar in motor cars round the curves of our highways; we build great soaring bridges and insure our lives; we let our money increase in the bank and decrease in lotteries; we curse statistics, yet cannot live without them; we know that chance governs our lives but is itself, like all things, subject to some law; we might at times be surprised that a flea's skill at jumping is so far in excess of our own or an elephant's. It is in fact true that we come across mathematical principles everywhere in our lives, but we remain as a rule only hazily aware of their real nature and significance.

This book attempts, therefore, to give the ordinary reader some understanding of mathematical principles. Its method is to present familiar phenomena from our own surroundings, aspects so often neglected in school, and to show how a mathematician would think about them, by letting one look behind the scenes in the mathematical "workshop." The list of contents forms a ready guide to the "workshop." It shows how an apparently simple question may involve a mathematical problem, and how calculating can be an art; it tells about the power of spatial conception, and of symbols and formulas; it tells of the rigor of mathematics and of its hidden depths, of visible and "invisible" curves, of the "primeval world" of geometry, of the fourth dimension, and infinity—in short, of all the paths of thought which mathematics has revealed to us.

Traditional nomenclature, which means nothing to the uninitiated, has been avoided, lest the reader think he has fallen amongst pedants. Only the pure essence of mathematics is presented, and so the book does not deal with the more advanced conceptions of earth and universe, or with the place of mathematics in cultural history or in art. Even so, there remains an incomparable kingdom of riches for our attention—"a truly wonderful landscape, fashioned by God."

KARL W. MENNINGER

Heppenheim an der Bergstrasse

MATHEMATICS IN YOUR WORLD

Chapter 1

COUNTING CAN BE AN ART

Counting is one of our earliest encounters with mathematics. It provides our sequence of ordinary numbers, where each number is followed by another which is one larger. This "sequence of magnitude" is one basic characteristic of numbers, and the other is their "combining power" in calculating. Let us just consider the first quality here:

HOW DO YOU COUNT A HEAP OF DRIED PEAS? You arrange them, either in actual fact or in the mind, in such a way that one follows the other, and you say: "One, two, three . . .," noting each one in turn. In this way you allocate to each pea one of the sequence of numbers. The last number used in the sequence, say "twenty," gives the total number of peas, and this is the number you wish to find when you count them.

Counting peas, then, is not difficult, even if the heap is large. But in other cases, when one has to count certain arrangements, the task can become very tricky. In order to appreciate this, let us visit the favorite inn-table of four well-known kings—the Kings of Clubs, Spades, Hearts, and Diamonds. These have been chosen because one can easily take a pack of cards and set up the various arrangements before one's very eyes.

HOW MANY "CLINKS"? Today our four friends are celebrating the King of Hearts' birthday. The innkeeper has brought up a good bottle from the wine-cellar and they are clinking glasses all round: "Clink—clink—clink!" How many clinks?

Now this is by no means as simple to count up as a pile of peas, because what we have to count is not lying neatly arranged before us but has to be established with reference to the special procedure followed. We can quickly find the total, however. The King of Hearts (1) clinks glasses with each of the other three: 3 clinks. Each of the four Kings in fact does this, hence $4 \times 3 = 12$ clinks. But as the clinking of 1 with 2 is the same as the clinking of 2 with 1, and so forth, the actual number of clinks, one with another, is only half as many, namely $4 \times 3/2 = 6$.

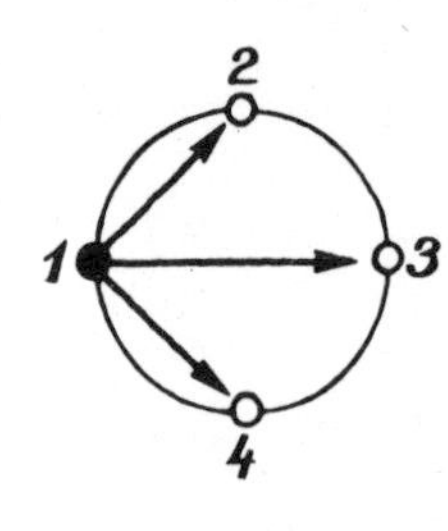

As we at the neighboring table have no birthday to celebrate, let us investigate a little further: how many times will the glasses clink if the four Kings have their Queens with them? There will then be eight sitting round the table, and, by the same reckoning as before, the total number of clinks will be $8 \times 7/2 = 28$. With the whole card-clan of fifty-two members present, there would be $52 \times 51/2 = 1326$ clinks. Thus, with n people taking part, the total of clinks is given by

$$C = \frac{n(n-1)}{2}.$$

Let us now develop the idea in other directions. When the four Kings met tonight, there were just as many handshakes as there were glass-clinks; if their four Queens had greeted one another with a kiss, there would have been the same number of kisses, namely $4 \times 3/2 = 6$. And if we consider the number of telephone connections needed so that each of the four could speak in turn with his three friends, the answer would also be $4 \times 3/2 = 6$. Each time we have the same relationship in different guise. In mathematics we are concerned only with the relationship between things. The things themselves are unimportant in comparison and serve only as means by which one can study relationships. Putting it differently, one could say that mathematics is concerned with the essential similarity underlying a set of given instances. To realize this similarity, to examine its significance and to represent it—these are the fundamental tasks of all mathematical thought.

A GAME OF THREE-HANDED "SKAT" has started at the table of the four jolly Kings while we have been talking. They have agreed to the following arrangement: they will play as many games during the evening as they can change places, one with another; each in turn is to sit out by the fire and stay there until the other three have gone through all the changes of place that are possible, one with another. How many changes would this entail? The Kings cannot work out the answer and are therefore appealing to us at the mathematical table for a ruling.

We assure them that it is not really a difficult problem. If there were three of them, A, B, C, then each would sit out in turn, while the other two changed places once to play two hands, for example: A (BC) and A (CB), where A is the one sitting out. Thus the three of them would go through six games. However, there are four of them present, so each of the four must sit out while the other three go through the six games as just calculated, changing places each time with one another; altogether there will thus be $4 \times 6 = 24$ games, each involving interchanging of places.

Twenty-four games in the course of the evening—"Just right!" thinks the King of Clubs. But we mathematicians are more interested in understanding the rule governing the total possible changes of place. Let U stand for the total and set it out as follows: $U = 1 \times 2 \times 3 \times 4$ (abbreviated 4!, spoken "factorial 4") = 24. Now one can see that if the four Kings sat with their Queens, the number of possible arrangements would be

$$U = 1 \times 2 \times 3 \times 4 \times 5 \times 6 \times 7 \times 8 \text{ (or } 8!) = 40{,}320.$$

The number of possible changes is given by:

$$U = n! \text{ (or } 1 \times 2 \times 3 \times \ldots \times n),$$

where n is the number of people taking part.

THE "PAIRING-OFF" GAME. "Yes," says the King of Hearts at this point, "but if we have our Queens with us, we don't just want to sit there anyhow: let us fix it so that during our place-changing, no King ever finds himself sitting next to his own Queen!" How many possibilities would there be in this?

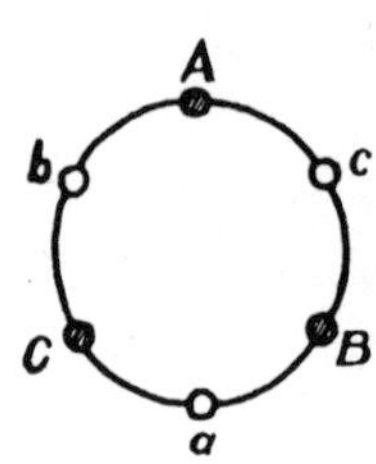

This is not so easy to solve, or to predict for any number, n, of couples. Among one or two couples, of course, no such arrangement is possible, and among three couples only one, this basic sequence being represented by

$$(b)\ A\ c\ B\ a\ C\ b.$$

See the diagram, with the husbands—capital letters—evenly dispersed around the table, and the wives—small letters (each couple being thus *Aa Bb Cc*)—seated between them. To keep the idea of the round table, with husband *A* between two women, wife *b* has been shown above in parentheses (*b*) at the start of the sequence and again, without parentheses, at the end. For the four royal couples there will thus be, as one can realize, two arrangements of this kind, namely

$$(b)\ A\ c\ B\ d\ C\ a\ D\ b \quad \text{and} \quad (c)\ A\ d\ B\ a\ C\ b\ D\ c.$$

However, in the basic sequence of the illustration, it will be seen that the men and women can change their places at the table and still retain the basic sequence. Let us try this with our four royal couples, numbering their chairs one to eight. First of all they sit in the basic sequence (*b*) *A c B d C a D b*, the Kings occupying chairs 1, 3, 5, 7, and their Queens chairs 2, 4, 6, 8. The Kings can now interchange amongst themselves to the extent of $4! = 1 \times 2 \times 3 \times 4 = 24$ times. A similar arrangement, using however the other basic sequence (*c*) *A d B a C b D c*, would give another 24 changes, making a total of 48. With each change, of course, the Queens make corresponding changes to retain the basic sequence. If now the Kings sit on their Queens' chairs and the Queens on 1, 3, 5, 7, yet another 48 changes can be made, giving a grand total of 96 different seating arrangements with no King ever sitting next to his own Queen!

The King of Spades now asks, "How many of these mixed basic sequences would be possible with more than four couples? What if our sons and their fiancées (i.e., the four Jacks and their Tens) were to join us?" It is just not possible to predict this by means of a convenient formula, but there will be with . . .

Couples	5	6	7	8	9	10
Basic sequences	13	80	579	4738	43,387	439,792,

and with 12 couples almost 60,000,000. Supposing now the eight couples who can form 4738 basic sequences were also to move about in each of their basic sequences, as did our four Kings and their Queens, then the number of arrangements would be $2 \times 8 = 80{,}640$ times as many, making the enormous total of 382,072,320.

Our four Kings agree that this would be a simply immense number and it just shows how counting, which can be a simple matter with peas, can become terribly difficult in such a case as this.

THE MIXED-UP HATS. And so the kingly session continued, with the innkeeper bringing quite a few more bottles. At last, however, the four stood up, reeling just a little, took down their hats from the wall, put them on and swayed regally out—each one wearing the wrong hat! It was so funny that it made us wonder in how many ways could each of the four find himself homeward-bound wearing a hat not his own? Let us give each King his corresponding Ace to wear as a hat and see how it works out: with two Kings, *A* and *B*, there is only one possibility (*A b*, *B a*); with three Kings, *A*, *B*, *C*, there are two:

A	*B*	*C*
b	*c*	*a*
c	*a*	*b*

Our four Kings, *A*, *B*, *C*, *D*, can go strolling home wearing no fewer than nine different combinations of the wrong hats:

A	*B*	*C*	*D*
b	*a*	*d*	*c*
b	*c*	*d*	*a*
. .	. .	. .	. .

(Complete this table for yourself, letting the small letters stand for hats.) For all four to have their own hats is only possible once; for all four to have the wrong hats is possible nine ways; there thus remain 24 — 10 = 14 ways in which one or the other will have the right hat and the other three the wrong ones, since four hats can be interchanged to the extent of 4! = 24 ways. (See three-handed "skat," above.)

FOR THE CALCULATOR. The intricate recipe for solving all problems of this kind: Given n people, H is the number of possible arrangements whereby each person would be wearing someone else's hat:

$$H = n!\left(\frac{1}{2!} - \frac{1}{3!} + \frac{1}{4!} - \ldots \pm \frac{1}{n!}\right).$$

This solution was established two centuries ago by Euler and Nicholas Bernoulli, in the matter of the "mixed-up letters." Suppose that someone wrote n letters and addessed n envelopes; in how many ways can the letters all find their way into the wrong envelopes?

Another version of the same problem: At a ball n couples are dancing; in how many ways can they pair off without any man dancing with his wife?

The matter of the Kings and the mixed-up hats is an intriguing one: that no King shall be wearing the wrong hat is possible once; that only one King shall be wearing the wrong hat is not possible at all! Put simply, the whole situation is as follows:

Kings with wrong hats	0	1	2	3	4
Possibilities	1	0	6	8	9

Two may have wrong hats as many times as there are possible different pairings among the four Kings, namely six; three may have wrong hats only twice (see above, p. 8); as however the fourth would be wearing the right hat each time and there are four Kings altogether, the number of possibilities is $4 \times 2 = 8$.

Now we too must prepare to go. What has our time at the inn table taught us? That counting can be an art when the items to be counted are specially arranged. There are three basic types of arrangement.

1. *The interchanging of* n *units*. As for instance the interchanging *ABC*, *ACB*, *BAC*, etc., in three-handed "skat."

2. *The random grouping of* n *units into groups each numbering* k *units*. As for example when the Kings paired in clinking glasses—*AB*, *AC*, *AD*, etc., there being no special regard paid to sequence of grouping, but only to the bundling together of units, like bunches of radishes. Here, then, *AB* and *BA* would be one and the same group.

3. *The planned grouping of* n *units into groups each*

numbering k *units*. Here the groups are arranged in a planned sequence; for example, from three units *A*, *B*, *C*, groups of two are selected in turn according to some plan, and arranged in an ordered sequence—*AB*, *BA*, *AC*, *CA*, etc. Here *AB* and *BA* are two distinct groupings, as when a number of people being photographed re-group themselves for successive shots. For an example of this see Chapter 8.

For these three basic types of arrangement (also called "permutation," "combination," and "variation") formulas have been devised to facilitate the number of possible arrangements. But when two or more of these types of arrangement are found operating together and leading to complicated new series of arrangements, as in the case of the "paired-off couples" or the "mixed-up hats," the calculating can become really difficult—much more tricky than counting a heap of peas, the simplest way of counting and the origin of all these more sophisticated approaches.

A GAME

Arrange any number of stones (matches, dried peas, or seashells would do) into three random piles, say: *A* 7, *B* 10, *C* 13. Two players now draw in turn, as follows. Each player takes any number of stones from any pile; he may take only one, or a number, or all, but may take from only one pile during any one turn, though he may vary the pile with each turn if he wishes. Whoever takes the last stone is the winner. Let us try this out as shown below:

	Pile	*A*	*B*	*C*
1. Start		7	10	13

I take from pile *B* four stones (written *B* 4); now we could have the following moves:

2.		7	6	13
3. You	(*C* 12)	7	6	1
4. I	(*A* 2)	5	6	1
5. You	(*B* 2)	5	4	1
6. I	(*A* 3)	2	4	1
7. You	(*B* 1)	2	3	1
8. I	(*B* 3)	2	—	1
9. You	(*A* 1)	1	—	1
10. I	(*A* 1)	—	—	1

You now take the last stone, *C* 1, and thus win the game.

This is a nice little game and so simple to prepare—a mere handful of stones picked up from the wayside. The rules are easy and the excitement lasts to the very end. There is something picturesque about it. Chinese road workers play it by the roadside; in fact it probably came to us from them. Every game develops differently, as in chess, and there is never a state of deadlock, as in checkers.

Each move of the game can be wisely considered, but how on earth should one set about it, when faced with, say, 23, 19, 15 stones? For a long time you are working in the dark and only toward the end can you really see the effect of your moves. If one knows how to play properly, however, one can see at any point, even with 23, 19, 15 stones, who is in the winning position. For even this apparent game of chance has an underlying pattern, which can be grasped with the aid of mathematics.

WIN OR LOSE? Let us take a situation in the game which a player (Number 1) has produced by his last turn. His opponent (Number 2) is now faced with a winning situation, and he can win if only he now plays correctly. Stage 9, above, in the game that we played, is just such a winning situation for you, and therefore a losing situation for me.

It works like this: a winning situation W is inevitably transformed into a losing situation L by the following draw, but this losing situation need not necessarily be re-transformed by the next draw into a winning situation — W'; it could become another losing situation — L'. Expressed in symbols, this is:

$$W \rightarrow L \rightarrow (W' \quad \text{or} \quad L').$$

Consider, for example, Stage 7 in the game we played: 2, 3, 1 is a winning situation for you. I now draw and make it into 2, 0, 1, with which I cannot win if you are on the alert and turn it into 1, 0, 1. If, however, you draw A 2 and leave 0, 0, 1 for me, then I can take the last stone and win. Thus you can make out of my losing situation a winning or a losing situation for yourself, and so you must play correctly.

Now how can one tell from such a situation as 7, 10, 13 whether it is a winning or a losing situation for oneself? This is how it is done: Write the numbers 7, 10, 13 in terms of powers of 2 in the order given, and then add them together. If the total, which we shall call the "indicator," consists only of the numerals 0 and 2, the situation is a winning one for you; if 1 and 3 are present in the total, however, it is a losing situation for you.

What are powers of 2?

Before answering this question, let us examine our familiar decimal numbers which are written in powers of 10. When we write the number 375, for example, we mean the number whose value is:

$$\underline{3}(10^2) + \underline{7}(10^1) + \underline{5}(10^0) = \underline{3}(100) + \underline{7}(10) + \underline{5}(1) = 375.$$

Every decimal number can be written as the sum of successive multiples of powers of ten. When it is written in its familiar form (375), the power of ten by which each numeral is multiplied is indicated by the position of that numeral.

Any number can be written in terms of powers of 2, instead of powers of 10. Successive powers of 2 are $2^0 = 1$, $2^1 = 2$, $2^2 = 4$, $2^3 = 8$, etc. For the decimal number 13, for instance, we can write:

$$
\begin{aligned}
13 &= \underline{1}\,(2^3) + \underline{1}\,(2^2) + \underline{0}\,(2^1) + \underline{1}\,(2^0) \\
&= \underline{1}\,(8) + \underline{\ }\,(4) + \underline{0}\,(2) + \underline{1}\,(1) = 1101.
\end{aligned}
$$

Such a number in powers of 2 is composed of only two numerals, 0 and 1, and is called a binary number.

Now let us return to the earlier question: Is 7, 10, 13 a winning situation? Let us write the numbers of stones in each pile in terms of powers of 2:

	8	4	2	1		
7		1	1	1	=	111
10	1	0	1	0	=	1010
13	1	1	0	1	=	1101
						2222 Total (the "indicator")

The total, or "indicator," consists entirely of 2, hence a winning situation!

Three heaps of the order 6, 10, 12 would also be a winning situation, having the indicator 2220 when treated as above, but 7, 11, 13, with indicator 2223, and 23, 19, 15, with indicator 21,233, are losing situations. It may also be noticed that all situations where two heaps have the same number of stones are also winning situations (e.g., 7, 7, 0).

One can easily see that the next turn will always transform a winning situation into a losing situation, for any draw out of one pile, for example 2 stones from 7, takes away one or more ones from the representation in terms of powers of 2; in this instance 111 becomes 101. This results in the intrusion of 1 into the indicator which previously contained only 2 and 0: 2222 becomes 2212. By a proper draw, however, an indicator containing 1 and/or 3 can always be transformed into one in which only 2 and/or 0 appear (a winning situation W'); by an incorrect draw, however, one can obtain an indicator which still contains 1 and/or 3 (a losing situation L'). The reader will find it interesting to play through a game or so to practice the manipulating of these indicators.

The matter cannot be considered more closely here, but one can see that this game, apparently one entirely dependent on chance, does have its underlying pattern, and that mathematics can play its part in helping the players to solve the weighty problem of how to play correctly. It may indeed be that many games become all the more exciting and challenging if they are based upon some such intricate underlying pattern.

Chapter 2

WHY THE ELEPHANT IS NOT A FLEA

FLEA AND ELEPHANT. A flea can jump 150 times his own length. An elephant cannot even jump his own length, for the simple reason that he cannot jump at all! John Smith thinks the matter over: "But what if a flea .08 in. in length were 1000 times as large? Then, with a length of 80 in. he would be about as big as a horse and could make jumps of $80 \times 150 = 12{,}000$ in., or 1000 ft. But a horse cannot do this. Why not, if a flea can? Has it to do with the fact that a flea is so small?"

It does indeed depend on the flea's tiny size. All prodigious jumpers, such as fleas, grasshoppers, and others, are little fellows. And from the flea's point of view even the great lion is only small fry when it comes to jumping, for he cannot manage more than three times his own length. The lion, in fact, stands fairly low on the list of jumpers, and the elephant, the most massive land-creature, is right at the bottom!

John Smith is reminded of the book *Gulliver's Travels*, which he read with such enthusiasm as a boy. Gulliver, an ordinary man, went to the kingdom of Lilliput and found he was a giant, who could put the king in his pocket; later he journeyed to Brobdingnag, the kingdom of the giants, where he was a midget and was very nearly drowned in the Minister's inkwell. "Well now," thinks John Smith, "if we put a flea in Lilliput, where he would have the size of an elephant, he would surely still be able to jump prodigiously, like a flea. Or, on the other hand, if we take an Indian elephant to Brobdingnag, where he would be only as big as a flea, wouldn't he then be able to jump, flea-wise, 150 times his own length?

The matter seems a simple one to John Smith and to Jonathan Swift, the author of *Gulliver's Travels:* Gulliver's surroundings in Lilliput are merely reduced in size, and in Brobdingnag they are enlarged; everything else remains ordinary and familiar, except for this enchanting paradox of great and small placed side by side.

But such a state of affairs can exist only in a fairy-tale world; in ours it is impossible. When a photograph is enlarged (keeping the negative quite flat), all items in the picture, both living and inanimate, are enlarged in equal proportion—that is to say, the size of all items *in relation to one another* and their positions *in relation to one another* remain the same. Moreover, in this matter of the size of living creatures in relationship to their surroundings, there have been times when certain circumstances of nature influencing life in our world have become so unfavorable that animals and plants have become extinct because of their too vast size. The dinosaurs of prehistory were not the last creatures to die out because of this disproportion. Trees may seem to grow so tall that they almost meet the sky, but they do not really—nor do animals or men.

THE MYSTERIOUS EFFECT OF ENLARGEMENT—how shall we explain it? John Smith has succeeded in taking a very nice landscape photograph, 2×3 in. in size, and he wants to enlarge it to 4×6 in. This is exactly twice as large ($4 = 2 \times 2$ and $6 = 2 \times 3$). The original print cost him 15 cents, so he expects now to pay, in cost of paper, twice as much—30 cents. He is amazed, therefore, when the photographic dealer asks him for

60 cents (four times as much). But the truth is, that when the linear dimensions of a rectangle are *doubled*, the surface area is *quadrupled*. Linear measurements tripled will result, then, in a surface area of *nine* times the original ($9 = 3^2$).

Hence one must distinguish between linear enlargement and enlargement of the area of a given figure, and the latter is always much greater than the former. Enlargement of linear dimensions k times results in an enlargement of area by k^2 times. The governing factor is k: if it is bigger than 1, as for example $k = 2$, then we talk of enlargement; if smaller than 1, as for example $k = \frac{1}{2}$, then we refer to reduction. So if a picture is reduced in linear dimensions by $k = \frac{1}{2}$, the linear dimensions are halved, but the area is now only a quarter as large as before.

When, in photography, one talks of an "enlargement," one usually means it in terms of an enlargement of linear dimensions. This same idea is present in the following instance: A microscope is said to have "a magnification of 200." This means that $k = 200$ (i.e., linear dimension a of an actual object viewed is multiplied by 200, to give a linear dimension a' in the resultant image. Hence $k = a' : a = 200 : 1$, or 200). The area magnification of this microscope is thus

$$k^2 = 200^2 = 200 \times 200 = 40{,}000.$$

A cross-section of a match with surface area $A = .001$ sq. in. will thus appear in image with an area of $A' = 40$ sq. in.

WHAT ABOUT ENLARGEMENT OF VOLUME? This is represented by k^3, so if linear dimensions are doubled, the resultant volume is *eight* times as large as before ($k = 2$; $k^3 = 2^3 = 8$). In the illustration the linear dimensions of cube 2 are twice those of cube 1; hence the area of each face is $k^2 =$ *four* times that of each

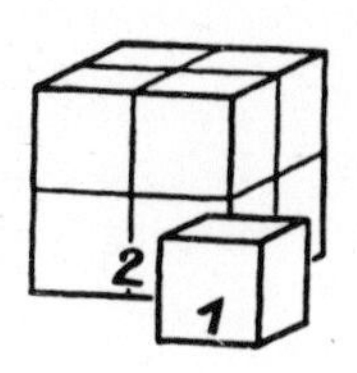

face in cube 1; the volume of cube 2 is k^3 = *eight* times that of cube 1. A cube with linear dimension of 10 ft. has a volume of 1000 cu. ft., i.e., 10^3 cu. ft.

Now we understand the strange effect of enlargement. When one multiplies each linear dimension by k, the surface area is multiplied by k^2, and volume by k^3. Area and volume therefore increase much more than the increase in linear measurements. This effect is seen not only in cubes, but in all bodies with volume: for example, a sphere whose diameter is doubled has its surface area quadrupled and its volume multiplied eight times.

Armed with this knowledge, let us now consider the effects of enlargement in size of living creatures.

DISTURBANCE OF BODY HEAT. The body of a mouse (its volume V) is a "stove," providing the warmth which the mouse needs for life; the mouse's surface area A is the "window" through which the warmth escapes from the mouse. So that the mouse's interior shall retain enough heat, there must be a balance of warmth between "stove" and "window." This is arrived at by a certain ratio $C = V : A$ (or V/A). C is in fact a measure of *the degree of compactness* of the body (see p. 226).

Let us now think of the mouse grown to twice its size. The new "window" (surface area) is now four times as large, and the "stove" (volume) is now eight times as large. Thus, the old relationship between "stove" and "window" is destroyed, for the new value C' is twice as large ($C' = 8V/4A = 2V/A = 2C$). It is as if, with the same "window" (surface area), there were now *two* "stoves" (volume $\times$ 2) in the mouse's interior. These overheat it, and if the mouse does not remove to some colder climate, where it would cool down more quickly (cf. p. 234), it will develop a fever and probably die.

This example shows us that when living creatures increase in size, some of their other characteristics are likely to become affected—certainly this all-important relationship between volume and surface area, which governs a creature's body heat. It is dependent on change in linear dimensions in terms of k, and thus increases with enlargement and decreases with reduction in size. John Smith thinks, however, that it remains constant and that an enlarged mouse is still the same mouse, only larger. But a mouse that would be basically healthy in our own normal environment would freeze to death if reduced to Lilliputian size, and would catch a raging fever if enlarged to Brobdingnagian proportions. Alternatively, if, as in the book *Gulliver's Travels*, the whole community were to be considerably enlarged or reduced in size, all would suffer the same fate as the poor mouse.

FOR THE CALCULATOR. In a cube with linear dimension a in., the degree of compactness C is generally given by $C = a^3/6a^2$, where a^3 is the number of cu. in. in volume, and a^2 the number of sq. in. in the surface area. It is thus in proportion to the linear dimensions. Likewise, the degree of compactness of a sphere is in proportion to its diameter and increases or decreases as the diameter increases or decreases.

This is not the only disturbance resulting from increased size in living creatures, however. Let us now consider another.

DISTURBANCE OF MOBILITY. We take a step S from C to D (see illustration). To move one's leg over this distance S, muscular force P is needed. The work done, represented by W, is measured by multiplying force P by distance of stride S: $W = P \times S$. If the distance is twice as far ($2S$), twice as much work must be done:

$$W' = P \times 2S = 2PS = 2W.$$

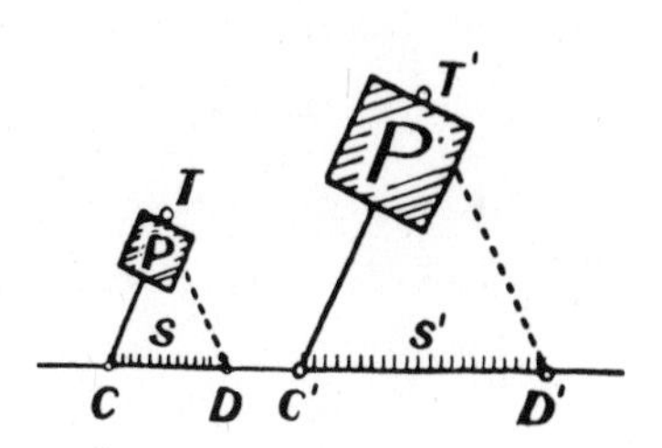

The strength to make such movements is contained in the muscles of men and animals. The bigger these are (in volume) the greater is their strength. Hence the force P which they may exert is in proportion to muscular volume V ($P \sim V$). In the diagram on p. 19, the force P is shown as a shaded square at the top of the leg.

If we now became twice as large ($k = 2$), our legs would be twice as long ($T'C' = 2TC$), and the volume of our muscles V' and their strength P' would thus be $k^3 = 2^3 = 8$ times as great. Thus, if we now take the stride $S' = 2S$ or twice the original distance, the work that must be done is:

$$W' = P' \times S' = 8P \times 2S = 16PS = 16W,$$

16 times as much work as before! But our strength P' is only 8 times as much as before. Hence, in order to take this stride, with our new strength P', twice as much work must be done as was previously necessary.

FOR THE CALCULATOR. With an increase in size by a factor k, the work to be done is, generally speaking

$$W' = k^3 \times P \times k \times S = k^4 \times W.$$

In other words, the work increases to the extent of k^4 times.

This fact is of vital importance. Any increase in our size increases the work necessary to move our limbs by a greater degree than that in which our strength is increased. Consequently, when our size is doubled, our strength is not sufficient to perform the work of moving, and we must either take strides of only half the distance one would expect, hobbling along like stilt-walkers, even though we are giants 12 feet tall, or we must have legs of half the size—that is to say, when we grow to twice our size, our legs must remain unaltered. Here our diagram shows, *l.* to *r.*: the normal person; the same, but twice as large; the same, but with legs, arms and neck not enlarged. In this last form, our steps would be, of course, the same as we took in our original form.

This state of affairs can actually be observed in nature. In most cases the larger the animals are, the shorter are their movable "appendages"—head, legs, antennae, etc., and conversely, the smaller they are, the longer are their limbs in proportion to the size of their bodies. A foal has excessively long legs, which do not grow as the animal develops full stature—or at any rate, they only grow much more slowly than the rest of the horse. Daddy longlegs, common spiders, and locusts have legs which are, in proportion to their bodies, out of all comparison with ours. The head of a gnat is .003 in. in length, and its legs .15 in. or fifty times as long; at this rate, with our heads of 8 in. or so, we should have to have legs of 33 ft.—as high as a house! Obviously, we just would not be able to move them. A certain variety of ichneumon fly has feelers which are seven times the length of its head. These must be as light as a feather, judging by the way the fly moves them about. If this creature were of human size, it certainly would not be able to move its feelers so delicately, for they would be 4.6 ft. long and as thick as fire hoses. And supposing it could, just think of the great mass of muscular tissue the fly would need! Its entire head would be a mass of muscle. It is true that in deep sea waters there are giant crabs with gigantic legs of this order, but here in the calm depths buoyancy helps appreciably to support the weight of such limbs.

At this point we now come to the third disturbance which results from enlarged size:

THE DISTURBANCE OF BONE STRENGTH. Bones carry the muscles and must remain rigid when the muscles are at work. If you lift an iron shot with your hand, the muscle *M* draws up the forearm with the sinew *MQ* (*G* is the elbow joint). The forearm bones must therefore be of sufficiently large dimensions to withstand the forces exerted upon them and not give way. The same is true of

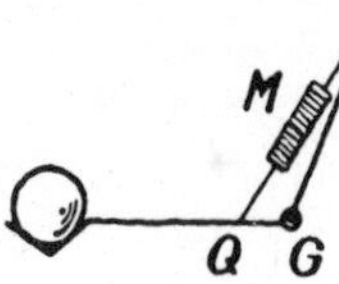

M
Q G

an animal's jawbones: these too must be able to stand up to the forces involved in chewing. A dog gnaws with all his strength at a bone, so that his jawbones only just stand the strain. If all were now made twice as large, including the degree of hardness of the bone he gnaws, then his jawbones would break, even though their dimensions had also been doubled, for the strength of a bone does not increase in the same proportion as its size.

Consider a plank which is serving as a bridge over a ditch. Its dimensions are breadth b, thickness (or height) h, and length

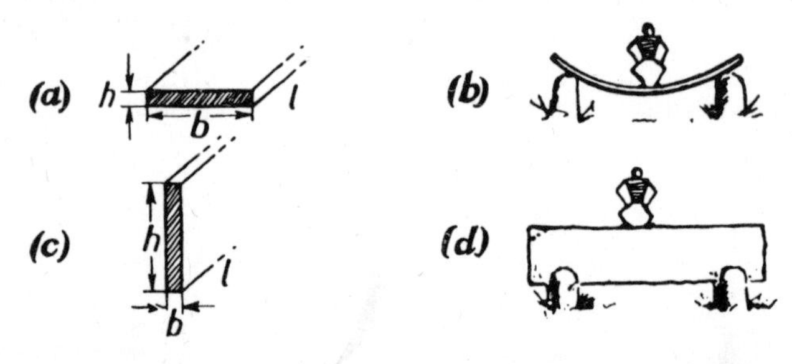

l (diagram a). If you walk over this plank, it will bend beneath your weight (diagram b). The amount it will bend depends on its dimensions, the load placed upon it, and the type of wood from which it is made. This last factor we shall disregard. When the load is constant, the plank will bend more and more as its breadth and thickness decrease and its length (the width of the ditch) increases. If, however, the plank is placed on edge (diagram c), the thickness h is now increased, and it would bend much less than before (diagram d). A pane of glass laid flat over the ditch would break with only a small load, but placed on edge it would bear a very heavy weight.

The technical explanation is as follows: The degree of bending of a plank, supported at the points C and D (diagram on p. 23), increases in proportion to the increase of the load P, but also in proportion to the cube of the length l; it decreases in proportion to any increase in breadth b but in proportion to the cube of the thickness h. Expressed as a formula, this is:

$$d \propto \frac{Pl^3}{bh^3}.$$

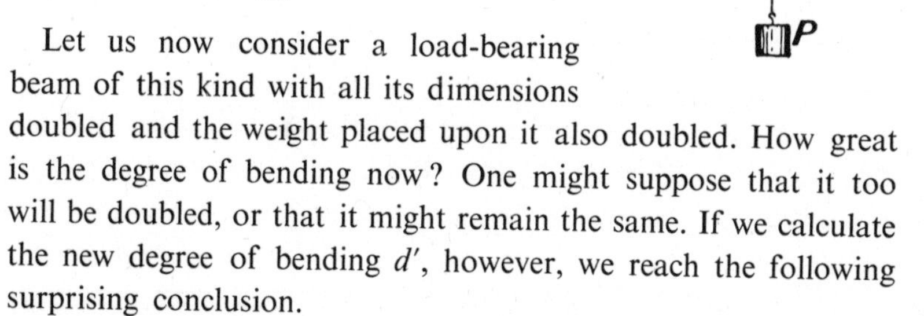

Let us now consider a load-bearing beam of this kind with all its dimensions doubled and the weight placed upon it also doubled. How great is the degree of bending now? One might suppose that it too will be doubled, or that it might remain the same. If we calculate the new degree of bending d', however, we reach the following surprising conclusion.

With an increase in size k times of a plank or beam or bone and of its load, the degree of bending increases k^2 times; with a decrease in size and load k times, the degree of bending decreases k^2 times.

FOR THE CALCULATOR. The degree of bending of the beam is increased in length k times. The new beam has length $l' = k \times l$; breadth $b' = k \times b$, and thickness $h' = k \times h$; the new weight (let us think in terms of a cube-shaped weight) is increased k^3 times, so $P' = k^3 \times P$. Thus the new degree of bending is

$$d' \propto \frac{P'l'^3}{b'h'^3} = \frac{k^3 \times P \times k^3 \times l^3}{k \times b \times k^3 \times h^3} = \frac{k^2Pl^3}{bh^3} = k^2d.$$

In words, with an increase in length k times, the degree of bending is increased k^2 times.

THE GIANT MATCH. Let us consider these ideas once again in relation to a match with length $l = 2$ in., breadth $b = .08$ in., and thickness (height) $h = .08$ in. It bends about .04 in. when resting on two knife edges, and carries a weight of 1 lb. at its center. Now let us suppose that all these figures are increased one hundred-fold ($k = 100$). The match thus becomes a beam of 200 in. by 80 in. by 80 in., and the load P becomes $P' = 1 \times 100^3$ lb. = 1,000,000 lb. = 500 tons, or the weight of five freight locomotives! For if we think of the original load of 1 lb. as an iron cube with edge 1.5 in., the new load will be an iron cube of edge 150 in. And the degree of bending? This would be $d' = 100^2 \times d = 10{,}000 \times .04$ in. $= 400$ in.—quite impossible! Our load-bearing match would have broken long before it grew to 100 times its size!

From all this one can realize that when a beam with load P (or a match, or a bone subjected to the pull of muscles attached to it) is increased in size k times, the ratio of the load or pull P to the resisting power of the beam is completely upset to the disadvantage of the resisting power. The balanced relationship between the load or pull and the resistance of the beam is altered, and the beam's power of resistance destroyed. A bone increased in size k times can no longer withstand a muscular pull that has also increased k times (assuming that muscle power is proportional to the volume of the muscles).

One solution might be for the bone to grow stronger than the muscles, but then it would also grow heavier, and the muscular tissue would have to grow stronger and larger in order to move it. In fact, the proportion of bone weight to total weight is greater in the larger animals. The bones of a mouse represent 8% of its total weight; of a cat 12%; of a dog 14%; of the human body 18%; of the wren 7%, the hen 12%, and the goose 13%.

Another possible answer to the problem might be for the muscles to grow weaker and so exert less pull upon the bones, but then they would not be able to move them. Let us assume that our match, increased by $k = 100$ times, could bend no further than $d' = 4$ in. without breaking (i.e., 100 times more than the original match $d = .04$ in.). Then the load could only increase to 10 times the original instead of 100 times, i.e., $P' = 1 \times 10^3$ lb. $= 1000$ lb. Thus the giant match could just about carry a heavy horse without breaking, but not five locomotives!

The situation is reversed with decrease in size. The relationship between load and resistance is again altered, but this time in favor of the beam's resistance. It can stand up to it better. Many beetles can fall from a height 10 or more times greater than their own length without injury. A man who fell about 60 ft. would certainly not live to tell the tale! Everyone knows that children fall "lighter" than adults, and this is partly due to their being smaller. Break a match in two at the center—it's so easy. Now try again with one half, and you will find it considerably harder. Every time the match length is halved its resistance to breaking is doubled and finally becomes so great that you cannot break it at all. On the other hand, if held at one end and enlarged to the length of a beam, it would break because of its own weight. Imagine, then, a giant's difficulty if he were to put a cigar in his mouth!

Let us now summarize all these ideas. As an animal increases in size, its mobility decreases. For a giant the work that must be done to move himself increases in excess of his strength. He would thus not be able to don his seven-league boots and carry you over land and sea; on the contrary, he would be hard put to move his own vast bulk as freely as can an ordinary man. If nature were to try to overcome this disadvantage, she would have to enlarge his leg muscles even more. The giant would then be not merely an enlarged man, but disproportionately massive and bulky. For this reason simple enlargement, whereby the giant retains normal human proportions, would be impossible. Moreover, if the bones are to withstand the increased muscular tensions, their volume would have to be further enlarged, resulting in an even more grotesque deviation from human proportions. And if the skeleton is to be matched up to the enlarged muscular tissue needed to move it, then the giant's body must be completely unlike the human form as we know it. This is not to mention the consequences of the disturbance of body heat, of which we spoke earlier.

Our conclusion is as follows. Every species of living creature possesses a certain distinctive and finely calculable size. This can vary within small limits, but beyond these the creature could no longer live. And so human beings, animals, and trees cannot grow upward to meet the sky, nor can a flea ever become as large as an elephant.

INCREASING AND REDUCING

All around us in the world there is growth. You are growing, the trees grow, rabbits multiply and so do the algae and bacilli. The population increases and so does the number of automobiles; even your money increases if you invest it at interest. Growth is a part of life, but there are varieties of growth, and we shall speak here of two main kinds, simple and relative growth.

SIMPLE GROWTH. You lend your friend $100 at 4% for five years. Each year you receive $4 interest, and in five years it amounts to 5 × $4 = $20. Your capital has thus in five years risen to $120. In diagram *a* (opposite page), which is not drawn to scale, the vertical axis of the graph represents capital, the horizontal axis time. At 0 years (the beginning of the period of the loan) the thick upright line *C* represents $100 capital. After one year it has increased by the addition of interest *I*, and so also at the end of each subsequent year. Note that with equal divisions of time equal increments of interest (*I*) are added to the capital. The graph shows this growth in the form of a straight line through the points A, A', A'', A''', etc. Simple growth depicted as a graph always gives a straight line. These figures emerge

Year	0	1	2	3	4	5
Capital ($)	100	104	108	112	116	120
Constant interest added each year @ 4%		4	4	4	4	4

To take a similar example, work for instance progresses or "grows" in the same way. Each day a street is lengthened by 15 ft,, or a hole deepened by the same. The graph would show the amount of work done at any intermediate points in time, say half a year or one day. Diagram *a* shows, with the perpendicular drawn at $1\frac{3}{4}$ years, the increased capital *B* which results at this point in time.

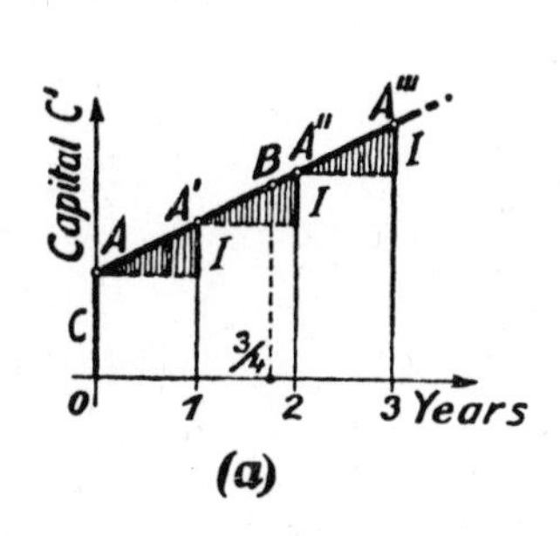

(a)

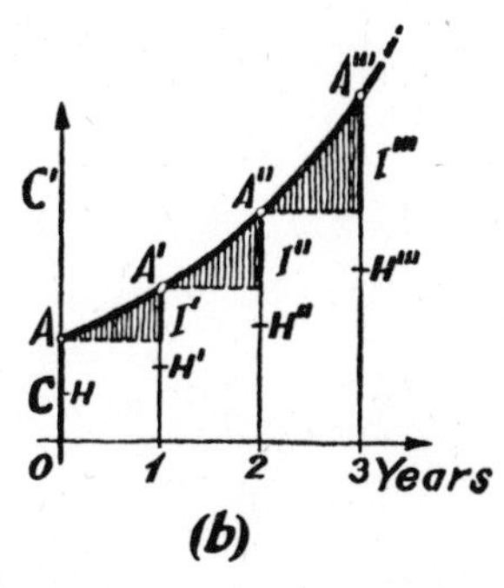

(b)

RELATIVE GROWTH. You put your \$100 in the bank at a rate of 4% interest and draw out the balance after five years. In this case your capital increases in a different way (see diagram *b*, not drawn to scale). After one year the interest I' (\$4) is added to the original sum. The new capital \$104 now earns interest at 4%, and its interest I'' is 4% of \$104 = \$4.16, which is \$.16 greater than before. During each subsequent year the interest earned grows in this way. It is not a fixed sum but each year amounts to 4% of the increased capital at the beginning of the year, i.e., the original capital added to the interest already earned. A graph representing growth of this kind is no longer a single straight line, but a series of short straight segments which slope upward increasingly through the plotted points A, A', A'', A'''. This we shall call "relative growth," because the amount accruing each year is not constant as with simple growth, but only the proportion of the constantly growing capital remains constant (in our example, this is 4%). In other words the annual growth bears always a fixed relation to the ever-increasing capital sum. Diagram *b* (p. 27) has been drawn to make this clear. It represents a capital sum increasing at the rate of 50% "compound interest" annually, i.e., the annual growth is a constant proportion of the rising capital, being 50% or half of it. The growth (interest) I' is $\frac{1}{2}C = 0H$; I'' is $\frac{1}{2}1A' = 1H'$; I''' is $\frac{1}{2}2A'' = 2H''$, etc.

Returning now to our former example of $100 increasing at compound interest by 4% per annum over a period of five years, the actual figures are as follows:

Year	0	1	2	3	4	5
Capital, in $	100	104	108.16	112.49	116.99	121.67
Interest added each year (4% compound interest)		4	4.16	4.33	4.50	4.68

The terms compound interest for relative growth and simple interest for simple growth are borrowed from banking.

A capital sum doubles itself at different rates of interest according to the following table:

Rate %	2	4	5	7	10
At simple interest, in years	50	25	20	14	10
At compound interest, in years	36	18	15	10	7

FOR THE CALCULATOR. The formulas for calculating the resultant capital, C':

Simple interest

Original capital $= C$, interest $= I$, rate of interest % $= P$, time in years $= T$.

$$C' = C + I = C + \frac{CPT}{100} = C\left(1 + \frac{PT}{100}\right).$$

In our example $C = 100$, $P = 4$, $T = 5$.

$$C' = 100\left(1 + \frac{4 \times 5}{100}\right) = 120.$$

Compound interest

$$C' = C\left(1 + \frac{P}{100}\right)^T.$$

In our example $C' = 100 \times 1.04^5 = 100 \times 1.2166 = 121.66$.

The amount (i.e., final value of the capital invested) is equal to the initial capital multiplied by the Tth power of the "interest factor," $1.0P$ (i.e., $1 + [P/100]$); from this is deduced the formula for continuous growth. This is called "exponential," and T is the exponent or power. In arithmetical terms a particular capital, e.g., \$108.16, is at the end of the second year to be multiplied by 1.04 in order to calculate the value for the third year: $108.16 \times 1.04 = 112.49$. The "interest factor" $1.0P$ is the growth or increase factor of the series of increasing capital sums.

TWO INTERESTING PROBLEMS INVOLVING THE IDEA OF RELATIVE GROWTH. A pond becomes covered over with weeds. Each day the area covered is twice that covered on the previous day. Today, after a month, exactly half the pond is covered. When will it be completely covered? (The answer usually given, but the wrong one, is "after another month." The right answer is, of course, "by the end of tomorrow.") If the covering over proceeds from one focus of weed growth which would need a month to cover the pond completely, how long would be needed if there were two sets of weed growth at work? (The wrong answer is "half a month," the right one, "a day less.")

The rumor snowball. Robinson has won \$100, and news of his good fortune spreads among the neighbors. One person tells another, and each time the sum is "increased" by 10%. Thus, when the tenth person has passed on the news, Robinson is supposed to have won \$260; after the twentieth it is \$670; and the 48th person talks in terms of $10,000. Rumor thus "invests" the prize at compound interest with a growth factor of 1.10.

RETROGRADE AND STEADY GROWTH. All living growth of plants, animals, and mankind is of the relative type. Nevertheless, such organisms do not grow without any restraint: a flea never becomes as large as an elephant. Nor do they grow at a uniform rate, but at differing rates during the various periods of their life span. In his youth a human being grows very quickly, reaching the limit of development in his twenties, and in old age actually decreases in size (a negative rate of growth of about .1 %). Trees grow at varying rates, according to their age and species—poplar trees most quickly, then spruce, beech, pine, and oak—and all grow more quickly in youth than subsequently. Their greatest actual degree of growth is reached in about their fiftieth year of life.

If we think in terms of an average rate of growth of 3 % per annum, then 1000 cu. yd. of forest timber would after 10 years become 1344 cu. yd. (If the growth were "simple," not "compound," there would only be $1000 + 10 \times 30 = 1300$ cu. yd.)

But a forest (or a living creature) does not grow in fits and starts. Unlike money in a bank where a fixed proportion of the balance is added as interest at the end of each year, a forest grows continuously, at all moments of its period of growth. The accretion (amount added) at any moment is proportional to the total amount of timber at that time. The moments of growth follow continuously, one upon another. Thus, in the graph of its growth, the points A, A', A'', etc. would also follow in this way, forming a smooth curve, not like the angles and straight segments of diagram *b* on page 27.

With mathematical formulas we can also describe this continuous or living organic growth, and we can indicate the total that will be reached at any given time, if the rate of growth is known.

For organic growth, the final mass K' is given by

$$K' = Ke^{PT/100}$$

($e = 2.718$ approx.). The mass of forest timber $K = 1000$ cu. yd. grows in $T = 10$ years at a constant rate of $P = 3\%$ to a total

$$K' = 1000 \times 2.718^{(3\times10)/100} = 1000 \times 2.718^{.3} = 1350,$$

compared with 1344 by the "compound interest" method of finance, and 1300 by "simple interest."

"REDUCTION" IS INVERTED GROWTH. It can be simple and shows as a straight line on a graph, e.g., from a weekly salary of $50 you spend each day 20 cents on bread. The sequence of reduction is 50, 49.8, 49.6, 49.4, 49.2, etc.

Reduction can also be "relative": consider the case of the black-market cigarettes in Berlin. Successive black-market middlemen handle the stocks and take as their payment 10% of the cigarettes. Thus out of an original 1000, after being handled by 10 middlemen, 349 are left, after 20, 122, after 50 there are only 5, and after 65 only one cigarette is left. The sequence is 1000, 900, 810, etc.; the common factor of the series is .9, and the remaining stock after the depredations of 10 middlemen is therefore, $1000 \times .9^{10} = 1000 \times .349 = 349$.

Depreciation. John Smith is a company director and runs a fine limousine that cost originally $8000; each year it loses value through use, and after 5 years it is shown on the firm's books as having no value. This depreciation of value could be reckoned either on a system of "simple reduction," or by "relative reduction." In the latter case the final value would be $1, not $0.

With "simple reduction" John Smith would subtract after

each year the same sum of $1600 (20% of $8000), giving this sequence of figures:

$8000, 6400, 4800, 3200, 1600, 0.

By "relative reduction" he would subtract after each year the same percentage of the value remaining (83.5%) in order to give the following figures:

$8000.00, 1320.80, 218.60, 36.07, 5.96, 1.00.

The income-tax authorities, however, would never approve such a drastic "writing down" by any business firm of its managing director's limousine. They would probably sanction a reduced depreciation rate of, say, 33% instead of 83.5%. This would lead after 5 years to a final value of $1074.34 instead of $1. The sequence would be:

$8000.00, 5360.00, 3591.20, 2406.10, 1602.00, 1074.34.

Connoisseurs of tax lore might agree that this would be a more realistic appraisal of the matter than simple depreciation at 20%.

This talk of relative depreciation brings us to the charming tale of the savory dumplings. A farmer's wife serves up a dish of dumplings for three farmhands. The first one comes in, and as the others are not there, helps himself to his share—one-third of the dumplings. After a hearty meal he returns to work. In comes the second and does the same, i.e., he takes one-third of the remaining dumplings. After he has gone, the third laborer comes and does the same. When the farmer's wife returns, there are still eight dumplings left. These eight remaining dumplings can be compared to the value on the firm's books of John Smith's car after 3 years' depreciation at $33\frac{1}{3}$%, or one-third. The original number of dumplings (how many were there ?) was equivalent to the purchase price of the car.

Incidentally, relative depreciation takes place in the natural world. A kettle of hot water cools off to the temperature of its surroundings in such a way that the amount of heat transferred is always a constant fraction of the heat present at the time of transfer.

AND RABBITS? HOW DO THEY MULTIPLY? Mathematics can predict the results of simple and relative growth by means of its potent formulas. But what sort of growth is the kind practiced by rabbits? When the breeding season begins let us say there is one pair only. In two months they are mature, and thenceforward

produce each month another pair. Each new pair also starts producing after two months. How many pairs of bunnies will there by at the year end? This is not a case of simple or of relative growth. You need to take pencil in hand in order to trace this sequence of growth:

1 1 2 3 5 8 13 etc.

Thus mathematics is again able to step in and calculate that at the year's end 233 pairs of young rabbits will be skipping about. You only need to follow up the family into the 13th generation (13, because the original pair was already alive in month 0).

At any rate, it is clear that there can be other forms of growth besides simple and relative!

BUYING A CAR: WHO, WHERE, AND WHAT?

Mr. Black buys a Ford. Mr. Brown buys his car in Chicago. The Buick is bought in New York. Is the Chrysler bought in San Francisco? What sort of car does Mr. Green buy?

Three purchasers, three cars, and three cities are jumbled together in this puzzle, and the task is to disentangle them and group them into three consistent sets, each stating who bought what, and where. At first the task seems impossible, but the solution is simple if you make a table.

Name	*Make*			*Town*		
	Ford	Buick	Chrysler	Chicago	New York	San Francisco
Black	X	—	—			
Brown				X	—	—
Green						

Thus you set down what the puzzle tells you. Mr. Black buys a Ford (cross in column 1, dashes in columns 2 and 3). The places remaining open can then easily be filled. Against each name there will finally be two crosses and four dashes. It is much clearer, however, if you make a diagram of the problem. Draw a triangle and mark along one side the purchasers, along another side the cars, and along the third side the cities. Now establish the actual links as far as possible by joining the points to accord with the information given. The correct groupings thus appear in the form of three triangles within the original triangle. These will be seen most clearly if three colors are used.

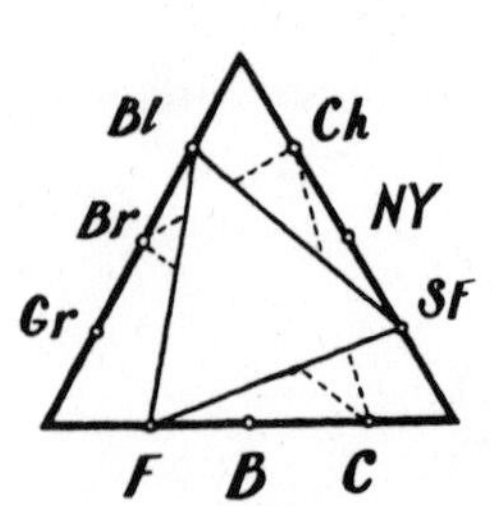

(Is the problem likely to be soluble if there are four buyers, cars, and towns? Actually, as you will see, it is very difficult even to frame a problem with these ingredients, let alone solve it.)

What is the mathematical element in this? To bring about the correct groupings of buyer, car, and place—to *arrange* these data. Systematic arrangement is a basic idea of mathematics. As holder of a driving license you have a certain number, say 31/691. This numbering of people, practiced so much in these days and yet so practical, is, mathematically speaking, an arrangement of persons to correspond with a sequence of numbers. If you count out ten nuts into a dish, you are arranging that each nut should correspond to one numeral of a sequence: One, two, three, etc. The last numeral indicates the total number of nuts.

When sunlight throws a shadow of the window frame on the carpet (see p. 215, text and diagram), the mathematician sees in this pattern, as he does in everything, an arrangement of two aspects. The object A is arranged in the form of the image A'. Similarly, a point in a landscape is represented on a map by a "map reference" (cf. "Function," p. 50).

Our problem of the cars teaches us something else mathematical: The translation of a problem into "visible" form, either a table of numbers or an actual diagram, enlists the aid of the eye in solving the problem, and this is indeed a very present help. Many people cannot think without seeing.

"My mother is your mother's mother-in-law. How, then, are you and I related?"

If you cannot visualize this tricky relationship in your mind's eye, then draw it and let your actual eyes help. Then you will see easily enough: father and child; or uncle (father's brother) and nephew or niece; or aunt (father's sister) and nephew or niece.

There is an amusing story, told by Mark Twain, about a poor man from Philadelphia, whose confusing relationships drove him to suicide. Before killing himself, he wrote the following account of his desperate plight on a scrap of paper:

"I married a widow with a grown-up daughter. My father fell

in love with my stepdaughter and married her, thus becoming my son-in-law. By marrying my father, my stepdaughter became my mother.

"Subsequently my wife gave birth to a son, who was the brother-in-law of my father and at the same time my uncle, because he was the brother of my stepdaughter.

"Then the wife of my father gave birth to a son, who was therefore my brother and at the same time my grandson, since he was the son of my stepdaughter.

"I finally realized that I had my grandmother as my wife, because she was the mother of my mother, and as the husband of my wife I was also her grandson. And because the husband of any grandmother is always the grandfather—I am my own grandfather!"

HOW A SIMPLE QUESTION CAN BECOME MATHEMATICAL

Nine coins lie before you. One of them is counterfeit and lighter than the other eight. How will you find the false one with the aid of a simple pair of scales?

It is very easy: Place one coin in one pan and the others in turn in the other. You may find the false coin in the very first weighing, but at least you are sure to find it at some time in the course of the eight weighings. There is nothing mathematical in this: you just go on weighing until you find it.

There is a change, however, if you limit the number of weighings permitted. What is the least number of weighings needed to isolate the false coin? At once the problem becomes mathematical. Is there in fact a least number that will guarantee the answer? If so, what is it, and how must we proceed to find the answer with this limited number of weighings?

You can do it in two weighings, if you work like this: Divide the nine coins into three equal groups, A, B, C; place group A on one scale pan and group B on the other, leaving group C out of it. Three situations are now possible (f represents the false coin, $<$ signifies "lighter than"):

$$A < B \quad (f \text{ is in } A)$$
$$B < A \quad (f \text{ is in } B)$$
$$A = B \quad (f \text{ is in } C)$$

Thus we find the group containing the false coin. Now divide this group, labeling each of its three coins a, b, c, and proceed again as before.

$$a < b \quad (f \text{ is } a)$$
$$b < a \quad (f \text{ is } b)$$
$$a = b \quad (f \text{ is } c)$$

If limitation of this kind transforms a simple problem into a mathematical one, the mathematical element is intensified as the opposite idea of extension is applied. In other words, how many weighings are needed if there are more than nine coins, say 100, or m, and there is one false coin among them?

Here, for the calculator, is the solution. One must consider two different situations:

(*a*) If the number of coins is a power of 3, as for instance $3 \times 3 \times 3 \times 3 = 3^4$, four weighings will suffice. Generalizing, if the number of coins is 3^k, *k weighings will suffice.*

(*b*) If m is any other number, say $m = 100$, it will lie between two powers of 3, one higher, one lower, e.g.:

$$3^4 = 81 < 100 < 243 = 3^5$$

The smallest number of weighings possible here is therefore five, i.e., the same as the index of the upper power of 3.

Now we come to the matter of the method of carrying out the weighings. We split the m coins into three groups, e.g., $m = 27 = 9 + 9 + 9$, and this splitting is written $S(9, 9, 9)$. Two of these groups are placed in the scale pans. If one is lighter, then we know the false coin is in this group; if the two groups are equal in weight, the false coin is in the third group. The isolation of the group containing the false coin is labeled F.

Situation (a)

Total number $m = 3^4 = 81$.

1. $S(27, 27, 27)$ — $F(27)$
2. $S(9, 9, 9)$ — $F(9)$
3. $S(3, 3, 3)$ — $F(3)$
4. $S(1, 1, 1)$ — $F(1)$

Situation (b)

Any other number, say $m = 100$. If three equal groups are impossible, we split it into two equal groups and a third unequal one, as for $m = 100$:

1. $S(34, 34, 32)$ — $F(34)$ or $F'(32)$

Place the two equal groups into the scale pans to determine whether the lighter coin is in the $F(34)$ group or in the $F'(32)$ group. Assuming it is in the $F(34)$ group, we continue with:

2. $S(12, 12, 10)$ — $F(12)$ or $F'(10)$
3. $S(4, 4, 4)$ — $F(4)$
4. $S(1, 1, 2)$ — $F(1)$ finish! or $F'(2)$
5. $S(1, 1)$ — $F(1)$

Five weighings are sufficient to isolate the false coin no matter what the result of any particular weighing; in favorable cases, as in the fourth weighing above, you may need less than five.

The task becomes even more involved in a situation like this: among 9 coins there is one false one which differs in weight from each of the others, but we are not told whether it is lighter or heavier. What is the least number of weighings needed to isolate this coin? The answer is: *three!* You will find that after two weighings you know what group contains the false coin and if it is lighter or heavier than the normal ones. Therefore, one more weighing is needed than in the case above.

In the situation (*a*) for $m = 3^k$ the answer is simply $(k + 1)$; in situation (*b*) the formula is much more complicated and cannot be dealt with here.

LIMITATION AND EXTENSION, in instances of this kind, transform a simple problem into one involving mathematics. Mathematicians could quote many examples of limitation. An old Greek one, which has turned out to be of quite unexpected significance, was the practice of using for the construction of a geometrical figure only the circle and straight line (compasses or dividers and ruler). The western world also toiled in vain for centuries with these instruments at the task of drawing a rectangle equal in area to a given circle (this too a limitation problem of Greek origin). This was the so-called "squaring of the circle," and eventually came the question, "Is it only a matter of time before the solution is found, or is the problem quite insoluble?" The challenge of proving that it was impossible could not be taken up until mathematical knowledge had made considerable advances into unexplored realms of algebraic and arithmetical lore. Not until 1822 was the proof of the impossibility of squaring the circle actually formulated—more than 2000 years after the problem was first promulgated. But if there is no limitation about using only ruler and compasses, there is nothing to this problem. Any tenth-grader could solve it nowadays: the task is to construct a square (of side x) with area the same as that of a circle (radius r). Thus $x^2 = \pi r^2$, i.e., $x = r\sqrt{\pi} = 1.7725r$ approximately. A circle with radius 10 in. has thus the same area as a square with side 17.725 in.

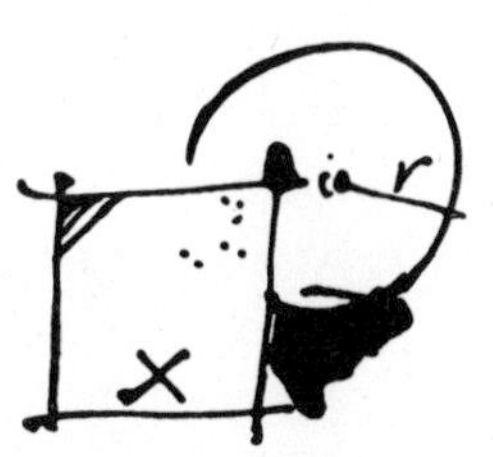

Just as fertile as limitation is the generalization or extension of the scope of a problem. If between 3 subscribers 3 telephone lines are necessary, so that each one can speak with any of the others, how many lines are needed for 4 or 10 or 1000 or in general n subscribers? This leads to the construction of a formula, using numbers and symbols that will have general application (see p. 78).

Probably the most significant instance of extension in mathematics is seen in the realm of numbers. The numbers 1, 2, 3, etc., were given to us, as it were, by nature. Mankind has extended these by the successive concepts of fractions, negative numbers, irrational, and complex numbers. Without this extension of the ranks of numbers, present-day mathematics could not exist.

In geometry a fruitful example of extension is the concept of space (cf. "The Fourth Dimension," p. 243). But even extension, as well as limitation, can be operated only within bounds. There are innumerable triplets of whole numbers (a, b, c) which satisfy the relation $a^2 + b^2 = c^2$. For example (3, 4, 5) and (8, 15, 17) give respectively $9 + 16 = 25$ and $64 + 225 = 289$. However, there seems to be no triplet of numbers satisfying a similar relation with powers higher than 2, such as $a^3 + b^3 = c^3$ or $a^5 + b^5 = c^5$. To give a proof of the impossibility of this is apparently an extremely difficult task. So far it has in fact only been given in the case of some powers, not yet for all.

Chapter 3

PEACH TREES, HONEYCOMBS, AND QUEEN DIDO

John Smith dreams of having an orchard of peach trees. He is always scheming how best to plan it, producing countless sketches of possible layouts. One day, when so occupied, he comes up against the question of fencing. As he considers the length of fencing in relation to the shape of the orchard he makes two curious discoveries.

THE FIRST DISCOVERY. He always believed that with an orchard or garden of a certain area, say 100 sq. yd., the length of fence required would also be a definite figure, 42 yd., for instance. With 200 sq. yd. he would expect to need twice as much fencing. He now notices that this is not so at all. He ponders this matter, using a sketch of a small garden of area 4 sq. yd. He draws it to the scale of 1 sq. in. = 1 sq. yd. and examines three cases.

First, suppose he has the customary rectangular garden. If it is very long then it will also be very narrow. The rectangle *R′*

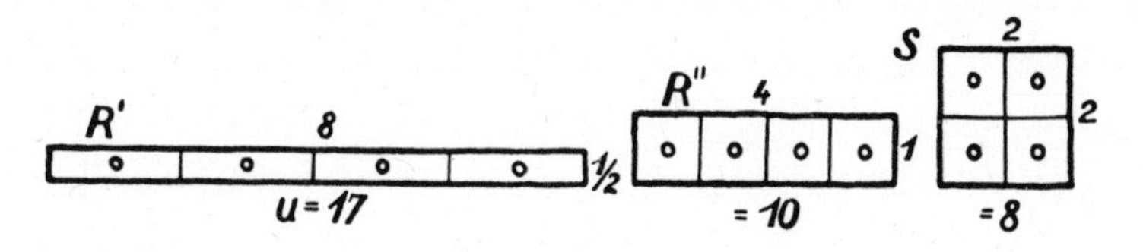

measures 8 yd. by $\frac{1}{2}$ yd., and so the length of fencing needed (u) is $u = 8 + \frac{1}{2} + 8 + \frac{1}{2} = 17$. With rectangle R'', which measures 4 yd. by 1 yd., $u = 2 \times (4 + 1) = 10$, which is 7 yd. shorter. If, again, the rectangle is square, like S, measuring 2 yd. by 2 yd., $u = 4 \times 2 = 8$. This is the shortest possible perimeter where rectangles are concerned. Thus John Smith recognizes the important fact that the fence length or perimeter depends not only on the size, but also on the shape of the garden. But in what way? John Smith considers the matter: Of all rectangles the square is the one regular quadrilateral, having all sides equal and all angles equal.

He now considers a second instance. In regular polygons how does the perimeter (u) depend on the number of angles? Does it increase with the number of angles, or decrease or remain constant? He tries an equilateral triangle with area 4 sq. yd., and finds that the perimeter is 9.12 yd.—which is more than with the square. With a hexagon he finds $u = 7.44$—which is less than the square.

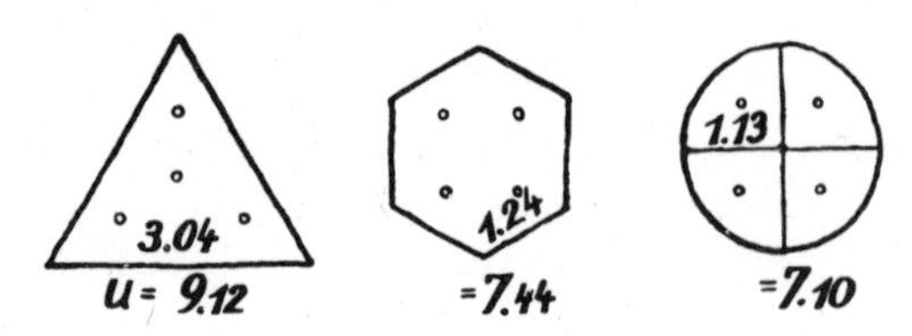

Thus, with regular polygons of equal area A (here 4 sq. yd.), as the number of angles increases, the perimeter decreases, and vice versa. This is curious. With an octagon the perimeter is less than that of a hexagon; with a polygon of one hundred sides it is less than with one having ninety sides. With a thousand sides the perimeter of the polygon is less than with. . . .

Forthwith John Smith moves on to consider the third case, that of the circle. The circle is the logical outcome of the idea of increasing indefinitely the number of sides or angles in a series of regular polygons. What does Mr. Smith find here? In a circle of area 4 sq. yd. the perimeter or circumference is 7.1 yd.—the smallest of all, so far. This is moreover the upper limit of the sequence of polygons, for no polygon has more "sides" than the circle. At the lower limit is the triangle, for no polygon has fewer than three sides.

Thus all values for the perimeters of regular polygons (the term here includes triangle, rectangle, and circle) of area 4 sq. yd. lie between 9.12 yd. for the triangle and 7.1 yd. for the circle—a span of 2.02 yd. The perimeter of the triangle exceeds the circumference of the circle by this amount, i.e., by $2.02/7.1 = .285$ or 28.5% of the circumference. Thus of all possible gardens of the same area (here 4 sq. yd.), a circular one would have the smallest length of fence. So much for John Smith's first discovery.

FOR THE CALCULATOR. The area of a triangle is half the length of its base times its height ($A = \frac{1}{2}bh$). With an equilateral triangle of side a and area 4, $(a^2\sqrt{3})/4 = 4$. From this a is 3.04 and $u = 3a = 9.12$.

The area of a hexagon comprises six identical equilateral triangles with side x. Thus $A = 6\,(x^2\sqrt{3})/4 = 4$, $x = 1.24$, and $u = 6x = 7.44$.

The circumference of a circle is $2\pi r$, where r is the radius and $\pi = 3.14$. The area is πr^2, which is 4. Hence $r^2 = 4/\pi$, $r = 1.13$ and $u = 2\pi \times 1.13 = 7.10$.

FENCING COSTS "PER PEACH TREE." Acting on what he has just learned, John Smith now makes a calculation. "As to the cost of the fence, I will bear the cost of construction, but the cost of maintenance ($1 per year per yard of fence) must be borne by the trees themselves, that is, out of the profits from the sale of peaches. Supposing on every square yard I plant a tree, then in my imaginary orchard of 4 sq. yd. there will be four trees. What costs are borne by each peach tree when planted in the various shapes of orchard so far considered? This is given by the ratio of fence length u to area A (number of trees).

Consider now each shape of orchard in turn. With the long narrow rectangle R' (see p. 41) where $u = 17$ the fence ratio $F = 17 : 4 = 4.25$ yd./sq. yd. This means that with this shape each peach tree has to bear $4.25 of the cost of fence maintenance per year. John Smith considers this too much: this garden has too much fence for its area.

He now compiles a table showing the maintenance cost, i.e., F, the fence ratio, $u : A$, which each tree must bear in the various shapes of orchard.

1 *Shape of orchard*	2 *Perimeter u (in yards)*	3 *Fence ratio F = maintenance cost per tree in dollars*	4 *F : 4 as a percentage*
Rectangle R'	17	4.25	106
Rectangle R''	10	2.50	63
Triangle T	9.12	2.28	57
Square S	8	2.00	50
Hexagon H	7.44	1.86	47
Circle C	7.10	1.78	44.5

Thus it can be seen that with the other shapes of orchard each tree would have to bear less of the fence maintenance costs than in the case of the rectangle R'. The smallest cost would be with the circular orchard—only $1.78. This reckoning in terms of money really brings home to John Smith the strange relationship between perimeter and area.

TAXES AND THE COMMUNITY. The ideas we have just been considering are so curious that we shall now look at them again in another context. Think of a square of area 1 sq. yd. We shall call it the unit square. It has a perimeter of 4 yd. John Smith's orchard comprises an area equivalent to 4 unit squares. Now, according to the shape of orchard into which these 4 unit squares are molded, each unit square must contribute in equal measure with its three fellows a proportion of the cost of its own perimeter, but how much? Column 3 in the table tells us this. If the 4 unit squares are remolded into a circle, each one has to contribute only 1.78 of its own 4 yd., i.e., 1.78/4 = .445, or 44.5%; with the square, 2 yd., or 50% (more!); with the rectangle R' 4.25 yd.—more than it possesses! (Column 4 shows these contributions in terms of percentage of unit square perimeter).

The diagram below shows us the situation clearly; the shaded line represents the contribution of the unit square perimeter to the total perimeter.

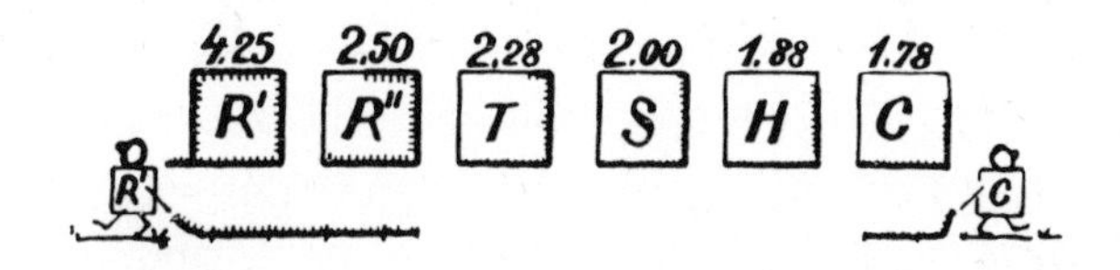

So if the 4 unit squares join to form a circular "community," the tax they pay (44.5% of their own perimeter) is the smallest possible; this makes the circular community the most advantageous: a noteworthy fact indeed, that there does exist a form of state which possesses some advantages! On the other hand, if the 4 unit squares act less cleverly and are constituted in a rectangular community as in R', then each must contribute not just his own perimeter of 4 yd., but $\frac{1}{16}$th as much again or 6% more (.25 yd.) than he possesses!

Thus emerges another significant fact, namely, that it rests with the unit squares as "subjects of the community," whether they work to form a "state" of greater or lesser advantage to themselves.

And so the curious relationship between perimeter and area, "exterior and interior," is at work not only in purely mathematical abstractions; it also affects John Smith's purse, and it has vital importance in the world of nature, as the next example shows.

HONEYCOMBS. Bees build for themselves a little town, and each house in it is a separate little apartment shaped like a hollow pillar with high perpendicular wax walls. The bees try to build their houses as economically as possible, achieving the maximum possible space with the minimum consumption of wax: these are their two "mathematical" stipulations.

The walls stand as a fence round the floor area. The best fence ratio ($F = u : A$, i.e., perimeter to area) is given by the circle: the bees learned this by buzzing round in John Smith's peach orchard, and they therefore considered the idea of building a community of circular houses. But no! This way there would be a waste of all the little spaces between the houses.

Circular shape may mean economy in wax for the walls, but it does not make the best use of the space available. If the ground space is to be used to the fullest extent, perhaps the square

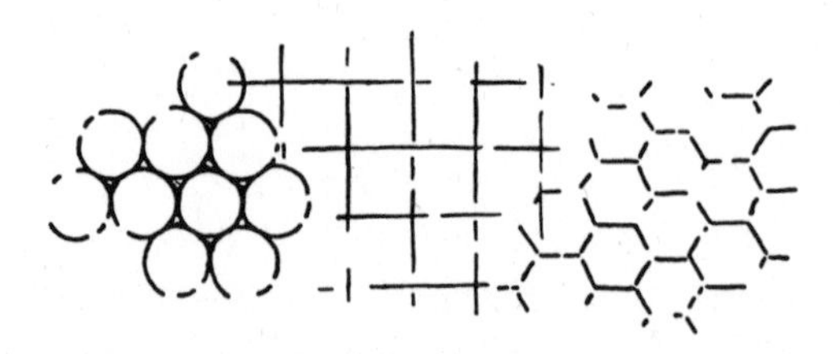

house shape could be used. However, this is not particularly advantageous in its fence ratio. What about using a polygonal shape to give a better fence ratio? Is there one which avoids all waste of space? Yes, there is: the hexagon avoids all loss of interstitial floor space, and as the nearest possible to the circle it also offers the best fence ratio. So all bees build their honeycomb houses in a hexagonal formation. Bees know what's what, and so do women. We shall now hear about just such a one, a woman of ancient times who possessed the wisdom of the bees.

QUEEN DIDO. Dido was the daughter of a Tyrian king. When her brother murdered her husband, she fled with faithful followers into Africa to the kingdom of Iarbus, and begged King Iarbus to give her some land. "How much do you want?" asked the king mistrustfully. "As much as I can span with the hide of an ox," she said. Well, that is hardly enough ground to build a hut on, so Iarbus agreed, and gave her the hide of an ox.

Vergil, the Latin poet who gave us this tale, does not relate what happened next. But there is no doubt that Dido cut up the hide into narrow strips, and knotted them together to make a long, endless thong. Whatever land she enclosed with this was indeed spanned with the hide of an ox, and this did not offend against the terms of the agreement. Of course, she thought things out just like John Smith: "How should I lay out the leather thong to enclose the greatest area of land? As a square? Or a hexagon? Or a circle?"

Just as John Smith was able to decide that with the circle he had the smallest perimeter for his fixed area of garden, so Dido could clearly see this the other way round, namely that a perimeter of fixed length must be arranged in the shape of a circle to enclose the largest possible area. The circle is, then, the unique plane figure which, of all others, encloses the biggest area for a given perimeter (Dido), and the smallest perimeter for a given area (John Smith).

So Dido had her followers lay out the leather strip in the shape of a circle, and taking possession of the land enclosed founded the city of Byrsa, later called Carthage. Vergil does not relate Iarbus' reaction to all this, but he does tell of Byrsa (Greek for oxhide), and how Aeneas came there as the sole survivor from the fall of Troy, fell in love with Dido, and later deserted her, causing Dido eventually to commit suicide. It is true that historians today tend to doubt the story of the oxhide and the cleverness of Dido. In a detached sort of way they suggest that the Tyrian word *birtha* means mountain, i.e., that on which the town's fortress stood, as does the Acropolis at Athens. This word they claim has been corrupted by the legend-loving Greeks to *byrsa*, so that they could spread the tale about the oxhide. But the historians cannot prove their story any more than the other, and as the latter is after all a better one, we shall stick to it.

Nature provides a wonderful supplement to the story of Dido and her circle. If you dip a wire, bent into a rectangular shape, into a soap solution, a thin film becomes stretched across it. If on this we place a tiny band of fine silken thread, corresponding to Dido's strip of leather, it swims about easily on the soap film, gradually changing its shape. If we now stick a needle through the film inside the silken band, it bursts and in a flash Dido's silken thread is pulled as if by magic into a perfect circle, not a square or a hexagon, but a circle!

What has happened? Every tiny bit of the soap film possesses, as it were, the power to pull at the film and help keep it stretched. In physics this is called surface tension. When the film inside the boundary of the silken thread is burst, causing the disappearance of the forces at work there, then the forces on the rest of the film outside the thread pull with all their might until the empty area inside is as large as possible—producing a circle!

JOHN SMITH'S SECOND DISCOVERY. We must return to his peach orchard, for meanwhile he has made a second discovery about perimeter and area. From his table (p. 44), we can see that the fence ratio F grows smaller, the more the orchard shapes approach the circular. With the circle it is at its minimum, that is, 1.78 yd. of perimeter per sq. yd. of area. This is assuming that the area is constant at 4 sq. yd. for all shapes of orchard.

But it also grows smaller, as John Smith finds, if one shape is maintained—say the square—and increased in area.

Area A in sq. yd.	4	16	100	10,000
Perimeter u in yd.	8	16	40	400
Fence ratio $F = u : A$ in yd./sq. yd.	2	1	.4	.04

If the shape of the figure remains constant as the area increases, the fence ratio becomes smaller.

In terms of John Smith's money reckonings, the larger the garden, whatever its shape may be, the smaller is the fence maintenance cost per peach tree.

BY THE CALCULATOR this is easily understood. With a square of side a, $A = a^2$, and $u = 4a$. Hence $F = 4a/a^2 = 4/a$, a fraction which grows progressively smaller as a grows larger.

Now John Smith summarizes his discoveries:

(a) If he gives his orchard a fixed area, he needs fencing of varying length, according to the shape of the orchard. Of all shapes the circle is the one needing least fencing.

(b) If he is not bound to a fixed area, he can, whatever shape he cares to choose, make the fence ratio as small as he likes, and thus reduce at will the fence maintenance cost per tree.

These are John Smith's two discoveries, and what a quandary he is in! He is so confused by all this that to this day he just cannot decide how to lay out his orchard.

FUNCTION: ONE FUNDAMENTAL CONCEPT

TABLE OF VALUES, CURVE, FUNCTION. Suppose you have a fever, and the doctor orders precise observations of your temperature. A table is compiled, showing time of day (t) and degree of fever (F).

Time of day in hours (t)	8	9	10	11	12	1	2
Degree of fever (F) °F (temperature)	100.3	100.4	100.6	101.0	100.7	101.0	101.0

If you are in hospital, the nurses keep a record of these figures in the form of a graph on which the horizontal axis shows the time t, and the vertical axis temperature F. The progress of the fever shows up as a line when the nurse joins the successive points recorded.

Let us put on our mathematical spectacles and ask what is actually being done here. The two values t and F are being associated or put in relationship to one another. At every point in time a certain temperature can be read from the graph: each point in time has a certain temperature value associated with it. Thus one might say, "The degree of fever F is dependent on the time t, or it is a function f of the time." Written in brief $F = f(t)$. This mathematical dependence of a value B on another value A by no means implies any genuine dependence or any system of cause and effect. The degree of fever is not caused by time: it merely means that with any given value of A (the independent variable, time) a certain value of B (the dependent variable, degree of fever) will be associated.

This idea of function has become a fundamental concept in mathematics. It is easy to understand, and would seem to provide an excellent way of expressing association between values, but at the same time it has a vast range of application. For one can appreciate that:

THE TASK OF ALL EXPERIMENT is to establish how a certain value A might depend upon one or more others, B, C, etc. (In mathematical language, to represent the value A as a function of the values B, C, etc.)

You are driving your car. A car in motion possesses, as distinct from a stationary car, kinetic energy, K, the power to do work, as would be abundantly clear were you to collide with something! In order to define this, the science of physics proceeds in two stages. It asks "where from?" and "how?"

Upon what values does kinetic energy depend? It has been established that the kinetic energy, K, depends upon two values: mass m and speed or velocity v. This is represented in symbols as $K = f(m, v)$: "Kinetic energy is a function of mass and velocity." Thus, if the values of mass and velocity are known, the kinetic energy associated with them can be determined.

How does kinetic energy depend upon these quantities? Experiment has shown that kinetic energy varies in direct proportion to both: it increases as they increase, but in the case of velocity kinetic energy increases to a higher degree. If velocity is doubled, kinetic energy is quadrupled: $K = mv^2/2$. Physicists have found the denominator 2 to be necessary. Thus the function has been determined and the problem under investigation solved. The value of kinetic energy can thus be predicted for any given instance.

FOR THE CALCULATOR. If your car weighs 3200 lb., and the acceleration of gravity is 32 ft. per sec.^{2}, its mass can be given as 3200/32 or 100 mass units, and if you drive at a speed of 72 ft./sec. (50 mi./hr.), the kinetic energy is $100 \times 72^2/2 = 50 \times 5184 = 259{,}200$ foot-pounds of energy. The car's capacity to do work is then as great as that of a crane which lifts a locomotive weighing nearly 130 tons one foot off the ground—an enormous amount!

What is the task of mathematics in such matters? It is to investigate the qualities of all possible 'pure' functions. It does not matter what the quantities m, v, and K are in reality; mathematics is concerned only with the manner in which the function K will vary as m and v change, i.e., how it grows, decreases, fluctuates, reaches its peak, and so on. Such purely mathematical knowledge has of course its practical importance.

THE REPRESENTATION OF A FUNCTION. A function can appear in three different ways:

As a *functional equation*, as in the instance of the formula for kinetic energy given above. This is a "prescription" for calculating purposes, by means of which if values of mass and speed are known, the momentum can be calculated. Further examples are the gradient of a road (see p. 98), and the earth's corset (see p. 202). By no means all the world's associated values can be expressed in this handy form (cf. the association between fever and time of day). There is thus a second method of expressing function:

As *a table of values* (cf. the temperature chart on p. 50). Tables like this are a common feature of modern life. There is one, for instance, that enables us to read off the price of a ticket for journeys of various distances. Other examples are the tables for expectation of life (see p. 249), or for frequency of vibration and musical pitch (see p. 69). But these tables of figures are often less convenient than graphical representation.

Graphical representation of a function. For example, in a graph of the temperature table on p. 50, the horizontal axis would be graduated in time units, and the vertical axis in degrees of temperature. (See also the details of a similar graph of mortality figures, p. 251.) At one glance can be seen the whole course of a patient's fever—when it rose, reached its peak, declined, and finally ceased.

If a quantity such as kinetic energy depends not on one but on several other quantities, then graphical representation is more difficult, but still possible (cf. "the calculating pictures," p. 152).

Functional equation, table of values, and graphical representation are thus the three forms in which a function may be illustrated. The fever and mortality curves are "curves of experience," and the associated quantities which constitute them are "functions of experience," for these values are not found by theoretical calculation, but by actual experience (e.g., by measurement or counting). In the case of the fever you cannot predict at 10 a.m. what the patient's temperature will be at 2 p.m. You just have to wait until 2 p.m. and measure it; at most one might guess at the likely progress of the fever. Thus one cannot construct a general formula for predicting the precise dependence of temperature on time, nor can one do this for the majority of functions in real life (weather, commerce, birth rate, coal production, etc.) Thus a function of experience can only be presented in two forms: as a table of values or as a graph.

FUNCTIONAL EQUATION AND GRAPH. A so-called "mathematical" function on the other hand is one that can be expressed also as a functional equation. Here arises the possibility of unexpected significance: the association of the equation, which belongs to the realm of number, and the graph, which is essentially diagrammatic or geometrical. Thus number and shape become associated.

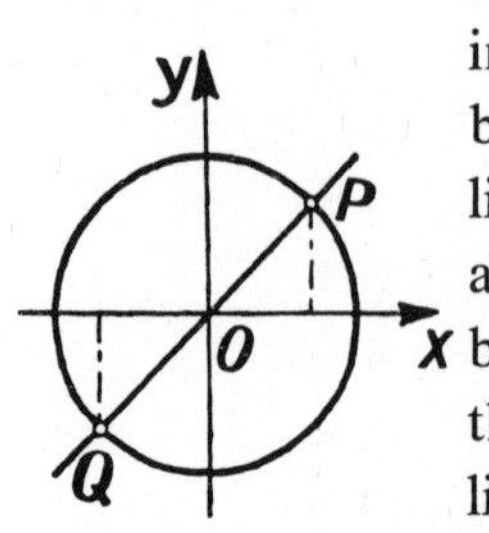

A circle with radius 5 drawn round the point of intersection 0 of the axes x and y may be represented by the functional equation $x^2 + y^2 = 25$. A straight line through the point 0 at an angle of 45° with the axes can similarly be represented by $y = x$. From both these numerical equations can be calculated the position of the points of intersection of straight line and circle: $P(3.5, 3.5)$ and $Q(-3.5, -3.5)$. The geometrical properties of a curve, such as gradient, curvature, continuity, segment, and angle can together with other features be calculated, and conversely the results of calculations can be interpreted as geometrical properties.

This interlocking of number and shape within the field of two crossed axes has proved itself to be one of the most fruitful ideas in the whole of Western mathematics. Without this calculating (or analytical) geometry, mathematics would never have achieved its present significance.

MATHEMATICAL RIGOR

Of what does this consist? Its demands are twofold: one must express precisely what one means to say, and one must prove all assertions. "The tangent to a circle is at right angles to the line drawn through the center of the circle and the point of contact of the tangent with the circle." When this mathematical "proposition" is considered, all such terms as circle, tangent, etc. must be clearly explained and defined, and then the proposition must be proved. Definition and proof are the two essential ingredients of mathematical rigor.

The nature of proof will be dealt with later (see "Prime Numbers," p. 58); for the moment let us consider definition. A definition must fit an idea exactly, like a tightrope walker's tights:

it must not be a loose, shapeless affair, full of loopholes or ambiguities. The art, which is none too easy, is to say neither too little nor too much, but just what is necessary.

WHAT IS A CIRCLE? Everyone knows this, but how can it be precisely explained? Suppose you say "It is an area, the edge of which is of equal roundness." But what does "of equal roundness" mean? If you say "It is an area that has the same breadth all round, so that one might place it like a coin between two parallel rails and roll it along (in the diagram, b = breadth)," then

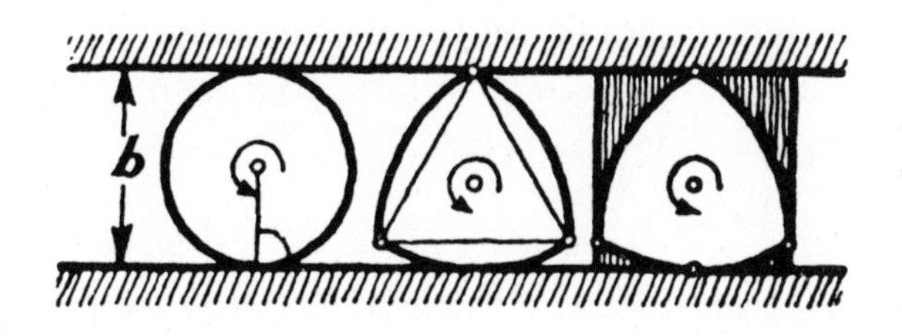

this does seem to be a quality that only the circle possesses: but in fact it is not so. An area with corners like the second shape in the diagram—we might call it a bow-sided equilateral triangle—can be rolled between two parallel rails, or rotated inside a square just like the circle. It is also "of equal breadth all round," and curiously enough it has the same perimeter as the circle ($\pi b = 3.1416b$). Thus if the "cornerless circles" went to law to establish their identity, and were declared in law to be "persons of equal breadth all round," then the whole tribe of bow-sided figures might slip through the same mesh. Such a pronouncement in law, or definition, has a loophole in it.

You would encounter a similar difficulty if you defined the circle as "a curve which can follow itself around," for a straight line can do this also, and so can a screw-thread, as for instance a corkscrew. There are curved Turkish scimitars which follow their own curve as they slide into their scabbards, and also straight ones and curly screw-twisted ones.

THE TANGENT to a curve is also very tricky to define. If you say it is a straight line which meets the curve at only one point, this is in fact true of the circle, but not of the sine curve or wave curve, for if the line touches, say, the crest of the wave it has also innumerable points of contact with all the other crests. And if you say a tangent is a straight line which does not cut the curve, this is also untrue of the wave curve, because at the point of inflexion (*W* in the diagram), where a left-hand curve changes to a right-hand curve, it both touches and cuts the curve.

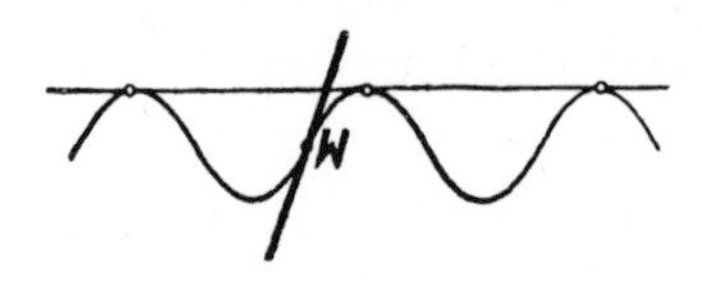

AGAIN, HOW SHOULD WE DEFINE A POINT, a term so familiar to all? A schoolboy once wrote "A point is an angle with its legs cut off," but this will hardly do. If you follow Euclid, the Greek thinker of 2000 years ago who was the first to work with mathematical rigor, insisting on definition and proof, you might say "A point is something that has no parts" (i.e., no magnitude). After much fruitless thought, you might be tempted to agree with what the great artist Albrecht Dürer wrote in his book of geometry: "In order that pupils shall become wise in practical knowledge, I shall describe a point as a tiny dot made with a pen, and write beside it the word 'point.' Then shall this dot be termed a point." We can all appreciate what he means, but the center of a circle is something rather different from one of Dürer's dots. The definition with which many will agree was expressed by the brilliant mathematician Hilbert: he called it "a circle with zero radius." Frankly, however, there are basic ideas which just cannot be defined. The point is one of them, and so is surface, as we shall learn when considering the twisted belt (see p. 75).

There are many others. Careful research into fundamentals has shown, however, that the whole structure of mathematics may be built up with suitable rigor.

THE VILLAGE BARBER. It is strange how one can be firmly convinced that an idea is understood quite clearly, and yet one becomes confused by it. What is a village barber? He is a barber who shaves all the people in the village who do not shave themselves. The definition of an idea *A* must of course be so clear that one can decide, when contemplating a certain thing, whether it is or is not *A*. Now what about this village barber? Does he shave himself or not? If he shaves himself, then, according to the definition, he must not shave himself, because he only shaves those who do not shave themselves. Worse, if he does not shave himself, then he must shave himself, as he shaves all those who do not shave themselves. What a quandary! You would never suspect that these snags might lurk in the harmless little definition quoted above. In mathematics also there are "village barbers" of whom one must beware. (E.g., consider *M* the class of all classes which do not contain themselves. Does *M* contain itself or not?)

Thus definition is not always simple. A definition must be complete, lucid, and definite, free from all contradiction and ambiguity. Therefore mathematicians do not have conflicting opinions about the meaning of a concept: contrast the way politicians squabble about such words as democracy, each interpreting it to suit his own ends.

The art of defining makes one appreciate the great miracle of language: a picture within one's mind is transformed into words, which will in turn be re-transformed into the same picture in the listener's mind. Poets seek to do this also; they busy themselves with the "echo" of a word, the associations aroused in the mind by it. For poets the best is often that which is read between the lines:

"The moon was a ghostly galleon . . ."

For mathematical purposes such emotional echoes are quite out of place: we are concerned only with the actual written word, with its fixed and definite meaning and application. It must not be subject to varied interpretation according to human emotional bias.

To the layman this may seem unpleasantly austere, but this is taking an emotionally conditioned view. If it is considered with the intellect, rigor makes for clarity, the goal of all intellectual striving. It is a great mistake to confuse rigor with dull pedantry, as so many people do. Clarity does not exclude imagination, nor rigor the riches of thought. The joy of making a discovery of mathematical purity is one of the greatest emotions in life.

HOW MANY PRIME NUMBERS ARE THERE?

PRIME NUMBERS AND COMPOSITE NUMBERS. Counting is easy: 1, 2, 3, 4—each figure is one greater than the one before. In spite of this common origin, however, the numbers do not all possess the same qualities. Some may be split into smaller factors, as for instance $12 = 2 \times 2 \times 3 = 2 \times 6 = 3 \times 4$. Numbers such as 12 are called composite, while others, such as 7, cannot be so divided except by one and itself (i.e., 1×7), and these are called *prime* numbers.

Every composite number can be made up of factors which are all prime numbers (e.g., $12 = 2 \times 2 \times 3$; $30 = 2 \times 3 \times 5$). 1 is not considered to be a proper factor for this purpose, and is neither prime nor composite. Prime numbers are, as it were, the atoms which make up the composite numbers. The smallest prime number is 2, which is, incidentally, the only even prime number.

HOW MANY PRIME NUMBERS ARE THERE?

Below	100	1000	10,000	100,000,000	
there are	24	268	1229	5,761,455	prime numbers,

and the biggest so far calculated (in 1957) has 969 figures ($2^{3217} - 1 = 2.07 \times 10^{968}$). Are there others beyond this?

We could compile a list of prime numbers and count them: it is not too hard. Write down the natural sequence of numbers, omitting 1, and then strike out in turn all multiples of 2 (4, 6, 8, etc.), that is, all the even numbers; after that all multiples of 3, 5, 7, etc.

Natural sequence	2	3	4	5	6	7	8	9	10	11	12	13	14	15	16	—
"Sieving" for																
multiples of 2	2	3	.	5	.	7	.	9	.	11	.	13	.	15	.	etc.
multiples of 3	2	3	.	5	.	7	.	.	.	11	.	13	.	.	.	etc.
multiples of 5	2	3	.	5	.	7	.	.	.	11	.	13	.	.	.	etc.

GENERAL PROCEDURE: After each "sieving," sieve once more for numbers which are multiples of that number remaining in your list immediately to the right of the number just used, e.g. if you have just sieved for multiples of 5, sieve now for multiples of 7, and after that for those of 11, 13, etc.

The right-hand neighbor of each prime number is always the next prime to be used. Thus this sieving process very neatly lays bare at each step the next prime number, and at last you will be left with the whole sequence of prime numbers in your sieve. However, one cannot go on sieving forever! Therefore, by this method, we cannot find out whether the sieving method breaks down—whether a stage is reached when all numbers to the right of the last prime have already been deleted: in other words, we never learn in this way whether there is an ultimate prime number or an infinite list of prime numbers.

In fact, there is an infinite number! Just consider the audacity of this statement; you do *not* know the numbers themselves, and yet you know that there is an *infinite* number of them! But how on earth can we be sure of this, when we can only count up to a finite number?

The proof, formulated by Euclid two thousand years ago, is as simple as it is clever, and a classic example of clarity—a fine chance for you to observe the illuminating power of a mathematical proof. First must come, however, a little preparation: a composite number such as $30 = 2 \times 3 \times 5$ is divisible by any of the prime numbers which are among its factors, e.g., 5. If you add 1 to 30, $31 = 2 \times 3 \times 5 + 1$, then any division by one of the prime factors will always leave a remainder 1; thus 31 is not exactly divisible by factors.

Now for the prime numbers: if their sequence is infinite, i.e., has no end, then there is no final prime number. This will be proved if we can find for every prime number p a following one p', which is larger than p.

Let us take a prime number p, and make with it a new number:

$$Z(p) = 2 \times 3 \times 5 \times 7 \ldots p + 1.$$

Thus, the product of all prime numbers from 2 to p is increased by 1, as for example:

$$Z(5) = 2 \times 3 \times 5 + 1 = 31$$

$$\text{or} \quad Z(13) = 2 \times 3 \times 5 \times 7 \times 11 \times 13 + 1 = 30{,}031.$$

What do we know about this new number $Z(p)$? It is greater than p, and it is not divisible by any of the constituent primes 2, $\ldots$, p. Thus 31 is not divisible by 2, 3, 5 and the new number $Z(p)$ is only divisible by prime numbers which are not contained in the sequence 2, $\ldots$, p, that is, by numbers greater than p.

The number 31 is a prime number itself and greater than 5. The number 30,031 $= 59 \times 509$ is composite, but the prime numbers 59 and 509, by which it is divisible, are both greater than 13.

Conclusion: In forming a number $Z(p)$ we always find at least one prime number p', which is greater than the prime number p. Therefore the sequence of prime numbers has no end: it extends to infinity!

If you have followed this proof, it will have given you also a glimpse of the true nature of mathematics, such as you could hardly have caught in another context. It will have shown you:

(*a*) What the act of proving means: every step an instance clearly thought out and its significance scrutinized.

(*b*) How forcefully this mathematical evaluation of the problem contrasts with the tedious "try it out" approach of the sieving method, and settles the whole question infallibly by the exercise of pure reasoning.

(*c*) How we can make confident statements about the realms of infinity, even though we can trespass into them only as far as our own finite numbers will take us.

(*d*) How the concern of mathematics is not with uses and applications, but with exploring the wonderful interrelations of numbers, and the pattern of basic conceptions familiar to our minds.

(*e*) How mathematical knowledge can be full of spirit and imagination, and made by clarity and rigor even more illuminating, not dry and dull as many ignorant persons believe.

In conclusion you have learned also something of the great mathematical ability of the ancient Greeks, for here, with a few deft strokes, the distinction between prime and composite numbers is made and the question of how many prime numbers formulated, the surprising answer given and cleverly proved.

Chapter 4

ORDER WILL OUT: STANDARDIZATION

UNIFORM SPACING. John Smith is planting dwarf trees in a section of his garden. The strip of land concerned is 10 yd. long; the distance between any two trees is to be 1 yd., and he wants a tree at each end of the strip. How many trees are needed?

His neighbor says 10—one for each yard. Another friend thinks 12—one at each end plus ten for the 10 yd. between. John Smith follows the old saying that truth lies between two extremes and tries 11—exactly right! Acting on this he devises a simple method for calculating the answer to this kind of problem.

Then, one day, a gardening friend comes to consult him. He wants to plant 6 trees at equal distances along a 10 yd. strip: how far apart should each pair be? "If there is to be one tree at each end, the distance between any two will be 2 yards," replies John Smith. "But there are 6, not 5 trees!" "Yes, that is

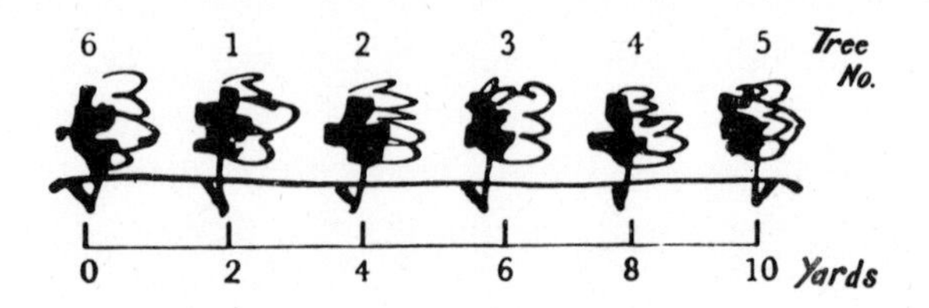

the reason: $10 \div 5 = 2$." "But $10 \div 6$ does not equal 2!" John Smith says, "Here in this sketch (p. 62), you have the strip of land 10 yards long, marked out in intervals of 1, 2, 3, ..., 10 yards. Divide this by one less than the number of trees you wish to plant. Plant the first tree at 2, the second at 4, etc., and the fifth at 10. You still have a sixth tree to plant; that one goes at 0—right at the beginning of the plot. This 0 is what you overlooked in your calculation."

The Standardized Nails

STANDARDIZATION. Why are we taking John Smith's gardening so seriously? It is because the planting of trees equidistant from one another is a suitable introduction to the subject of standardization, which is so important today in industry, technology, commerce, and daily life. What is it? Briefly, the restriction of the number of possible sizes of an article to a limited range.

Suppose while cycling you lose a nut from your bicycle. This would be nothing serious nowadays, because in the next town there is always a bicycle dealer. Sixty years ago, however, you might have sought a long time without success, and then managed to get only one from a dealer who stocked your particular make of bicycle. In those days individual factories had to make the whole of their product, down to the tiniest spring, screw, or nut. Thus widespread variations existed, and those seeking spares had to go to the original makers. This is still so today, in the case of spares for the most expensive cars and radio sets, for instance, and it is understandable even though some may grouse about having to pay through the nose for a spare cogwheel.

The last war showed how important standardization of spare parts can be. The Russians had to a large extent standardized wheel sizes for military vehicles, and if a wheel was damaged on an otherwise sound vehicle, it could readily be replaced by a sound wheel from any wreck by the roadside, regardless of type.

The pursuit of over-refinement in cars—"This car is unique"—always creates difficulties in the matter of spare parts.

The advantages of standardization are obvious. Let us consider the homely example of nail sizes. Assume that we have to reduce the vast number of nail sizes to 11 standard sizes 0, 1, 2, 3 . . . , 10. First of all we fix the two extremes, size 0 (the smallest) and size 10 (the largest). These are to be, in accordance with prescribed technical needs, 1 centimeter and 10 centimeters (.4 in. and 4 in. approx.). Now we have to fit between these two the remaining 9 sizes—in effect a task identical with that of John Smith and his trees. Standardization is thus in mathematics the task of "interpolation."

John Smith planted his trees at equal distances apart. Let us try this with the 9 nail sizes, interpolated between size 0 and size 10, so that each nail in the sequence is longer by a fixed amount than the one before it. The difference in length between the smallest and largest sizes (9 cm., or 3.6 in.) is to be divided into 10 equal parts. The fixed difference in length from nail to nail is therefore .9 cm (.36 in.). (In John Smith's garden terminology, the plot is 9 cm. long, and 11 trees are to be planted. Thus, according to John Smith's system the spacing is 9 cm. ÷ 10, i.e., .9 cm.) Accordingly, the nail sizes are as follows:

Size	0	1	2	3	4	5	6	7	8	9	10
Length in cm.	1	1.9	2.8	3.7	4.6	5.5	6.4	7.3	8.2	9.1	10

But this type or interpolation is not really satisfactory. If we buy a nail of size 0 and one of size 1, the second one is 90% larger than the first: nearly double. But if we buy one of each of sizes 9 and 10, the larger one is still .9 cm. longer than the other, but only 10% larger. There is thus not much difference in nails of such sizes. In other words, this classification seems hardly worth while where the larger sizes are concerned (see diagram on page 66).

How else can we grade the nails? Not with a uniform increase in length from size to size, but with a proportionate increase, so that the ratio of the lengths of nails of any two consecutive sizes shall be constant. The proportionate rise from one size to the next will then not decrease with the higher sizes as before, but will remain the same in relation to their lengths.

This type of interpolation is not so easy to work out as the last type. We have to find a fixed ratio q, with which to multiply the length of one nail size in order to find the next. If we take, for a trial, $q = 2$, then for the sizes 0, 1, 2, 3, 4 the nail lengths will be respectively 1, 2, 4, 8, 16. But since size 10 of 10 cm. length is to end the required sequence, this "common factor" ($q = 2$) is too big, for even size 4 would contain nails longer than 10 cm. On the other hand q must be greater than 1, for if only 1, all nails would be 1 cm. long. The correct value therefore lies between 1 and 2; it is in fact approximately 1.2589, say 1.26. Using this factor, we can calculate the lengths of the sizes: size 1 is $1 \times q = 1.26$; size 2 is $1 \times q \times q = q^2 = 1.59$, and so on, until at the end $q^{10} = 10$. The final scale looks like this (the numbers have been rounded off: see also "For the calculator," p. 67):

Nail size	0	1	2	3	4	5	6	7	8	9	10
Length in cm.	1	1.25	1.6	2	2.5	3.15	4	5	6.3	8	10

If we now investigate the "jump" from one length to the next, we see that each consecutive nail is about $\frac{1}{4}$ (25%) longer than its predecessor in the series: Sizes 0 and 1, difference in length $1.25 - 1 = .25$ and proportion $.25/1 = 25\%$; Sizes 3 and 4, difference .5 and proportion $.5/2 = 25\%$; Sizes 9 and 10, difference 2 and proportion $2/8 = 25\%$. Thus, as we pass from one size to another at any part of the scale, the "jump" is the same, because the proportional variation in size is constant.

Standardization is in fact carried out along these lines so

that consecutive sizes vary in the same proportion. (See: Din sizes used in Germany for writing paper, p. 70.)

The diagrams *a* and *b* below show the two methods of grading. In diagram *a* the difference *PQ* between the lengths of any two consecutive nails never varies; each successive nail is longer than its predecessor by this amount, so that the line *QQ′* runs parallel

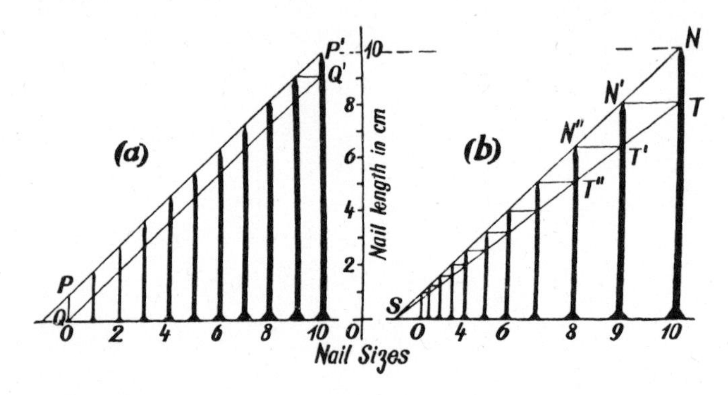

to the line *PP′* joining the nail points. In diagram *b* the ratio $q (= 1.25)$ of the length of any two consecutive nails is constant: each successive nail is longer than its predecessor by the same fraction ($\frac{1}{4}$) of its predecessor's length (e.g., $NT = \frac{1}{4} N'9$). The actual difference in length is not now constant, but varies, as is shown by the lines *SN* and *ST*. The difference increases as the nail length grows.

There is an interesting way of drawing the standardized nail lengths. Draw at the point 10 of a horizontal line a perpendicular representing the nail *N*10 (i.e., nail size 10, 10 cm.). To one side, at a point 9 of the line draw a perpendicular representing the nail *N′*9 (8 cm.). Join the nail points *NN′*, and extend the line to meet the horizontal line at *S*. Join *S* to the point *T* on *N*10, so that $T10 = N'9$ (8 cm.) and let it cut *N′*9 at *T′*. The horizontal line *T′N″* through *T′* meets the perpendicular representing nail 8, which is drawn through the nail positions, giving the point *N″* of the next nail in the series (size 8). This process can be repeated down to size 0 (1 cm.), each time taking the point T', etc., where ST cuts the nail last drawn.

For the calculator is the determination of the common factor q. The individual lengths

$$1, q, q^2, \text{etc., up to } q^{10}$$

diverge increasingly from one another through multiplication by q. They form a "geometric" series in which the successive terms are in constant ratio, each one to the next. (When the difference between successive lengths is constant—cf. John Smith's trees—the series is termed "arithmetic.")

Size 10 has the length $q^{10} = 10$ cm. The task is to find a number q, which, when multiplied by itself 10 times, gives the number 10. It is $\sqrt[10]{10} = 1.2589$, approximately 1.26 (usually rounded off for standardization purposes to 1.25). To use the technical terms of standardization, q^{10} is called the "norm" (N) and the series is called the "norm series." There are finer gradations of the "nail" sequence with 21 or 41 sizes. For instance, in a list of 21 sizes, $N = q^{20}$ and $q = 1.122$; a list of 41 sizes has $N = q^{40}$ and $q = 1.0593$. In calculating these roots logarithms are of course used.

Tuning the Piano

THE STANDARDIZED MUSICAL SCALE. Very many objects in our daily life are standardized. We might even say that the notes of a piano are standardized. This musical standardization was in fact an early example of the "geometric" kind: it took place about 1700 in the days of the great composer J. S. Bach.

A musical scale or octave has as its lowest note the key note (e.g., C), and as its highest note the octave (C′). Because of the characteristic sounds, the notes in between are not equally spaced, but are placed at varying "distances." The problem was to make the gradation uniform for the purposes of the piano. It was a task of standardization just like that of the nail sizes.

How can all this be explained?

The sounds from a piano are caused by tightly stretched vibrating strings. The larger the number of vibrations per second, the higher is the note that comes to our ears. With 128 vibrations we hear the note C, with 256 vibrations its octave C′. A strange relationship exists between musical notes and the human ear: we hear successive notes of the scale if the rates of vibration (frequencies) producing them are in constant ratio one to the other. The three notes produced from the frequencies 100, 150, and 200 do not sound to us as being equally "spaced," even though the frequencies are, with an increase of 50 between each pair. The first frequency ratio $150 : 100 = 1.5$ is greater than the second, $200 : 150 = 1.3$, and so the first interval as we hear it is greater than the second. The second note does not seem to our ears to be midway between the first and the third, but nearer to the third. If now the frequency ratio between the lowest and highest notes in the octave is $2 : 1$ (the rate of vibration of the higher note is always put first), then the following problem of interpolation presents itself: between the lowest and highest notes of the octave, 11 more notes must be introduced with uniform spacing, i.e., between the frequencies 1 and 2, 11 numbers must be interpolated to form a geometric series.

Stating this in terms of nails, the nail size 0 represents the lowest note with frequency 1, and the last nail size represents the highest note of the octave with frequency 2. Apart from this, the only difference is that instead of 9 nails 11 notes have to be interpolated. They are C, C #, D, D #, E, F, F #, G, G #, A, A #, B, C′. This octave (without C′) comprises on the piano keyboard one complete playing unit, which is then repeated along the keyboard on either side. The sharp notes are those made by striking the black keys.

The common factor of the series is calculated from the norm: $N = q^{12} = 2$, and it is therefore the 12th root of 2. Its value is

1.05946. With this number it is then an easy matter to find the frequencies of this standardized scale, the notes of which are uniformly spaced. To the ear these notes will sound "equidistant" from one another, because their frequencies are in the same ratio, one to another.

Musicians call the unstandardized scale "natural tuning," and the standardized scale "tempered tuning." Mathematicians might well call the latter "proportional tuning" because of the constant proportion or ratio of frequencies. Technologists would call it "standardized tuning."

Note	*Tuning*		*Actual frequencies from C′ — C″*
	Natural	*Tempered*	
C	1.000	1.000	259
C#		1.059	274
D	1.125	1.122	290
D#		1.189	308
E	1.250	1.260	326
F	1.333	1.335	345
F#		1.414	366
G	1.500	1.498	388
G#		1.587	411
A	1.667	1.682	435
A#		1.782	461
B	1.875	1.888	488
C′	2.000	2.000	517

In the second column are the frequencies for the notes of the major scale in natural tuning; in the third are the frequencies for the notes in tempered tuning. We see that except for D and G the frequencies for natural tuning are lower than those in tempered tuning. Because the frequency of the lowest note is fixed and all subsequent frequencies are based upon it, they are called "relative" frequencies. The actual frequencies, e.g., for the middle octave C′–C″, are found by assigning to the note A′ an agreed frequency of 435 (the so-called "concert pitch"): then, to obtain the frequency for the next lower note (G #), divide 435 by the common factor 1.059, giving 410.6, or 411 to the nearest unit. For the next higher note (A #), multiply 435 by 1.059 to get 461. Thus we can progress from note to note, and the fourth column shows these frequencies, all rounded off to the nearest unit.

"*Din*" *Sizes*

THE CURIOUS RECTANGLE. John Smith is in a shop in Bonn buying writing paper. "Do you want a Din A 4 or A 5?" asks the sales lady. "It's for a typewriter," John says. "Din A 4, then," says the girl, and brings him just what he wants. This Din-size business is a new one to him, however, and on the way to his hotel he decides to find out all about it.

In his room he takes out one of the new sheets of paper; it is of course a rectangle (*I*). When he measures it with a metric ruler, he finds to his surprise that it is 21 × 29.7 cm. (8.3 × 11.7 in. approx.) Why not 21 × 30, or even better 20 × 30? Now he folds the rectangle in the middle to make one of half the size (*II*), and measures it again: 14.8 × 21. He scratches his head, folds again, and measures the still smaller rectangle (*III*): 10.5 × 14.8. Ah! here is something. On arranging the measurements in order of size: 10.5, 14.8, 21.0, 29.7, he makes his first discovery. The shorter side (21 cm.) of the rectangle *I* becomes the longer side of rectangle II, and similarly with rectangles *II* and *III*.

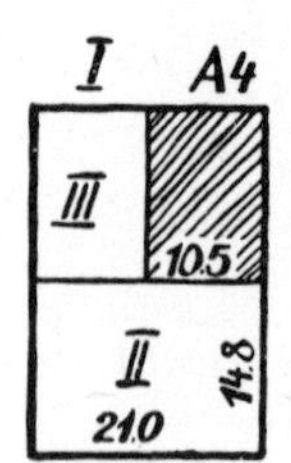

Now the second discovery: the shorter side 14.8 of rectangle *II* is half the longer side of rectangle *I*, and the same is true of rectangles *II* and *III*. John Smith draws a plan of this, and is already on the track of finding the rule governing Din-size measurements. Stubbornly he follows it up, and also inquires about the curious name Din. Eventually the whole truth is revealed.

Writing paper is rectangular, and there can be a great variety of rectangles, long and narrow, short and broad, square, or any intermediate shape. If every writer were to insist on his own favorite size, as teen-agers often do, there would be difficulties in the world of office supplies: difficulties of manufacture, with increased costs, difficulties of ordering and delivery of supplies, of matching up refills for loose-leaf books and writing cases, etc. Here, then, is a clear case for standardization.

In Germany there is a committee for *Deutsche Industrie Normen* (German Industrial Standardization), which is abbreviated to Din, and often re-rendered as *Das ist Norm* ("This is standardized"). This committee determines, in the case of items which exist in many sizes and styles, certain standard sizes and styles. The details of these standardizations are published on Din leaflets, and are obtainable by the public, each bearing a reference number. Thus, on Leaflet 476 are given the recommendations concerning paper sizes.

THE THREE DIN DEMANDS. Which rectangles out of all possible sizes did the Din Committee select? They were those which fulfill these three conditions:

(a) Halving or doubling of one size is to result in a size which also belongs to the standardized Din range. For example, a sheet of typing paper *I*, folded in half, gives rectangle *II*, which is also a member of the Din range. This is the substance of John Smith's discoveries.

(b) All rectangles shall be similar, i.e., rectangle *II* is a smaller version of rectangle *I*, and a postcard (rectangle *III*) is a smaller version of rectangle *II*. This is ensured if the ratio of length and breadth in each size is kept constant. Rectangle *I* has the ratio of length to breadth 29.7 : 21.0 = 1.41; rectangle *II* has 21.0 : 14.8 = 1.41, and rectangle *III* has 14.8 : 10.5 = 1.41. All these three ratios are the same, 1.41.

This is a special quality, not possessed by every rectangle. If, for instance, I fold in half a sheet measuring 40 × 20 cm. (twice as long as it is broad), then it becomes a square, 20 × 20 (see diagram). If now it is folded again to put into an envelope 20 × 10 cm., it again becomes twice as long as it is broad. Between the two similar rectangular shapes, with length-breadth ratios equal to 2, is the dissimilar square, with length-breadth ratio 1 : 1.

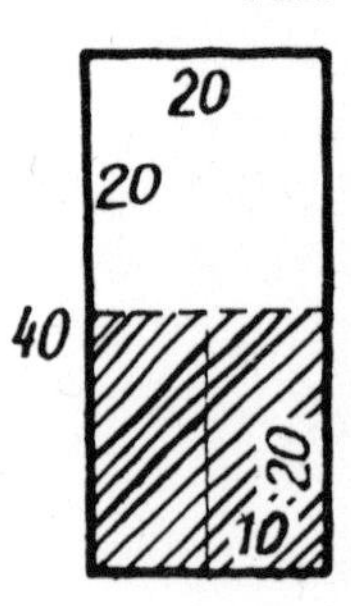

It is true, however, that there are other sets of rectangles which fulfill conditions (a) and (b), but do not have the measurements of those in the Din range. For instance, a rectangle *I'*, measuring 50 × 35.3 cm., can be halved to make a rectangle *II'* measuring 35.3 × 25. In both cases the ratio of their sides is 1.41 : 1, the same ratio as in the Din range. But these measurements are not included in the Din range, for a third condition controls the membership of that select group.

(c) The largest size in the Din range is to have an area 1 square meter (sq. m. = 10.76 sq. ft.), and on this the subsequent smaller sizes must depend. The measurements of the largest size work out at 118.9 × 84.1 cm. (3.90 × 2.76 ft.). Using these figures and keeping condition (a) as a guide, we can work out the whole Din range from A 0 to A 10. The longer side of the second rectangle A 1 is the short side (84.1 cm.) of the preceding rectangle A 0, and the short side of A 1 is half the long side of A 0 (118.9/2 = 59.4), and so on.

These are the complete results:

Classification	*Description*
A 0	Quadruple sheet
1	Double sheet
2	Sheet
3	Half-sheet
4	Quarter-sheet
5	Bill
6	Half-bill
7	Quarter-bill
8	Ticket
9	—
10	—

Din A 4 is the whole sheet of typing paper, A 5 is half of it, A 6 the postcard. In addition to the A series, there are two others, B and C, for such items as envelopes. The measurements in these ranges are dependent on those of series A. The Din sequence A 0–A 10 is a genuine standardized sequence, because any two consecutive Din rectangles bear the same relationship to one another: The smaller rectangle is half as large as its larger next-door neighbor (p. 65: nail-length ratio). The quarter-sheet A 4 results from the fourth folding of the master quadruple sheet A 0, and thus the classification number indicates also the number of foldings. Hence, from one sheet of A 0 are produced 2^4, i.e., 16, quarter-sheets. Printers have therefore a general formula: from one A 0 with k folds are obtained 2^k smaller sheets of size A k.

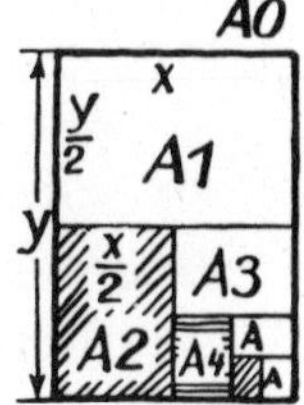

FOR THE CALCULATOR. The general method for determining the size of the Din rectangles: if the largest (master) rectangle has sides measuring x and y, condition (a) requires the next smaller rectangle to have sides x and

$y/2$; condition (b) that the ratios of length to breadth in both rectangles shall be the same, so that $y : x = x : y/2$. Hence $y^2 = 2x^2$ or $y = x\sqrt{2}$. Thus the length of a Din rectangle is equal to the product of its breadth by $\sqrt{2}$, (1.41). In other words, the ratio of the sides is a constant, and equals 1.41. (See below for a geometrical explanation of this relationship.) Condition (c) requires the area of the largest rectangle to be 1 sq. m., hence $xy = 1$, and as $x = y/\sqrt{2}$, so $y^2 = \sqrt{2}$, $y = \sqrt[4]{2} = \sqrt{1.41} = 1.189$, and $x = .841$. These in meters are the measurements of sheet Din A 0 in the table above.

The geometrical property of a Din rectangle is also very interesting. Form the square $ABC'D'$ using the short side x of the rectangle as the side AB of the square. The diagonal AC' of this square is $x\sqrt{2}$, and may be shown by measuring to be equal to the long side AD of the rectangle. Thus, if the corner B of a sheet of Din paper is folded over to the point D' on AD, the line of the fold AC' will equal the long side AD of the rectangle.

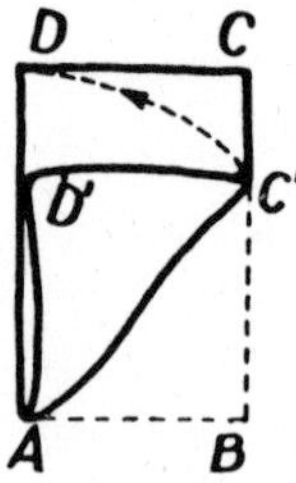

For the old mathematicians the square was the perfect straight-sided figure, just as the circle was the perfect curve. A rectangle made from a square by taking the square's diagonal for the longer side represented for them a most exceptional type of rectangle. As a result it was much used by medieval artists. Albrecht Dürer chose it for his series of woodcuts of the Apocalypse. The side ratio is 39.4 : 28.1, i.e., 1.4—practically the same as the Din ratio, even though it is not actually a Din size: it lies between A 3 and A 4. The wonderful pictures of the German *Minnesängern* (medieval poets) in the so-called Manesse manuscript (*Manessische Liederhandschrift*), show almost the same ratio of length to breadth, and the serious observer cannot fail to realize that the medieval artists were influenced in the composition of their pictures by the special dimensions of this type of rectangle.

A TWISTED BELT

How often have you fastened a belt round yourself, only to find to your annoyance that it was twisted? But if you were to ponder on this mistake, you might well hit on a surprising discovery. The belt in this diagram, when properly fastened 1 to 1′, 2 to 2′, forms a shallow cylinder, shown here with its inner surface white, and its outside black. If the belt is twisted, and fastened 1 to 2′ and 2 to 1′, then its surfaces are still black and white, but not white inside and black outside, because there is no longer an inside or an outside!

Why? Let us consider the diagram of the twisted belt on p. 77. Move your finger along the outside counter-clockwise, from 1 2 along the center line shown; after a time the surface, over which your finger moves, no longer faces outward, but inward; up to the points 2′1′ you remain on black, but thereafter continue on white—first facing inward, but later again facing outward, until the original starting points 1 2 are reached. Moving along the middle line and without touching the edges of the belt at all, you traced your way along the whole length of both white and black surfaces.

If the belt had not been twisted this would not have been possible without either lifting the finger from the belt or moving over one of the edges. If you try with a pencil to trace a path over an untwisted paper "belt" you will get two quite separate continuous lines, one inside and one outside; but when it is twisted there is only one continuous line. Another remarkable fact is that the twisted belt has only one edge—trace your finger round it and see!

What is the difference between these two belts? The untwisted one has two surfaces, the twisted belt only one. So there are actually surfaces with only one side! Apart from the twisted belt there are other one-sided surfaces. It is only during the last century that these have been discovered, so clearly you will have to revise your idea of surfaces having necessarily two sides. A top hat, a hollow sphere, a box, a coat—these can all be colored red outside and blue within, but not so a twisted belt. If you were to try to color it with the outside red, both sides of the belt would end up as red.

A basic quality of any surface would seem to be that it has two sides. But in the light of the above this must be altered: *it must always have either one or two sides.*

This cannot be altered by any kind of distortion short of actual division, i.e., cutting or tearing. If you want to make a twisted, one-sided belt into a two-sided one, you cannot do it by knotting or further twisting but only by dividing or unclasping it.

TOPSY-TURVY PROPERTIES. As one might expect, a twisted belt has twisted properties. It is like a river with only one bank, but yet at any given point it seems to have a bank on each side. But the point is, you don't have to cross the river to get from any place to "the opposite bank."

If you cannot yet grasp this phenomenon of onesidedness, you will not be able to predict what will happen if you cut the belt in two, the whole way along its center line. If it is untwisted, you will get two separate belts, each one half as wide as the original. But if you try this with the twisted belt, you will get a surprise. And if after the first cutting, you cut the half along its center line, your astonishment will increase! For the result will be alternately belts of twice the length and interlinked rings, and they will occur as often as you repeat the cutting. If you find

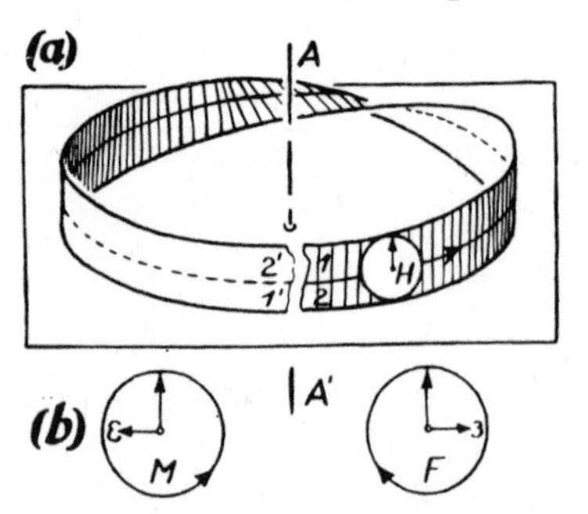

this game entertaining, twist the belt twice before fastening it, and cut as before.

You can make an intriguing party game out of this, one which will baffle all who are not in the know: how can you make two interlinked paper rings out of one by making only one cut with a pair of scissors?

Here is yet another topsy-turvy property. With a one-sided surface like the twisted belt, there is no fixed direction of turning, that is, no fixed clockwise turn, as for instance with a coffee mill. To explain this let us discuss:

THE ENCHANTED WATCHES. Suppose the twisted belt is a world inhabited by tiny insects of a curious kind. They are quite flat, and live embedded in the surface of the belt, and we look down upon them just as God looks down upon us. One of the male insects, *M*, lives with his wife, *F*, in their house, *H* (diagram *a* on p. 76). Both possess watches of a curious kind, for the insects themselves are the faces around which the watch hands move clockwise. *M* says to his wife one day, "I am going for a walk." His wife replies, "It's now twelve o'clock. Be back at three." And so *M* wanders with his watch over his topsy-turvy world toward the right, round the axis AA'. Eventually, after a long walk, he spies his house *H* again, and re-enters it from the left on the stroke of three. "Hello dear, I'm back." "But, my dear man, whatever is the matter with your watch? It's going round the wrong way!" *M* and *F* hold up their watches and compare them (diagram *b* on p. 76). Sure enough, *M*'s watch hands are going round counter-clockwise! At three o'clock the hands are set as for nine o'clock by his wife's watch. *F* weeps bitterly, fearing that some sinister mischance has destroyed the harmony of their lives. But we, who watch over their topsy-turvy little world, know a simple cure: she must take a trip round their world, just as her husband did, or send him round once again. What she doesn't realize is that in their world there cannot be specified an unchanging direction of turn. If the watch had been a coffee mill, the same thing would have happened, but of course she cannot view her world from outside, and so does not realize, as we do, that there is a twist in it.

To help you understand all this, try the experiment of moving a watch round a twisted, fastened belt, from buckle back to buckle, imagining all the time that the watch is an "insect-watch," moving in, but not on, the belt. In a normal untwisted belt the watches always move their hands clockwise, so long as they do not pass over the edge of their belt-world to the other side, which is a forbidden zone. For them there is an underworld. But this is not so for those who live in the world of the twisted belt: these have no fear at all of a Hell!

THE POWER OF SYMBOLS: THE UNKNOWN QUANTITY *X*

How many minutes is it to six o'clock, if fifty minutes ago it was exactly four times as many minutes past three? There's a headache for you! However can anyone unravel such a tangle of times?

THE UNKNOWN QUANTITY x. Let us outline the basic idea with a simpler example:

If you multiply a number by 4 and then add 2, the answer is 30. What was the number you started with? If you cannot see how to do this, try working backward from the answer: 30, in this case, must be decreased by 2 to give 28. This, divided by 4 gives 7. That is the answer.

Working backward, however, often fails in more complicated cases like our original problem, nor is it good mathematical method to work backward. One should always work forward, after setting down the number relationship, as given in the problem:

? times 4, add 2, result 30

But how can you work with a number which you do not know? This is the whole point: use a symbol instead! Let x represent the number, until you can determine what it really is. In this way we are able to write down the whole statement, as indicated in the problem. This can then be simplified according to the rules of arithmetic.

If you multiply a number by 4 (in short $4x$), and then add 2 ($4x + 2$), the result is 30. In full, $4x + 2 = 30$.

In this way the wordy wrappings of the problem are stripped away, laying bare the essential relationship between the numbers in the form of an "equation." (An equation is a statement which contains the sign $=$, which means that the numbers on each side of it are equal.)

FORMALISM: FOR AND AGAINST. The next task is to extricate the unknown quantity, by reaching a stage in the calculations at which it is stated "x is so much." In this case, $x = 7$. The equation is then said to be "solved," and the symbol x has served its purpose.

The methods used for solving all types of equations constitute an important branch of mathematics, which is called "algebra." Algebra is an Arabic word dating from the 9th century, and so gives no hint as to what the subject really is. It merely illustrates how the unintelligent use of pedantic terminology can at once envelop a straightforward matter in clouds of mystery. The algebraic solution of our problem is:

Equation	$4x + 2 = 30$		
adjusted (— 2)	$-2 \quad -2$		
gives	$4x = 28$		
Divide by 4	$x = 7$	Solution	

You can see how the steps in calculation follow quite naturally, independently of the significance of the individual numbers. This is the great power of symbols: they permit the essential relationships between numbers to emerge for our scrutiny, unhampered by the things these numbers measure, such as times of day (as in the problem above), or sisters or pheasants (featured in later problems, p. 81). In this way methods of general calculating procedure are made clear, and can be applied to many different individual problems. Unnecessary brain-work is avoided, for once the appropriate equation has been written down the recognized formal steps in the solution follow as a matter of course.

This is, then, a mechanical process, a type of formalism, but not to be lightly regarded for that reason. On the contrary, one of the main aims of mathematics is to put particular instances into their proper framework of general validity. We can divide 365 by 29 formally, that is, without stopping at every step to ponder why we are doing it. We must be able to pursue particular ideas through the medium of some such general mechanical system of elucidatory processes, if we are ever to pass through the entanglements of thought on to new knowledge. In this sense formalism is a virtue. It can, however, become a vice, if seen as an end in itself and not as a means to elucidation. Formalists are people obsessed by the formal methods themselves; for them the living, creative significance of mathematics has become merely incidental. These are "mathematicians" to be avoided. As teachers they can stifle every trace of natural enthusiasm.

Here are three more examples of the usefulness of x, the unknown quantity. First let us take our time problem from p. 78.

Let us say that at the moment it is x minutes to 6 o'clock. Don't you feel already that this gives us a start? Now we can get organized. Fifty minutes ago it was $4x$ minutes past 3. Between

3 and 6 o'clock there are 180 minutes. If all this is sketched, as in the diagram, you can see at once that:

$$4x + 50 + x = 180.$$

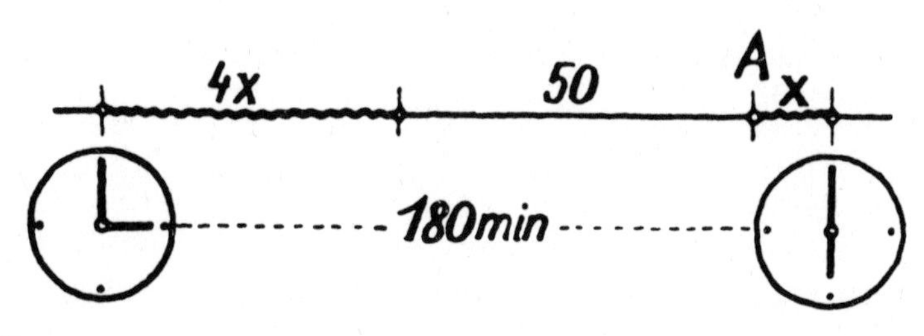

Thus

$$5x = 130 \quad \text{and} \quad x = 26.$$

Therefore it is now 5:34 o'clock. Putting this answer to the test: 50 minutes ago it was 4:44, i.e., 4×26 minutes past 3.

A charming Chinese problem presents us with a picture of hares and pheasants in the same cage. Between them they have 20 heads and 56 legs. How many creatures of each kind are there?

Does this seem at first sight too difficult a problem? Then see how easily you can solve it if you start thus:

There are x hares.

The rest follows, simply enough. There must be $(20 - x)$ pheasants. x hares have $4x$ legs, and $(20 - x)$ pheasants have $2(20 - x)$, i.e., $(40 - 2x)$ legs. The total number of legs is 56. Thus:

$$4x + 40 - 2x = 56.$$
$$2x = 16, \text{ and therefore } x = 8.$$

Hence there are 8 hares and 12 pheasants.

THE COMPLICATED PROBLEM OF ANNE AND MARY demands our consideration. Mary is 24 years old. She is twice as old as her sister Anne was when Mary was as old as Anne is now. How old is Anne? Here is another problem that at first reading makes your brain reel. Nevertheless, put your trust in the power of symbols, and also transform the problem into a diagram.

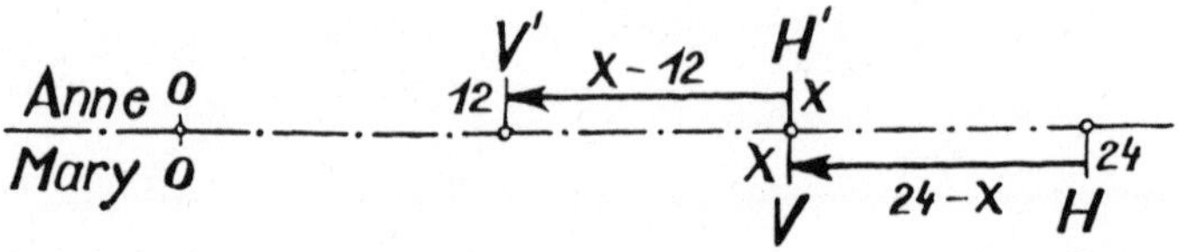

Anne is now x years old (H'), and Mary is now 24 (H). When Mary was as old as Anne is now, she was also x years old (V). This was $(24 - x)$ years ago, and is shown on the diagram as the distance VH. At that time Anne was 12 years old (V'), and younger than Mary by the same number of years. Thus, $H'V' = HV$, i.e., $x - 12 = 24 - x$; $2x = 36$, and $x = 18$. And so Anne is 18 years old.

To test the result; when Mary was 18, 6 years ago, Anne was 12, exactly half as old as Mary is today.

There is a little story which illustrates the power of the formula in everyday life. Some people at a party were talking of "beautiful" women, "interesting" women, and "charming" women. Most of them agreed that it was entirely a matter of personal taste as to how one placed a woman in any of these categories. One person disagreed—a scoffer who said, "I have a formula for this. Let A be the dazzling appearance of the woman, and V her intellect. Then the charming woman is $A + V$, the beautiful woman $A - V$, and the interesting woman $V - A$."

GETTING THE BEST OUT OF IT: ECONOMY IN SHAPE AND FORM

Making the best use of materials is one of the great problems in which technology has to enlist the aid of mathematics. Here is a practical example.

A firm wishes to manufacture an open tin box, using a sheet of tin plate 1 yard square. From each corner of the sheet a square of side x will be cut out, giving 4 rectangles which will be bent upwards to form the sides of the box. The volume V of the box is to be as large as possible. Obviously, the dimensions of the finished box will depend on the size of the squares which are cut away. If these are very small, the box will be shallow, with a large base area and low sides; if the squares are large, the box will be tubular in appearance, with a small base and high, narrow walls. If the cut-out squares have sides of $\frac{1}{2}$ yd., the volume of the box will be zero, there will be no tin-plate left for the base and therefore no box! The problem is to find, from all possible values of x between 0 and $\frac{1}{2}$, the particular value (x_B) which will give the box the largest volume V_B. How can this be done? We could take many successive values for x, and calculate for each one the volume of the box, gradually working towards the maximum volume. This is quite straightforward, but tedious. Mathematics works more directly: the volume V is set down as a function of the side x of the squares. A direct calculation of a certain kind then gives the value of x_B as 1/6 yd. This gives the box with the "best" or maximum volume, $V_B =$ .074 cu. yd. $\approx$ 15 gallons.

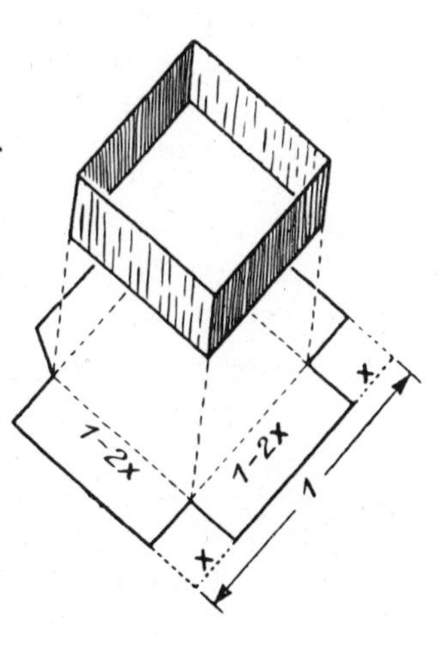

The formula for the volume V of the box is $x(1 - 2x)^2 = 4x^3 - 4x^2 + x$. The graph of this function is a curve with a highest point and a lowest point. This curve is called a "cubic." At the highest point the

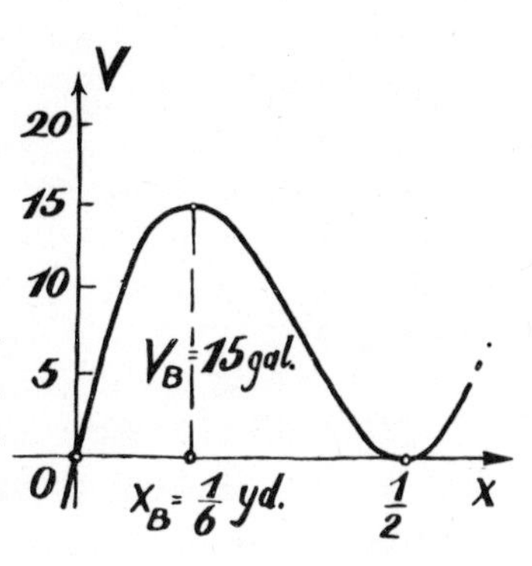

gradient of the curve is zero; in mathematical terminology the "derivative" of the function is zero. In this case the derivative = $V'(x) = 12x^2 - 8x + 1 = 0$, and from this $x = 1/6$. Hence the maximum volume of the box is $V(1/6) = .074$ cu. yd. = 14.95 gal.

The lowest point of the curve in the diagram at the bottom of p. 83, where the gradient (and derivative) are zero, is at $x = \frac{1}{2}$, and gives a quite useless minimum volume for the box, i.e., $V = 0$.

OTHER "BEST VALUES"

(1) Closed boxes (i.e., with lids) of 1 gallon volume are to be manufactured, using the least possible quantity of tin plate.

(2) A tent in the shape of a pyramid is to be erected on a square base, using four poles for support. How far apart must the lower ends of the poles be placed from each other, in order to give the greatest possible volume to the tent?

(3) What elevation must be given to a gun barrel to fire a shell with maximum possible range?

(4) On a wall *I* sits a spider *S*; on the opposite wall *II* of the room *III* is a mosquito *M* (see diagram). By what route *SABM* will the spider be able to reach the mosquito in the shortest possible time? Clearly by the shortest route, and this can be found by drawing the two walls *I* and *II* as if they had been turned through a right angle to lie flat on the floor. Points S' and M' are then connected by a straight line, which crosses the foot of each wall at points *A* and *B*. *SABM*, which gives the required shortest distance, can now be completed. A technical version of this problem is as follows: Let S' represent a transformer, *B* a factory, and *III* a river flowing between them. Let us suppose that it is three times cheaper to lay cable through the water than to carry the same

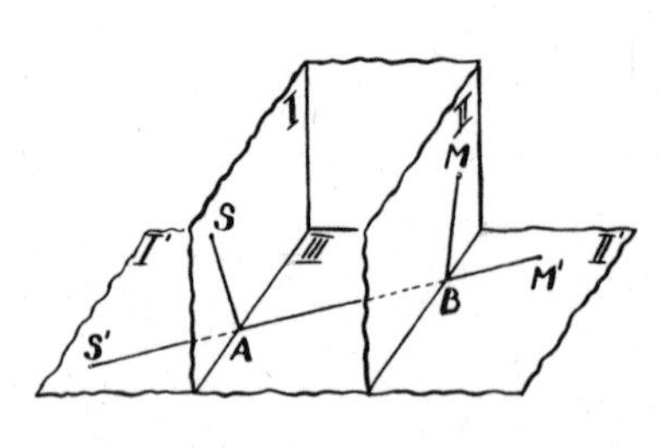

length on pylons overhead. If all distances are known, by what route should the cable be laid in order to achieve maximum economy? It would not generally be along the straight line $S'AB$ but along a route which bends at a point A' on the bank.

THE "BEST SHAPE." Suppose you have knotted together the ends of a piece of string 1 yd. in length, and you throw it on a table three times in succession. Three different closed curves are the result, and each of the three encloses a different area, but with the same perimeter. What would be the "best shape," i.e., which curve of all those possible would enclose the largest area?

There is a great variety of such curves, with which we can include also rectangular shapes, both narrow and wide, squares also, and ellipses, all having the same perimeter. Which is the one we want? The answer is—the circle. Somehow we might have known this, but the proof is not easy (cf. "The Tale of Queen Dido," p. 47).

In the next problem, however, in which we also search for a best shape, your guess might well prove to be misleading. Here it is:

A ball-bearing is to roll from A to B, both of which points lie in the same vertical plane (see diagram). *By which route will it travel most quickly?*

Think of both points as being on a wall, A at ceiling level and B on the floor. Once again there is a great variety of possible tracks between A and B. Which is the one giving the quickest journey for the ball-bearing? Surely it would be the straight line II, since that is the shortest? The result, obtained by calculation, comes as a surprise: it is not the straight line, but curve I, a half-cycloid, which is of course longer.

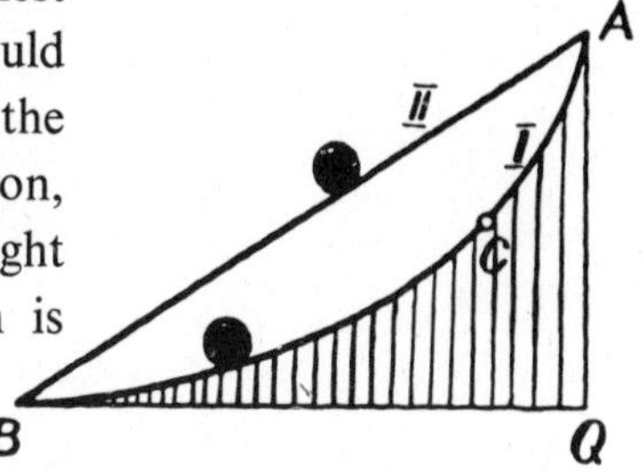

A
II
I
C
B
Q

(A cycloid is the kind of curve traced by a point on, within, or outside the circumference of a circle, as the circle rolls along a straight line (cf. BB', diagram on p. 128).

If you were to construct two such tracks and start two identical ball-bearings rolling down them at the same time, you would see the ball on the curved track arrive first at the bottom.

If you choose for your figure the dimensions of the ski jump at Oberstdorf in Germany ($AB = 440$ ft., with average gradient 53 in 100 [cf. p. 94]), the time of fall of the ball-bearing can be calculated, friction being ignored, as 7.6 sec. for a straight track, and 6.3 sec. for the curved one—about $1\frac{1}{3}$ sec. (i.e., 17 %) less. If the distance of a skier's jump depended on his coming down the slope AB in the shortest possible time, the best type of slope would be the half-cycloid, and not one with constant gradient.

It may come as a shock to the non-mathematician that, in spite of the fact that the times taken to move down slopes *I* and *II* are different, the final speeds reached by identical objects moving down them are the same: 115 ft./sec., or 78 mi./hr.

FOR THE CALCULATOR. Estimating the time taken to move down the different slopes:

Let t' be the time for the "straight" slope (inclined plane, cf. p. 90). Let $AB = d = 440$ ft. The final speed reached is given by $v = \sqrt{2db}$. In this equation, b is the acceleration down the slope, with an angle of slope of 28° (see p. 94):

$$b = g \sin 28° = 32 \times .47 = 15 \text{ ft./sec.}^2$$

(g, the acceleration due to gravity, is 32 ft./sec.^{2})

Thus, the time of descent t', during which the maximum velocity v is reached at B, is given by the formula $v = bt'$.

$$t' = v/b = \sqrt{2d/b} = \sqrt{2 \times 440/15} = \sqrt{58} = 7.6 \text{ sec.}$$

The time of descent t'' down the cycloidal curve ACB is 6.3 sec., but to explain this fully would mean going into topics beyond the scope of this book. The cycloid is not only "the curve of quickest descent," called a brachistochrone, but is also the curve of "equal times of descent"—a tautochrone. (Greek "chronos" = time; "brachistos" = shortest; "tauto" = same.) These terms suggest the peculiar characteristics of this curve. A spherical object falling from the upper point A reaches the bottom at the same time as an identical sphere which starts simultaneously at a lower point C on the curve (cf. diagram on p. 85). The time of descent of a sphere on this type of curve is independent of the height of its starting point above the horizontal BQ.

In fact $t'' = \pi\sqrt{r/g}$, where $2r = AQ$, the diameter of the circle which generates the cycloid (cf. diagram on p. 128 and definition, p. 86).

OTHER EXAMPLES OF "BEST SHAPE." Which is the shortest path between two points A and B? The straight line AB—anyone can see that. But what about the shortest distance between two points A and B on the surface of a sphere? The answer is the "great circle" through A and B, but this term needs some explanation.

Between Naples and New York, both of which are in the same latitude, the shortest route by air is not due west, along the line of latitude, but northwest from Naples, following part of a great circle, the center of which is the center of the earth.

An even more difficult problem to solve is how to trace along the surface of the ground the shortest path between a point A on the side of one hill and a point B on the side of a neighboring hill.

In conclusion, both quests—for "best value" and "best shape"—have this in common—that is to find, from among innumerable possibilities, one definite answer (or at any rate a very much smaller number of possibilities). The quests differ only in that the "best value" emerges as a numerical value of an already known function, while "best shape" emerges as itself a function, from among many possibilities. Mathematics has been able to indicate the methods of solving problems of both kinds by the aid of what is known as "calculus." Students in undergraduate mathematics courses tackle problems relating to "best value" (maximum or minimum); those relating to "best shape" are, however, more appropriate to a higher branch of mathematics called the calculus of variations.

Chapter 5

STREETS AND HIGHWAYS, GRADIENTS AND CURVES

In earlier days, when John Smith still thought of himself as a pedestrian, he never bothered much about what streets to use, whether they went uphill or down, or what sort of bends they had. But now he drives a fast car, and suddenly the inclines and curves of the roads have taken on a new significance. Often, of late, as they have rushed into view before him, he has been made uncomfortably aware that they might well decide between life and death for the motorist. We shall now tell him why.

The Gradient

THE TRIANGLE OF GRADIENT. John Smith is touring by car in Germany. One day he sets out to drive up the Feldberg, a fair-sized hill in the Black Forest. He leaves Freiburg (about 1000 ft. above sea level), drives up the Hollental Valley to Lake Titisee, and then follows the lovely road via the Seebachtal Valley to the Feldbergerhof (about 4200 ft. above sea level). The total distance driven is about 30 mi., and in the course of this he has climbed 3200 ft.

"What do you mean by gradient?" asks John Smith. "How do you calculate it?"

Let us think of his whole journey as being in a straight line, viewed in longitudinal section; this gives the gradient triangle FBQ of this journey (see diagram). The distance traveled, FB, is 30 mi.; FQ or w is the horizontal projection of this distance, and is obtained by dropping a perpendicular from B to Q. BQ (h) is 3200 ft., or .6 mi. and is the height of the Feldberg above the starting point Freiburg. The angle BFQ between the line of the road and its horizontal projection is the angle of inclination.

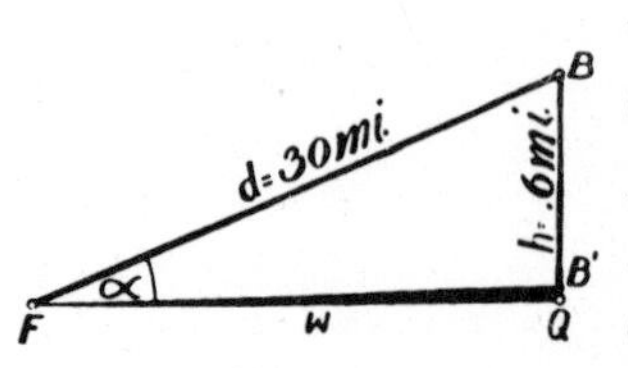

The gradient (s) is the ratio of the height gained (h) to the horizontal distance traveled (w). Gradient = height gained : horizontal distance traveled. In algebraic symbols, $s = h : w$.

The road engineer always relates gradient to horizontal, not actual distance, because his plans are all drawn up in terms of horizontal distance, and it is this to which he constantly refers. With small gradients, however, we can in fact take the ratio of height gained to actual distance traveled, without incurring serious error (see p. 95).

John Smith's drive had therefore an average gradient of .6 : 30 or 6 : 300 or 1 : 50, which is 2 : 100 or 2%.

For calculating purposes this ratio can be regarded as a fraction, which can be indicated in three ways:

(a) As a *general ratio* of the actual figures (using one standard of measurement, e.g., in this case miles). Thus,

$$s = .6 : 30.$$

(b) As a "*unit*" *ratio* with numerator 1. Thus $s = 1 : 50$, implying that over each 50 mi. of horizontal distance there is a gain in height of 1. (This method is used on railways, cf. p. 95.)

(c) As a *percentage*. Thus $s = 2 : 100$ or .02 or 2%. This implies a gain in height of 2 mi. for every 100 mi. of horizontal distance. Highway engineers and motorists usually think of gradient in this form.

SCALES OF DISTANCE AND HEIGHT. If we draw the gradient triangle on a scale of 15 mi. to 1 in., the 30-mi. distance traveled is shown as 2 in., and the height gained QB' is 2% of 2 in., or .04 in. (see diagram on page 90). But then the triangle FQB' becomes almost impossibly tiny, and for this reason when plans of road gradients are drawn the heights are usually exaggerated. If h is made 1 in. instead of .04 in., this means a twenty-five fold exaggeration or distortion of height as compared with horizontal distance. In this way the gradient triangle does indeed become of reasonable size, but now John Smith's uphill journey looks much steeper than it actually was.

For example, the scale M of a map is the ratio of map distance k to actual distance n, using the same unit of measurement for both. Thus $M = k : n$.

Scale for horizontal distance (M) = 1 in. : 15 mi.
Scale of vertical distance (M') = 1 in. : .6 mi.
Magnification of height (Z) = $M' : M = 15 : .6 = 25 : 1$.

Where small gradients (up to 9%) are involved, the actual distance, d, is so little different from its horizontal projection, w, that we might use the "unofficial" but convenient formula for gradient $s' = h : d$, instead of the "official" $s = h : w$. In a car, d can be read off directly from the mileage indicated. With an angle of inclination of 5°, $s' = 8.72\%$ and $s = 8.75\%$; with an angle of 20°, the corresponding values are 36% and 34%; with 45° (a typical mountain slope), they are, however, 71% and 100%.

A diagram showing the downward flow of the Rhine (or any other river) to the sea would be quite unimpressive, were it not for magnification of the heights. With a magnification factor of 1000, however, it becomes quite spectacular. With an average downward gradient of only .4 %, the Alpine section of the Rhine (*AR* in the diagram) simply hurtles down into Lake Constance, and the falls at Schaffhausen (*S*), with a maximum height of 82 ft., look as if they were a lock gate. From there onward the 330-mi. stretch of the Upper Rhine (*UR*) which passes through Basel (*B*) and Mainz (*M*) flows down in a lovely

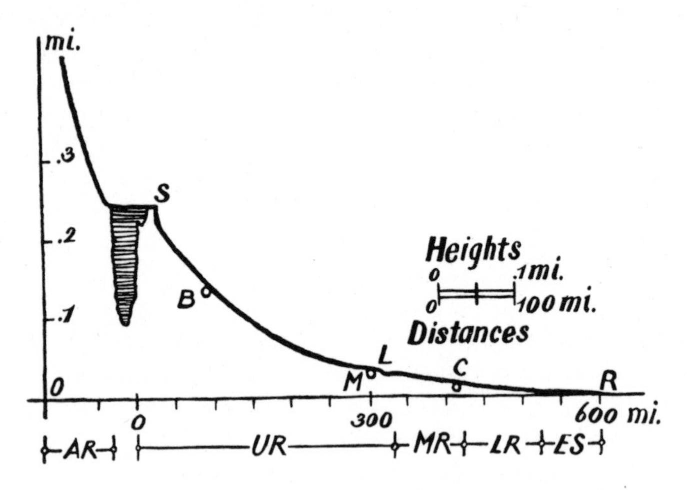

curve, with an average downward gradient of .07 %. Then the river passes through Cologne (*C*) as the Middle and Lower Rhine (*MR*, *LR*), with an average gradient of .02 %, into its estuary (*ES*) at Rotterdam. The gradients are given as average values, for the river does not of course maintain constant gradients over long stretches. Between Oppenheim and Mainz the Upper Rhine has its smallest gradient of .004 %, i.e., 4 ft. in 100,000 ft. At the Bingerloch (*L*) is the largest gradient which is 8 : 1000 or 1 : 125. (The current here flows at 11.5 ft./sec. or approximately 7.8 mi./hr.) In the Middle Rhine, near the Lorelei Rock, it flows for a short distance over its smallest gradient .001 %, or 1 ft. per 100,000. The normal speed of the current lies between 3 and 6 ft./sec. (2 to 4 mi./hr.)

It is much of a surprise to note, in the table which follows below, that gradients which to the eye seem very steep are in fact expressed by numerically small ratios. The Brenner railway rises on a gradient of only 2.5 % with an angle of inclination of 1.4°, and the Rhine here flows with a downhill gradient of one-third of a minute of arc, which is 1/180th of a degree, and expressed as a gradient this is 1 : 10,000. In fact most people tend to over-estimate the steepness of such things as roads, mountain slopes, and river courses.

A few actual gradients:

Gradient	1 : *w*	%	*Angle of inclination in degrees*
Rhine at Basel	1 : 1250	0.08	0.5
Rhine in Holland	1 : 10,000	0.01	1/150° = 24″(!)
Alpine Roads			
Brenner	1 : 7	14	8
Gotthard	1 : 6	17	10
Zirlerberg	1 : 4	25	14
Turracher Höhe (the steepest)	1 : 3	33	18
Railways			
Black Forest (Triberg)	1 : 50	2.0	1.1
Brenner	1 : 40	2.5	1.4
Gotthard	1 : 37	2.7	1.5
Funicular Railway			
Hungerburg (Innsbruck)	1 : 1.8	55	29
Ski Jump			
Oberstdorf	1 : 1.9	53	28
Nürburgring Racing Circuit			
Steep Part	1 : 3.7	27	15

This is due in part to perspective creating an illusion of shortening distances. If we stand on a hilltop, where the road begins to dip down into a valley, and look across, the slope of the road up the opposite side of the valley looks very steep indeed, but as we descend, it seems steadily less steep.

A SIMPLE GRADIENT INDICATOR. With the unaided eye it is difficult to estimate the gradients of roads, staircases, roofs, etc., but a simple indicator can easily be made. Take a rectangular board, say 5 in. by 3 in. and fasten a short plumbline (on the diagram, *AL*) to it. (A button attached to strong thread will do.) This will act as an indicator arm, moving over a scale showing angles from 0° to 90°, which is fixed to the board as shown, so that *AO* lies parallel to one edge. The indicator is now complete. Suppose it is set up as shown on a staircase; the plumbline will hang in the position *AL* and the angle of inclination of the staircase can be read on the angle scale, as it equals the angle *OAL*.

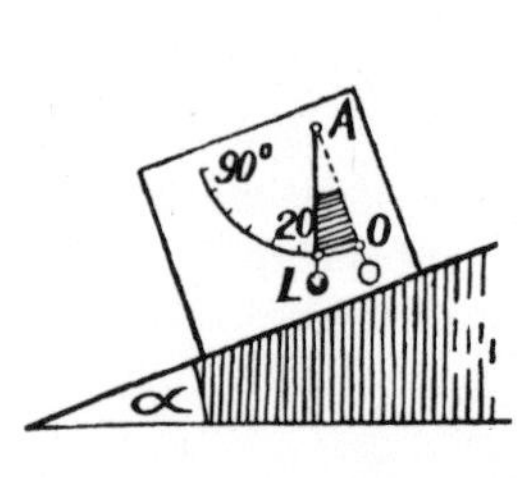

The following table shows how to express angles in degrees ($A°$) in terms of percentage gradient ($s\,\%$).

Angle

$A°$	1	2	3	4	5	6	7	8	9	10	15	20
$s\,\%$	1.7	3.5	5.2	7	9	11	12	14	16	18	27	36

$A°$	25	30	35	40	45	50	60	70	80	90
$s\,\%$	47	58	70	84	100	119	173	275	567	∞

FOR THE CALCULATOR. The angle indicated by the plumbline on the scale equals the actual angle of inclination, because the plumbline *AL* is at right angles to the horizontal and the zero line *AO* is at right angles to the slope itself. The gradient resulting from a given angle of inclination is actually the trigonometrical ratio known as the tangent. The values of the gradient can therefore be read from tangent tables, e.g., $A = 30°$; $\tan 30° = .5774$; $s = 57.74\,\%$.

In road building gradients are determined with great precision in the following way: a telescope F, set horizontally on a stand at a distance b

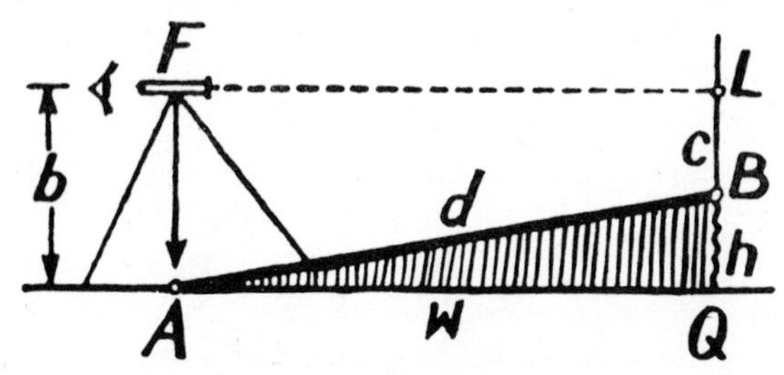

from a point A on the ground, is focused on a vertical surveying pole BL, at a distance $w = AQ = FL$. The length of the pole is c and the increase in height $h = b - c$. The gradient is thus $b - c : w$.

DIAGRAM OF GRADIENTS ALONG A STRETCH OF RAILWAY TRACK. For all sections of its railroad network the German railways have prepared a diagrammatic timetable. In this the time schedules of the trains are shown as straight lines, along which are marked the times of arrival, departure, or passage through the various stations (see p. 96 for details of its preparation). Above each of these diagrams is another which shows all the gradients along a given stretch of track (*AB* in diagram on p. 96). The length of the stretch is drawn to the scale 1 : 200,000 with a base line here set at 1000 ft. above sea level. Along this base line the various heights, usually of stations and shown by little flags, are given in figures, e.g. 1070, 1221, 1129, and are drawn to the scale 1 : 3000. Thus the ratio of the scales used (horizontal distance to vertical distance) is 200,000 : 3000, which is approximately 70 : 1. Thus all gradients along the track are shown in a very exaggerated form (cf. p. 92).

But each individual gradient, such as 1 : 40, is also precisely indicated. (In the diagram, for the sake of simplicity, only a few have been shown.) If any section of track is quite flat, it has zero gradient, but it is written as $1 : \infty$. This latter designation is used in order to keep in line with the notation used for all other gradients. It can be thought of as denoting a rise in height of

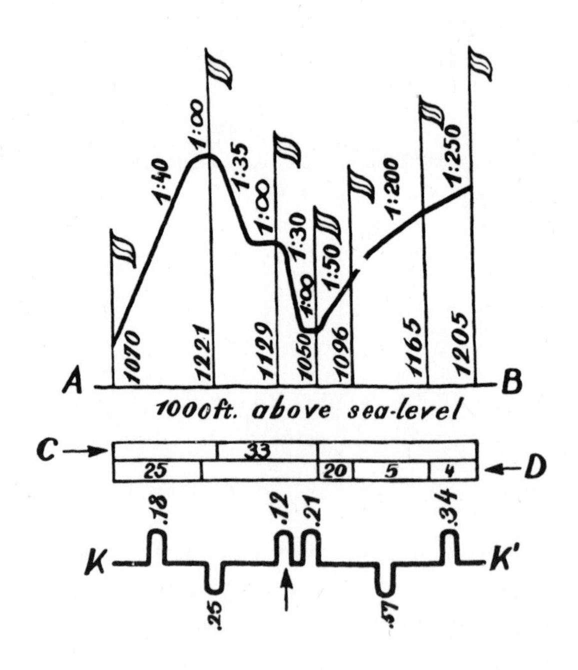

1 ft. over an infinite distance. In addition there is shown beneath this diagram the "standard average rate of downhill gradient," expressed as a percentage, for each section of track. (There are two rows of figures, according to direction of travel, e.g., 33% in *C* of the diagram.) As a rule, the maximum gradient of a railway track does not exceed 2.5% or $1 : 40$, but in certain special instances, to accommodate heavy freight traffic, it may be as much as 5% or $1 : 20$. Inside the bounds of a station it is never more than .25% or $1 : 400$; this is to insure that a train

will stand motionless with the brakes not applied. The resistance to movement of a railway train amounts to 1/400 of its weight, and this just balances the component of gravity produced by the downhill gradient. (This component is calculated by gradient × weight, and is in this case 1/400 of the weight. Cf. p. 99.)

At the main points where changes in gradient occur along the railway track are placed gradient signs for the benefit of engine drivers. If there is a notice: 580 (in meters, the equivalent of 1900 ft.) 1 : 180, then you know that for the next 1900 ft. the gradient is 1 : 180, either up or downhill, according to whether the arm of the sign slants upward or downward. In Bavaria the figures are inside a triangle, which points downward for downhill gradients.

Another diagram shown beneath those already described is that which is lettered *KK′* in the diagram on p. 96. This indicates the bends in the track (see p. 107). John Smith, I suppose, is wondering why it is so necessary to make all this fuss about an accurate measurement of gradients, etc., in road and rail-track building.

For one thing it is necessary because there are distinct limits to a vehicle's power to climb slopes. For example, a heavily loaded freight train cannot climb as well as a fast passenger express, nor a heavy truck as fast as a motorcycle. But the main reason is that a downhill slope can have a powerful effect on a vehicle.

John Smith knows this from his motorcycling days. At the very moment when a vehicle enters a downhill stretch of road, a certain additional power impels it, invisibly and maliciously, like the devil in the fairy tale, and drives it on at ever increasing speed. This is the component of gravitational force. Woe to the driver who does not take this into account, and who has not made sure that the brakes are dependable.

This component, which increases with the gradient, is in the case of the small gradients of roads and railways measured by the product of the gradient s and the weight of the vehicle W. Thus, ignoring the effect of friction and air resistance, $H = sW$. John Smith's car, which weighs 3200 lb., experiences on its journey up the Feldberg a component of gravitational force equal to .02 times the gravitational force (32 ft. per sec.^{2}) acting on the car ($.02 \times 3200/32 = 2$ units of force called poundals).

On the downward journey this force is added to that exerted by the engine and so increases the speed; on the upward trip it retards. If the car were to stop on the slope the friction, brought into play by the brakes, would have to exert an opposite force of 2 poundals, otherwise the car would roll downhill at an ever-increasing speed. If it rolled right down the Feldberg, when it reached Titisee after 12.5 mi., it would be moving at 200 mi./hr. or 294 ft./sec., and this would be entirely the result of the component of gravitational force. A ski jumper on the jump at Oberstdorf (average gradient 50 %) achieves on the way down the short slope of 440 ft. a speed of 78 mi./hr., or 115 ft./sec. (see p. 99), comparable with that of an express train. And this is from a standing start. (The effects of friction and wind resistance are again ignored, and the jumping slope considered as a constant gradient.)

The speed of a car would not be potentially dangerous if it were not for the fact that its kinetic energy—its power to do work, malicious work in the case of a collision—increases with the square of the speed. In fact, doubling the speed results in four times the kinetic energy! For this reason, the matter of gradients and the positioning of roads and railway tracks receive the most careful attention, with due regard to the braking and climbing powers of the vehicles destined to use them. In particular the fast modern highways show very clearly how much care has been taken, as we shall now see.

CALCULATION OF THE COMPONENT OF GRAVITATIONAL FORCE. In accordance with the rule known as the triangle of forces, a weight W on an inclined plane divides into two components: a force F, acting at right angles to the inclined plane toward the ground, and the force H, acting down and parallel to the inclined plane. Because the angle α is equal to the angle of inclination of the plane, the triangle WRH is similar to the gradient triangle. Thus, the gradient $s = h : w = H : F = \tan \alpha$ or, with small angles of inclination, e.g., $\alpha < 10°$, $s = H : W = \sin \alpha \approx \tan \alpha$, and so $H \approx W \tan \alpha = Ws$. But if $\alpha = > 10°$, with $s > 17\%$, then $H = W \sin \alpha$.

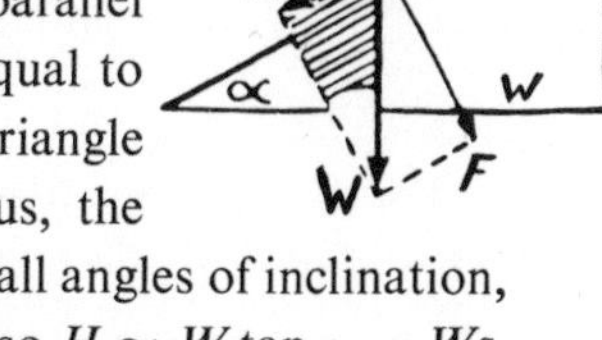

The final speed (ignoring friction) of a vehicle as it rolls down an incline is given by the formula $v = \sqrt{2db}$, where $b =$ the component of gravitational acceleration, and $d =$ the length of the slope. In the case considered $b = gs$ where $g = 32$ ft. per sec.², the acceleration caused by gravity. Thus, the final speed $v = \sqrt{2d \times 32 \times s}$, which is $8\sqrt{ds}$.

For John Smith's car coasting down to Titisee, $d = 12.5$ mi. $=$ 67,000 ft. and $s = .02$. Thus $v = 8\sqrt{.02 \times 67{,}000} = 294$ ft./sec. $=$ 200 mi./hr. For the ski jumper (see p. 86) the angle of inclination, A, is 28°, and so $v = 8\sqrt{d \sin A} = 8\sqrt{440 \times .47}$, which is 115 ft./sec., or 78 mi./hr. Note that this calculation must be made with $\sin 28° = .47$, and not with $s = \tan 28° = .53$.

FAST HIGHWAY AND GRADIENT. "Thruway" is the term now applied to the new roads reserved for fast motor traffic. They have no crossing and no left turns, and usually avoid passing through towns. Above all, their bends and gradients are planned with due regard to the high speeds, and the braking and climbing qualities of modern automobiles.

The German thruways (*Autobahnen*) are, in general, as shown in the diagram on p. 100. The total width comprises two outer grass borders each 6.6 ft., wide, two outer edging strips of 7.4 ft., two highways of 24.6 ft., two inner edging strips of 1.6 ft., and a central grass strip of 13.1 ft.

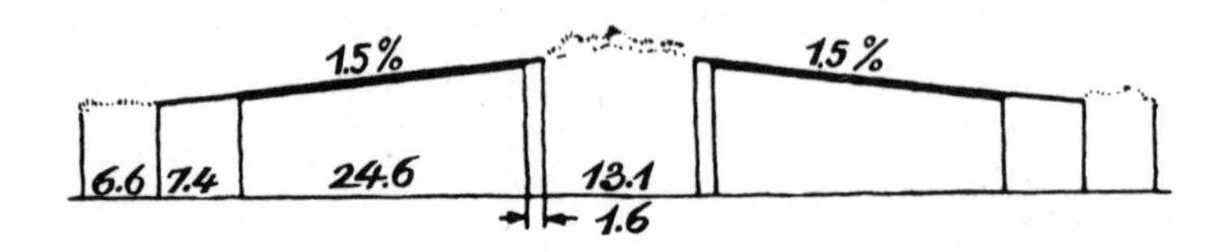

To allow rainwater to drain off, the highways are planned with a lateral slant toward the driver's right, i.e., to the outside of the road. This lateral slant is one of 1.5% and so the inner edge of each highway lies $24.6 \times .015 = .37$ ft., or 4.4 in. higher than the outer edge.

To counteract the effect of centrifugal force, any bend in the line of the highway must incorporate a lateral slant of the road surface downward and toward the center of the curve (see p. 108). Thus, in a right-hand bend, the lateral slant will be greater than the normal: it increases steadily (see diagram below) from 1.5% to 4% at the line UU', and thereafter decreases uniformly back to 1.5%. On a left-hand bend, however, the surface of the highway is twisted: the normal slant toward the right at AA' decreases to zero at BB', and then changes over to a left-hand slant toward the center of the curve, reaching 1.5% at CC'. Hold a strip of paper firmly at each end, and turn both hands in opposite directions: the flat strip of paper twists like the twisted belt seen on p. 76. By means of this twist in the surface of the road, a car is helped to move smoothly into the curve, and subsequently back to a

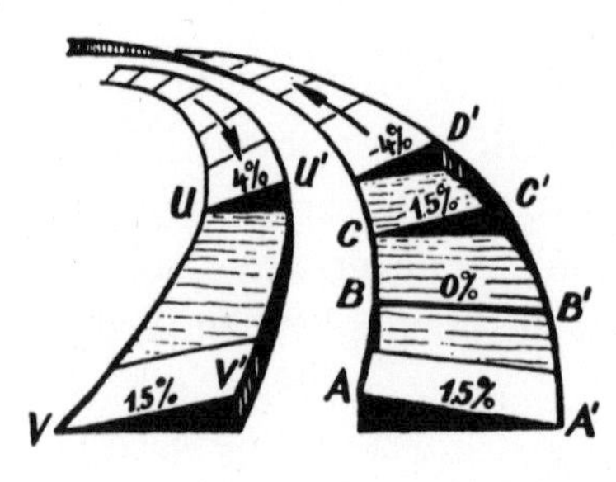

straight course. But those who do not know that the twist is there would not notice it at all.

A slope or gradient is termed by a road engineer "longitudinal inclination." Its upper limit is 4 % (1 : 25) in relatively flat country, where one might reckon on a maximum speed of 100 mi./hr. In hilly country it is 6 %, and in mountainous districts it can reach 6.5 % corresponding to a maximum speed of, say, 75 mi./hr. These gradients are far less than those of the old Alpine roads (cf. p. 43), because the limited climbing power has now been taken into account, and an attempt made to lessen the danger inherent in the acceleration due to gravitational force. For the same reasons, steep stretches are not made too long, but are relieved at intervals by gentler slopes.

Besides the lateral inclination of the road there is, on a longitudinal slope, a diagonal inclination, which must not exceed 7 %, but which, under wet or icy conditions, can be very unpleasant, because of the diagonal pull toward the outer edge of the road. The alteration of gradients in the *Autobahnen* is not effected abruptly. The diagram here shows sharp changes in gradient, at points *W* and *K*, but they are made gradual by a series of slight alterations (see the rounded crests and troughs).

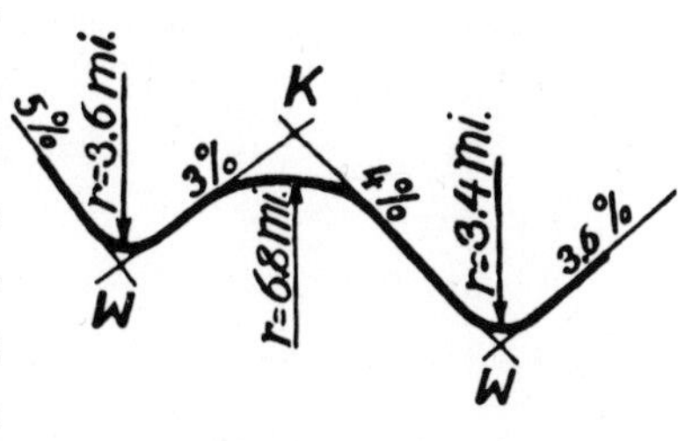

Between the straight lines of the two slopes an arc of a circle with large radius is inserted. The radius is of the order of 5 mi. As a result, in the trough the car's springs are preserved from the kind of shock which is experienced when a vehicle is driven quickly over a narrow subsidence or pothole; on the crests, moreover, there is no feeling of flying off into space while the wheels strive to hold on to the ground. Because of the horizon of visibility, which in flat country should not be less than 1000 ft., the crests of road gradients are rounded off even more than the troughs.

Often in a trough the road is supported on a bridge across the valley, positioned like a plank between the two opposite inclines. Even here, the engineers try to enhance the smooth flow of the roadway by making the bridge slightly concave along its length. Not only cars, but also human eyes are uncommonly sensitive to abrupt changes in a road, and are consequently all the more appreciative of a rhythmic, even progression through the countryside.

The railway, when rounding off a change from one gradient to another, varies the radius of the curve (r), so that it increases with the speed of travel (v) on the particular stretch in question.

Clearly then the planning of a fast highway makes necessary all sorts of considerations, which just would not occur to the ordinary man. There is also the economic factor: would it, for instance, be in the long run cheaper to incur the high building and maintenance costs of a bridge, to help carry a road across a valley, or should it simply lead down one slope and up the other? At any rate, we can see that road design is not the simple matter one might think.

The Curve

THE CURVATURE OF A CURVE. A road consists of straight stretches and curves. Now, a straight line is so to speak an "uncurved curve." But what is a curve? Railwaymen will tell you very nicely that it is a place where you can see the engine from the caboose. In road and railway engineering, a curve is always an arc of a circle, with center M and radius r, which leads from direction I into direction II. Thus, it is based on the circle and not on the ellipse or any other curve encountered in mathematics.

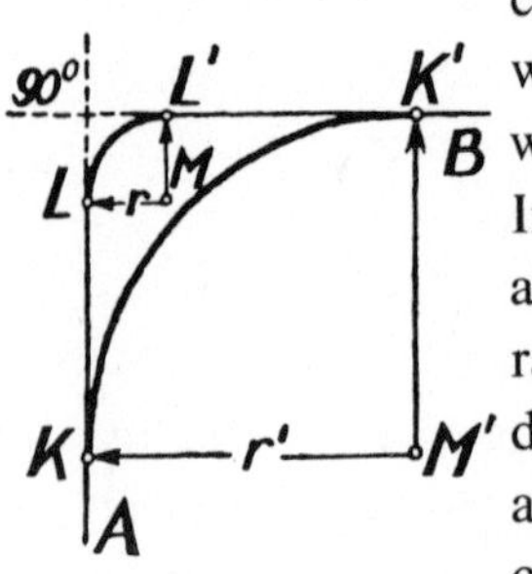

Such a circle, if no special dimension is prescribed, can be as large or as small as required. We may refer to a gentle curve, as KK', or to a sharp curve, LL'. The radius of the circle is thus a measure of curvature: large radius—gentle curvature; small radius—sharp curvature. This significance of the radius in measuring curvature is expressed by the formula $C = 1/r$. Road builders prefer to speak of the curvature of a road, and in their plans the radius of curvature is always specified. The center of the circle is referred to as the center of curvature. The change of direction shown in the diagram on p. 102 is 90°, and the curve is a quarter circle. A straight line may be thought of as a curve with zero curvature, and its center of curvature lies at an infinite distance to right or left (cf. M'' in the top diagram on p. 115). When one drives round a bend, the curvature is sharper for the inner wheels than for the outer. Thus, as the car is steered into the bend, the inner wheel (α) enters at a sharper angle than the outer (β). When $\alpha = 10°, 20°, 45°$, then $\beta = 9°, 17°, 33°$.

A HARMLESS YET DANGEROUS QUALITY. Think of the curve KK' as a road 10 yd. wide. Its outer edge AA' is, of course, longer than the inner edge JJ', in this case by 15.7 yd. There is nothing special in that, but it is surprising to realize that this difference in length does not depend on the radius of the curve, but on the breadth of the road (b) and the angle (α) subtended by the curve at the center (here it is 90°). Now this means that with the sharp but short curve LL' (diagram on p. 102), the difference in length of 15.7 yd. is exactly the same as with the gentler but longer curve KK'.

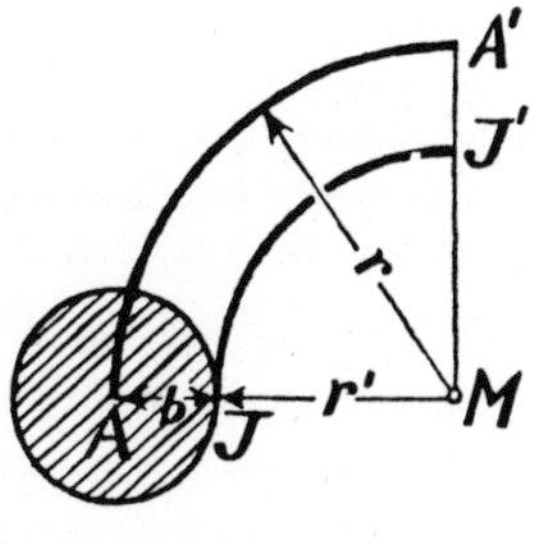

Furthermore, it means that with a car of track $b = 4$ ft. the outer wheels travel farther on a bend than the inner wheels. This distance W in no way depends on the nature of the curve, whether long or short, sharp or gentle, but only on the change in direction α. Thus, if one day you were to start driving due south, to return from due north after a long circular trip to the west, the left-hand or outer wheels of your car would have moved, in all, 25 ft. farther than the others. This can be precisely stated, because the complete trip can be thought of as a full circle. The extra distances traveled by inner and outer wheels in the course of the various right and left bends on the road almost cancel one another out, leaving in the end only an extra distance of 25 ft. traveled by the left side wheels.

The extra distance traveled along the outer edge of a curved road is calculated as follows (see diagram on p. 103).

$$\begin{aligned} r &= \text{radius of outer track} \\ r' &= \text{radius of inner track} \\ \text{Breadth of road} &= b = AJ = r - r' \\ \text{Extra distance } w &= \text{arc } AA' - \text{arc } JJ' \\ &= 2\pi r\alpha/360 - 2\pi r'\alpha/360 \\ &= (r - r')\,\alpha\pi/180 \\ &= \alpha\pi b/180. \end{aligned}$$

If $b = 10$ yd., $\pi = 3.14$, and $\alpha = 90°$, then $W = 15.7$ yd.

For the full circle, α is 360°, and the extra distance traveled by the outer wheels is given by $W = 2\pi b$. As the road width b becomes, in terms of a car, its track, so the extra distance W becomes the same as the circumference of the circle which has the track width as radius (around A, shaded: we might well call it the "track-circle." For the car in question, $W = 2 \times 3.14 \times 4$, about 25 ft.; for a railway track of width 4.71 ft., it is $2 \times 3.14 \times 4.7$ ft. $= 29.5$ ft., quite independently as to whether it is a track encircling a whole town, or a little tramway describing a tight loop.

When an outer wheel of radius R makes one revolution, it covers a distance on the road equal to its own circumference, given by the well-known formula $c = 2\pi R$. Thus it makes $W/c = b\alpha/360R$ more revolutions than the inner wheel. In a full circle ($\alpha = 360°$) the extra number of revolutions is b/R, which is exactly 2.

These extra revolutions with a car having $b = 4$ ft. and $R = 2$ ft. number only two, never more, not even if the car tours the whole country. In a car the two front wheels are free to revolve independently, each on its own short axle. The back wheels are fitted firmly to their axles (or half-shafts), but the differential mechanism is provided to allow them to revolve at different rates. The wheels of railway trains are also firmly secured to their axles, but have no differential. Both inner and outer wheels make the same number of revolutions, but they have a conical rim, so that when a freight car is pressed toward the outer side of a curve, the outer wheels are pushed up to a bigger radius, and thus cover a greater distance per revolution than the inner wheels (always providing, of course, that the centrifugal force is not countered by reduced speed and "super-elevation" of the outer rail). If it is, then the outer wheels must cover their extra distance by skidding instead of rolling; where the curves are gentle, the extra distance will be small.

So much for a curious but harmless property of curves. But John Smith knows only too well that they are in fact potentially very dangerous.

It is not only because on a bend the driver's arc of visibility is narrowed, with resultant danger to crossing pedestrians; more dangerous is the fact that a car is subjected to a strange force, which acts sideways, and tries to hurl it off the road ("centrifugal force," F; see diagram). This force takes effect quite without warning and strives with devilish strength to overturn any vehicle driven unsuspectingly into a curve at a speed of, say, 45 mi./hr. or more.

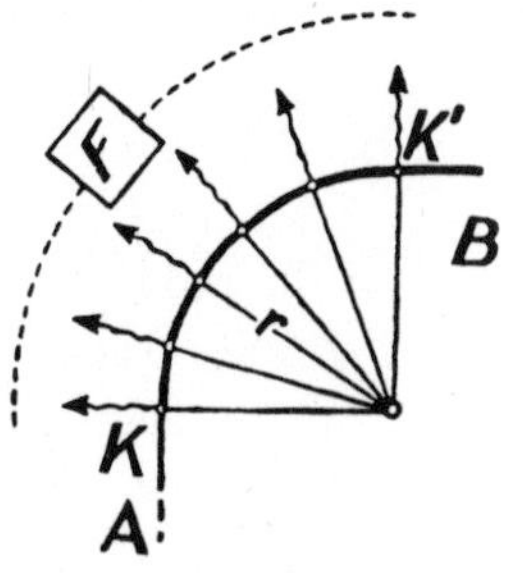

Every motorist and bicyclist has experienced this force in some degree, and maybe can recall with beating heart a situation when he only just got away with it.

Two methods of taming this monster are used in the design of fast highways. These are:

(a) "super-elevation" of the outer edge of the road as it leads into a curve;

(b) a transverse arc which removes or at least minimizes the initial shock of the curvature at both ends of a bend.

The reasons for the measures will now be explained.

CENTRIFUGAL FORCE. Fasten a stone to a piece of string, and whirl it round above your head: the string of course is tightly stretched. It is centrifugal force which pulls the stone outward, away from the end of the string round which it revolves. If the string is elastic (i.e., "stretchable"), the quicker the stone is whirled round, the more the string will stretch. It is clear that centrifugal force (hereinafter referred to as F) increases with the speed; actually doubling the speed means multiplying the force by 4. If the string breaks, the stone will fly outward in a straight line away from the center of the circle. If the string is lengthened, the centrifugal force decreases; if it is shortened, the force increases, provided that the speed of rotation of the stone remains constant. The centrifugal force results from the inertia of the stone: at every point it wants to fly off outward in a straight line, but is reluctantly pulled into a circular orbit by the string.

Centrifugal force is calculated by the formula $F = mv^2/r$, where m is the mass of the moving object (stone or vehicle), v its velocity, and r the radius of the curve in which it is moving. Thus a heavy truck with its relatively large mass is subjected to a greater centrifugal force than a bicyclist under the same conditions.

All this teaches us a useful lesson about bends in roads. A person who drives slowly is subjected to only a small centrifugal force, and a pedestrian would never go flying off at a bend in the road, but a speeding bicyclist might well do so, and land in the ditch. Moreover, on gentle curves the danger of this occurring is less than on a sharp curve, since the large radius is equivalent to a long string on the stone.

But a modern road is built to serve fast-moving traffic. A car driving at 45 mi./hr. on the straight should not have to reduce speed to 15 in order to negotiate a curve. Hence an attempt is made to make the radii of all curves as large as possible and thus the curves themselves as gentle as possible.

On the German *Autobahnen* the following minimum values for radii of curves are specified: in flat country, 1.24 mi., for a maximum speed of 100 mi./hr.; in hilly country .75 mi. for 87 mi./hr.; in mountainous country .5 mi. for 75 mi./hr.; on very high mountains .3 mi. for 60 mi./hr. The radii can, of course, be larger, but must not be smaller.

On the railway the corresponding values are as follows: main lines in mountainous countries .12 mi.; in flat country, not less than .37 mi.; for minor tracks, radii as low as .06 mi., or 300 ft., are allowed. The German Federal Railway prepares for all stretches of track an accurate "diagram of curves," which shows the radius and nature (i.e., left or right hand) of each curve. This diagram is accompanied by others, which give information on gradients, etc. (See diagram on p. 96.) Small "bumplike" deviations from the straight line represent curves which are read as left or right according to the direction of travel. Beside each bump is given its radius; the smallest, .12, is further emphasized by an arrow.

A relevant question: how can curves with a radius as large as .37 mi. be marked out on a given terrain? Certainly in practice they cannot be drawn on the ground with a cord .37 mi. long, pegged at one end! It is done by calculating the distance of a number of points from the line of the tangent (see diagram on p. 112, line *AK*6, e.g., 4–4′). These relatively short distances can easily be measured on the ground.

THE SUPER-ELEVATION OF THE ROADWAY. The string holds back the stone and keeps it on the curve: how, then, can we attach a similar "string" to a car on a bend in the road, to hold it on the curve?

The road surface is laid with a lateral slant, sloping downward toward the center of the curve. On the *Autobahnen* this slope has a gradient somewhere between 1.5% and 6%.

The outer rim of the curve is thus raised above the inner by (24.6 × the gradient) in feet, or between 4.5 and 18 in. (see p. 100). This has the effect of "laying the car into the curve," much as the string compels the stone, as will now be explained.

A car is being driven along a straight stretch of road (diagram *a*).

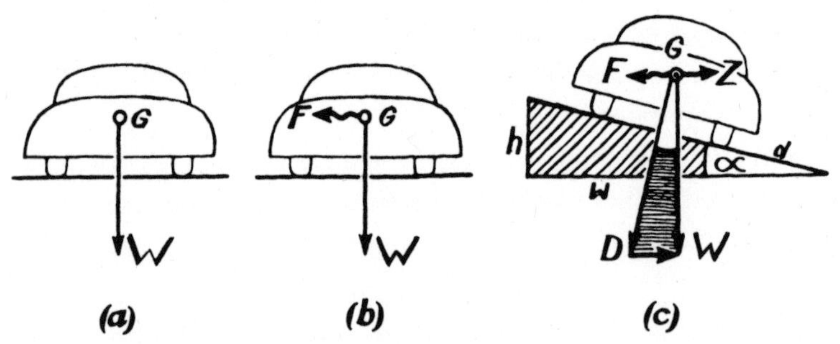

Let us consider its mass as being concentrated at a point *G*, the center of gravity, through which all forces acting on the car will be aligned. The car's weight *W* is supported by the road. So far, so good: now, however, comes a right-hand curve (diagram *b*). At the very moment when the driver turns his steering wheel, the centrifugal force begins to pull at the point *G*, striving to draw the car toward the outer edge of the curve. This force will affect the stability of the weight to some extent, depending on the radius of the curve and the speed of the vehicle. In an extreme case, it could overturn the car.

But if the road is laterally inclined toward the center of the curve in the ratio $h : w$ (diagram *c*), a different situation arises.

Consider first the car at rest on such a bend. We can then ignore the centrifugal force F, which is shown in diagram c, but which is now not operative. The weight W in the triangle of forces WGD can be resolved into a thrust D, perpendicular to the road surface, and a horizontal force Z. This latter is the "tension in the string" which strives to draw the car toward the center of the curve, and which increases with the lateral slope of the road.

If the car is at rest, this force will tend to pull it down the slope. If the car is in motion, however, the centrifugal force F is set up in opposition, and, given a proper combination of speed, lateral slope, and curve radius, it will be exactly balanced by the force Z. Both forces would thus be pulling like two boys of equal strength, one at either end of a barrow. Obviously the barrow would move neither forward nor backward, and similarly the car is able to travel round the curve quite unencumbered by any pull to either side. As the design of an *Autobahn* always includes a small lateral slant toward the outside, for drainage of rainwater, the "super-elevation" on a left-hand curve will result in a twisting of the road surface, as was mentioned on p. 100.

If the speed of travel v is given in mi./hr., and the radius of the curve in feet is r, the lateral slope required to balance the forces has a gradient q calculated by the formula $q = .067v^2/r$. Accordingly, if v is 75 and r is 2600, the lateral gradient needed is $q = .067 \times 75^2/2600 = .145 = 14.5\,\%$. On an *Autobahn*, however, it must not exceed 6 %, because much slower, heavier vehicles, such as trucks, also need to use the road. If the lateral slope were too steep, such vehicles would experience too severe a lateral force (Z), and under icy conditions they might slide down the slope and go off the road.

It is clear that the dangers of centrifugal force can be countered by this so-called "super-elevation" on curves. As, however, a definite speed of travel must be specified on these curves to win the benefit of perfect balance between the lateral forces, all vehicles moving at a slower speed would experience a lateral thrust toward the center of the curve, and faster vehicles would experience a pull toward the outer edge of the curve. In either instance the friction of the tires must hold the vehicle on the road, or else it would skid off to one side or the other. This is a common experience of passengers in trains: if the train travels too fast round a bend, they are thrown, in spite of the super-elevation, toward the outer edge of the curve; if the train travels too slowly, the passengers sense that the coach is leaning over, and feel themselves slipping toward the center of the curve.

Railway engineers calculate the gradient for the lateral inclination of a train, resulting from the super-elevation S, in inches, of the outer rail, by the formula $S = 2.5\ v^2/r$. Thus if the speed v is 60 mi./hr. and the curve radius 3000 ft., $S = 2.5 \times 3600/3000 =$ 3 inches.

FOR THE CALCULATOR. The derivation of the formula for the balancing lateral inclination, $q = .067\ v^2r$.

The triangle of forces DWG, with a right angle at W, is similar to the gradient triangle hwd (diagram c on p. 108). Let α represent the angle between d and w which is equal to the angle DGW. Hence $q = h/w = Z/W$, and also is equal to F/W, if the horizontal force Z is to balance the centrifugal force F. The centrifugal force $F = mv^2/r$ and the weight $W = mg$, where g, the acceleration due to gravity in ft./sec.^{2}, is approximately 32. Therefore, $q = mv^2/mgr = v^2/gr$, r being measured in feet and v in ft./sec. Thus, if, as is usual, v is given in mi./hr., then v mi./hr. $= v./.682$ ft./sec., and:

$$q = v^2/(32 \times .682^2r) = v^2/14.88r = .067v^2/r.$$

The "balancing" speed v for negotiating a curve can be calculated, given the radius r in feet and the lateral gradient q, from the formula $v = 3.8\sqrt{rq}$. If r is 2400 and q is 6%, then $v = 3.8\sqrt{2400 \times .06} =$ 46 (in mi./hr., of course).

The super-elevation S of a railway line (or the same value as h in diagram *c* on p. 108) is given by multiplying the track width by the lateral gradient q. The track width in Germany is 56.5 inches.

Hence $S = 56.5 \times .067v^2/r = 3.8v^2/r$. This is in inches; v is in mi./hr. and r in feet. As slower trains also use the same curves, the railway authorities reckon with only about two-thirds of this, i.e., with $S = 2.5v^2/r$.

THE NÜRBURGRING. This most famous German motor-racing track in the Eifel, which is about 18.6 mi. long, is not intended to be a safe, fast thoroughfare for the ordinary motorist, as are the *Autobahnen*. Its outline is shown here. (*A–Z* marks the starting and finishing line.) The carefully restricted values for gradient and curve radius do not apply here: the Nürburgring has uphill gradients as steep as 17%, and downhill 12% (the track is used in only one direction); there is in addition a stretch of special steepness (*S*) with a gradient 27%. Altogether, the total difference in heights over the whole track amounts to 1000 ft. Of the 89 left-handed and the 85 right-handed bends (which include many without "transitional arcs," cf. p. 114), the sharpest, at the so-called Roundabout *K*, has a radius of 100 ft. (!), and a lateral slope of 30%, necessitating an appropriate "balancing" speed calculated by $v = 3.8\sqrt{100 \times .3} = 21$ mi./hr. (p. 110). Not all the bends are built up in accordance with radius and "curve speed," and this is done intentionally: the track is not meant to give ideal motoring conditions, but conditions such as are encountered on roads other than the *Autobahnen*. Cars brought here for testing can thus be subjected to extreme stresses, and the circuit itself offers the racing driver a whole range of difficulties and obstacles as a challenge to his skill.

As a contrast, a famous bend on the north side of the Avus track in Berlin, which has a radius of only 260 ft. (!), had to be given a lateral slope with $q = .96 : 1$, almost $1 : 1$, in order to "balance" a speed of 60 mi./hr. Expressed in the more familiar degree measure this track slopes at an angle of 43.5°.

THE ONSET OF "LATERAL PULL." The lateral force, exerted on a vehicle as it negotiates a curve, is, as has been seen, neutralized, on at least lessened, by building up the outside of the track. Thus there is one danger which the road builder has successfully overcome. The other danger is caused by the initial onset of lateral force, which a vehicle experiences at the point of transition K, when it changes from a straight course into the curve KK', and again at the point K' where it resumes a straight course (diagram a).

The curve KK' is an arc of a circle with radius r. To negotiate this bend, we should have to turn the steering wheel through a certain angle β (say 5°), (and hold it it steady in its new position. For every angle through which the steering wheel might be turned, there is a corresponding "turning circle" for the car, and this grows smaller as the angle is increased. If the angle through which the wheel is turned is nil, then the car does not turn at all: the radius of the turning circle can be considered as infinite. Circle and straight line are the only curves with a constant rate of turn—that is, they are the only curves that can be negotiated with a constant angle of turn on the steering wheel.

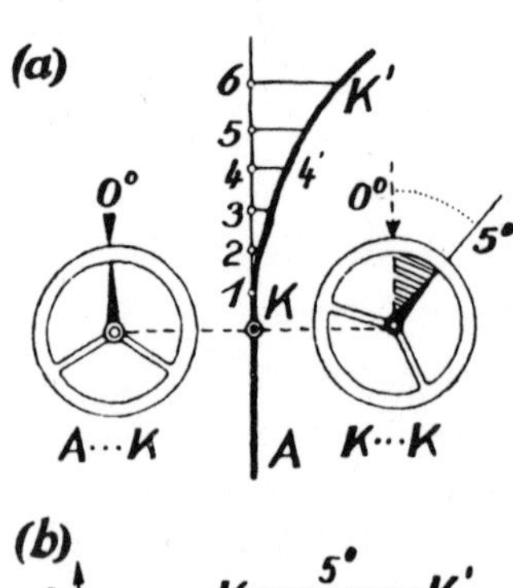

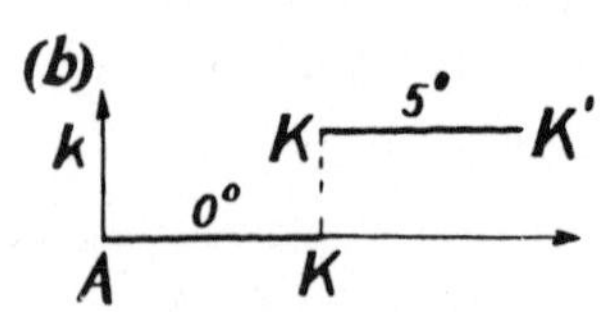

Now let us drive along the stretch of road AKK' (diagram a). At the point K the steering wheel must be turned through an angle of, say, 5°. In fact, it would have to be jerked round, as we pass from a straight course into the bend. At this point the wheel has to jump, without gradual transition, through a turn of 5°, because the curve is joined directly to the straight, also quite abruptly. This is the cause of "pull" on the steering. It is made clear by diagram *b*, which shows a graph of the curvature on this stretch of road. The horizontal axis represents the road distance, and the vertical axis marks the degree of curvature of the road (or, what is the same, the angle of turn of the steering wheel). It can be seen that the line of curvature from AK to KK' does not remain *continuous* at K. It is broken at this point by an abrupt shift from 0° to 5°.

"Steering pull" is caused by the sudden onset of the lateral force $F = mv^2/r$. In the case of a Volkswagen, weighing 2240 lb. (mass units = weight/gravity = 2240/32 = 70), passing at a speed of 45 mi./hr., or 66 ft./sec., into a curve of 300 ft. radius, the lateral pull F would be equal to $70 \times 66^2/300 = 1016$ lbs. It is rather as though the car at K were suddenly pulled toward the outside of the curve by a force of more than 1000 lbs.! This lateral pull on going into a bend can be readily observed with a child's toy train, when it passes from a straight to a curved rail. It is plainly jerked straightaway into the curve, sometimes so forcibly that it becomes derailed. You can feel the force yourself when traveling on very old and badly planned stretches of rails.

Vehicles which run on rails cannot escape this effect. John Smith, however, riding his bicycle or driving his car, can to some extent: he can "cut" a left-hand bend, and a right-hand turn can be negotiated with "counter swing." It is not that he likes to do it, or because he is tempted to infringe the law: He just cannot do otherwise! How can he in fact turn his wheel through 5° without passing through all intermediate stages, i.e., 1°, 2°, etc. ? He would have to stop at the point K, jack up his front axle, turn the steering wheel through 5°, remove the jack, and then proceed!

THE TRANSITIONAL ARC. John Smith negotiates a bend with abrupt onslaught of curvature by continuous alteration of steering in the following way: In the case of a left-hand bend *AB*, from the point *U* he turns his steering wheel steadily, until he reaches the point *L*; now he travels round the arc *LL'* with his wheel held steady at the angle of turn which he has chosen; from the point *L'* onward he reduces continuously the angle of turn, so that it is 0° at *U'*. In this way he describes before and after the arc *LL'* a so-called "transitional curve" (*UL* and *L'U'*), which leads him from the right-hand lane to the crown of the road: he "cuts" the curve. Instead of the arc *KK'*, he travels a much shorter distance *LL'* on an arc with smaller radius.

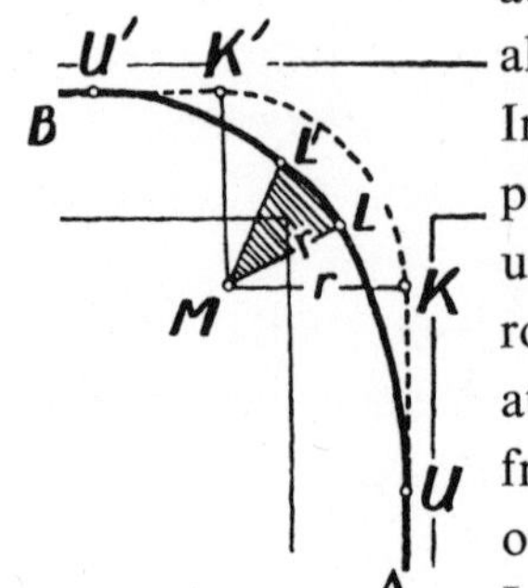

When taking a right-hand turn, John Smith, especially when he rides a bicycle, swings out in a left-hand arc (*UL*), moving round a larger arc *LL'* instead of *KK'*, and then, after an inward swing toward the right-hand arc *L'U'*, he regains a straight course at *U'*.

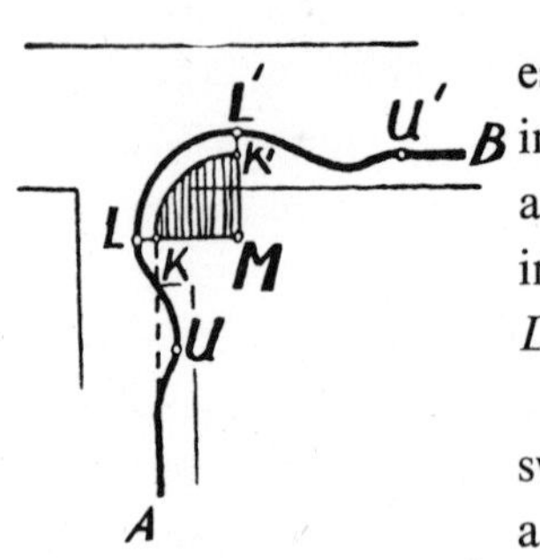

Usually, before and after this counterswinging, i.e., after *U* and at *U'*, he will make a slight swing in the opposite direction. This helps him to apply the actual counterswinging, and to recover from it. The transitional arcs, *UL* before and *L'U'* after the arc *LL'*, have no other purpose than to avoid, or at least tone down, the onset of lateral pull, i.e., to render an abrupt transition from one bend to another capable of negotiation by a *continuous* steering technique on the part of the driver.

The most urgent need for transitional arcs is on railway tracks. An express cannot cut the curves, and without the aid of these arcs it would be fatally susceptible to the sudden onset of lateral pull on curves. Thus, as the maximum speeds of trains have increased it has become necessary to incorporate transitional arcs into track layouts. They are based on the section *UK* of an *S*-shaped (cubic) curve *PUP'*. This has at its turning-point *U* the same curvature (i.e., zero) as the straight line *AU*. Then for a certain distance it increases its curvature more and more sharply, and subsequently eases it off. At the point *K*, where the curvature reaches that of a circle, a change is made by joining on an arc *KK'* of a circle with center *M*. (The center for the "straight arc" at *U* is at infinity.)

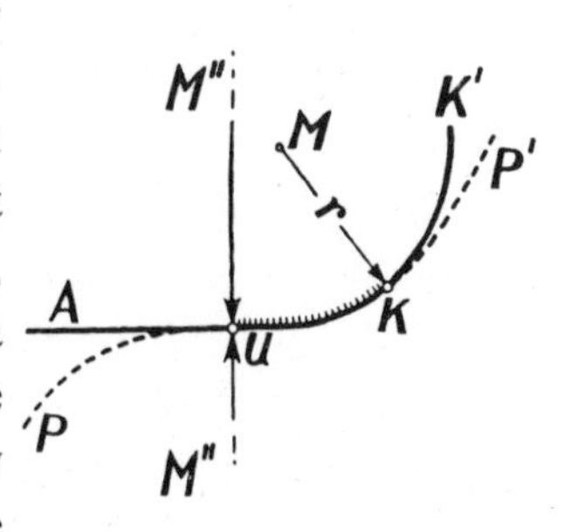

Some really interesting considerations arise from a study of transitional curves on the German *Autobahnen*. If a car is to negotiate a bend without cutting or counter-swinging, there must be a continuous transition from zero curvature to the curvature $1/r$, which is that of a circle with radius r.

First consideration. One might proceed by stages from curvature 1 to curvature 2 by interpolating an arc of a circle with twice the radius (diagram *a*). By this means the jump in curvature from 1 to 2 is eased by an intermediate stage 2a, as the graph of diagram *b* shows.

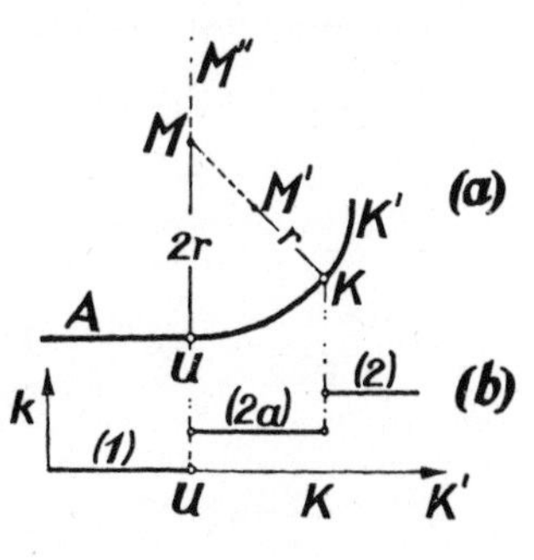

The radius changes from infinity through the value $2r$ to r. Of course, further intermediate stages can be added, whereby curvature 1 is gradually altered to its smallest value, and then changes back again at the end of the curve. An arc such as *UKK'*, which is made of several adjacent arcs, is called curve-fitting. It smooths down the abrupt change of curvature into several smaller changes, but the jumps in curvature are still there, just as stepping stones, when placed nearer to one another, will still fail to provide a continuous bridge across a stream.

Thus it does not completely provide for a continuous turning of the steering wheel by cutting out the sudden wrench. In the design of all major roads, however, the use of curve-fitting is specified, and it is also found on the *Autobahnen* quite frequently.

Second consideration. Let us choose for a transitional curve one which curves gradually from a straight line, much as is done by the S-shaped curve used on the railway (this curve is in fact not practicable for use in road design for other reasons). From many similar curves of this type, let us choose one, the curvature of which is proportional to the length of its arc: that is, one which doubles its curvature as it doubles the length of its arc. Is there such a curve? The little-known clothoid or Euler's spiral, fits this specification. It bends from a point U of zero curvature, either to right or to left, reminiscent of a bishop's pastoral staff, or a young, unrolled fern frond. At the end point E, which it continually approaches after innumerable turns, but never reaches, it achieves infinitely great curvature because at this point the radius of curvature is zero.

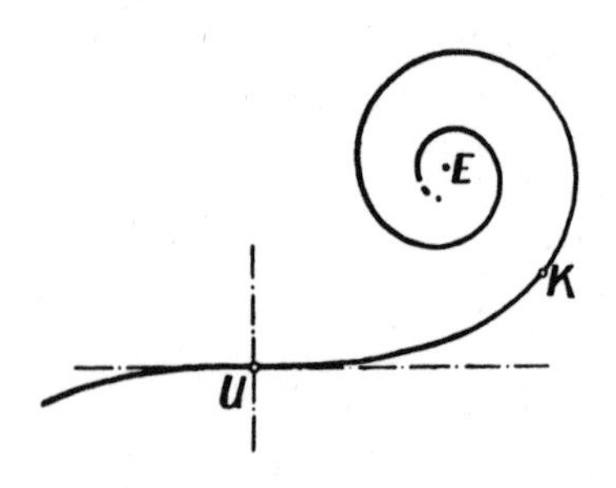

If the section UK of this curve is fitted between straight line and circle (diagram *a*), John Smith can then drive his car (see diagram *b*) from the point U by turning his steering wheel at a constant rate to give a continuously increasing angle of turn. The angle is doubled as the distance traveled is doubled, and when he reaches the point K, where the arc of

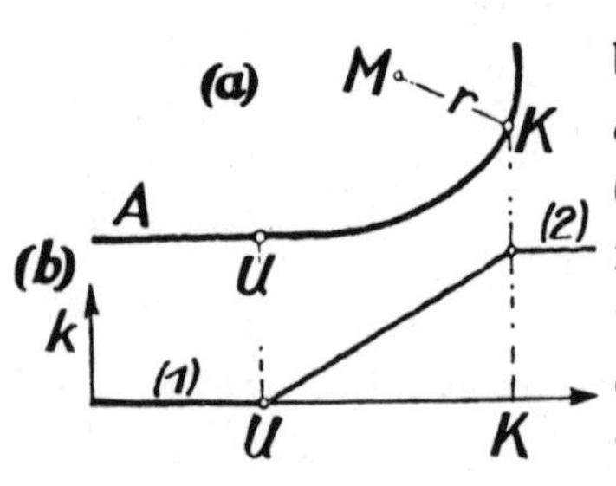

the circle commences, the angle of turn on his steering wheel remains constant. Thus continuous transition is made possible, and all trace of an abrupt onset of lateral pull is eradicated. This kind of transitional arc was first used on the *Autobahn* between Vienna and Breslau.

The cubic curve used on railways approximates fairly closely in one of its sections to the spiral, so that both graphs of curvature coincide. Incidentally, with arcs of smaller radius than 1000 ft., the width of track must be enlarged by as much as 1.2 in., so that the wheels shall not be constricted.

Try pushing a baby carriage, which has no steering, round a bend on a narrow path between two curbstones. It will stick fast, unless the wheels have sufficient room to move.

Third consideration. In seeking to provide a transitional curve fully suited to practical driving conditions, let us try to provide one that will match the degree of turning, which would be intuitively placed on the steering by a driver—the same sort of intuition that would make him cut a curve. The graph of curvature for such an ideal curve would not show a sudden bend at the point *U*, as does that of Euler's spiral (diagram *b*, p. 116), but would pass without any sudden bend from curvature 1 to curvature 2. For John Smith does not turn his wheel from point *U* onward, in strict relation to the distance: after traversing twice the distance, the angle of turn of this steering wheel is not completely doubled, but rather less. In a similar way he "understeers" the turn, as he passes into the arc commencing at point *K*.

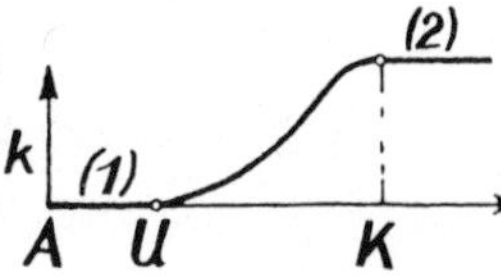

Mathematically speaking, a curve could be designed to fill these conditions; in actual road building, however, this would involve calculations so complicated as to make the idea completely impracticable. So far, therefore, the clothoid spiral remains the best form of transitional arc. The curves on older roads, built for earlier traffic, have no transitional arcs at all. Carts and pedestrians took the curves without any need for cutting or counter-swinging. The modern car driver, however, soon shows the road builder what is needed at points where it is missing: his tire tracks on roads show this only too well. If you examine these on a curve (in snow the tracks are seen best of all), you can soon tell whether the curve is well designed or not. From the curves themselves, it is not so easy to spot the technical considerations (if any) which underlie their design. Two short examples will soon demonstrate this. We are going to negotiate three closed curves, a circle and two ovals. When

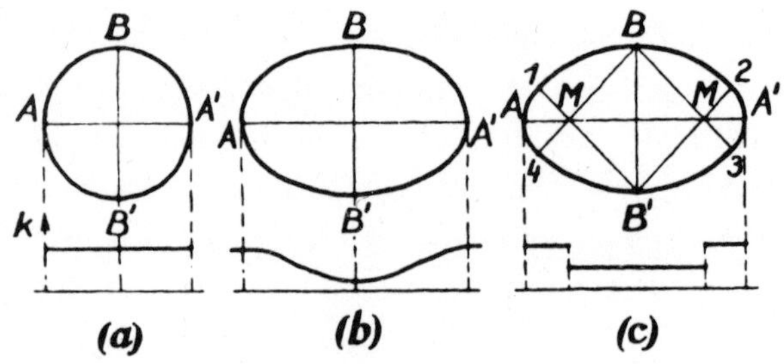

going round the circle (diagram a), the angle of turn of the steering wheel remains constant: constant curvature means no sudden onset of lateral pull (cf. graph of curvature beneath the circle, for the arc ABA'). As to the ovals, the first seems very like the second, and we might well assume that both have continuously changing curvature, and would thus allow us to negotiate them without experiencing an abrupt lateral pull. In the first instance (diagram b) this is indeed the case: the curve is an ellipse, and the curvature changes continuously from a maximum at A to a minimum at B. The second oval, however (diagram c), while resembling an ellipse, is actually made up of a series of fitted arcs. It comprises four distinct arcs, 1-2, 2-3, 3-4, 4-1, circular, with centers at B', M', B, and M, respectively. Its curvature does not alter continuously;

each of the four arcs is negotiated with a different angle of turn on the steering wheel, and at the transition points 1, 2, 3, 4, abrupt jerks on the steering are needed. (See graph beneath the figure.)

Let us now summarize all these ideas about curves. By super-elevation of the road surface a fast-moving car is guided into a curve and enabled to counter the lateral pull of centrifugal force. Transitional arcs help a car to be driven, by a gradual and continuous turning of its steering wheel, from a straight course into a curve, without braking or experiencing any abrupt lateral pull, which would result from a sudden sharp bend. Just as the transitional arc leads continuously into the curve, so does the upward sloping curve $B'C'D'$ in diagram on p. 100 lead to the full super-elevation at D'.

So when John Smith is revelling in the safe pleasures of the great new thruways, he ought to thank mathematics for taming the malicious demon that lurks in the bends of our minor roads. All he needs to do is to exercise reasonable care. But for the reckless motorist, on whatever road he may be, the demon still lies in wait, and will strike with lightning speed and ferocity.

A CHART OF MOTION

TIME AND SPACE. Movement takes place in both time and space. The Bergstrasse is a well-known stretch of straight road, which skirts the edge of the Odenwald in Germany. We set off from Bensheim B (see diagram on p. 121) at 12 noon on foot, and reach Heppenheim H, 3 mi. away, one hour later. If we draw a graph marking out distance in miles on the horizontal axis, and time in minutes on the vertical axis, our page constitutes a space-time "field," on which our walk can be plotted as a continuous line of points from B to E. It shows not only our course in terms of space (i.e., distance), as a map would, but our motion, which includes also the time dimension.

Think for a moment of the space axis on its own, isolated from time. Suddenly, at 12 o'clock, time "switches on." From every point of the distance axis, perpendicular lines arise (shown here only at half-mile intervals from 0 to 3). They all grow at the same rate, their uppermost extremities lying, at any given time (say 12:10, 12:20, etc.), along the same horizontal line.

Every point in this space-time "field" expresses both position and time: e.g., *Q*, .5 mi., at 12:10 p.m.; *E*, 3 mi. at 1 p.m. (Heppenheim). As our position changes a track is left behind on the field: it is the graph of our motion. Thus the straight line *BE* is the graph of our walk from Bensheim to Heppenheim.

TRAFFIC ON THE ROAD. If we walk at constant speed the graph of our motion is a straight line with constant gradient, because in equal intervals of time we traverse equal distances, e.g., in 10 minutes we always cover .5 mi. (cf. the first is from *B* to *Q*). If we take a rest after 2 mi. the line representing our motion stops and resumes higher up the perpendicular through the stopping point at 2 mi., at a point in time when we resume our walk. If a car leaves *B* at 12:40 p.m., and reaches *H* after 5 minutes, it overtakes us at the point *U* (2.2 mi.), the point where the two straight lines representing the two journeys cross. Because the car travels more quickly, its line on the graph does not slope as steeply as ours.

All the traffic on the highway can similarly be plotted on this "field" of time and distance, and, what is even more interesting, we can see from the graph what is going on on the road, at any selected time and place. If an observer were to sit beside the road 1 mi. from *B*, a motorcycle will pass at 12:03 p.m. making for *H*, and another at 12:17 bound for *B*; at 12:18 p.m. a motorcycle will be traveling toward *H*, and at 12:20 p.m. we

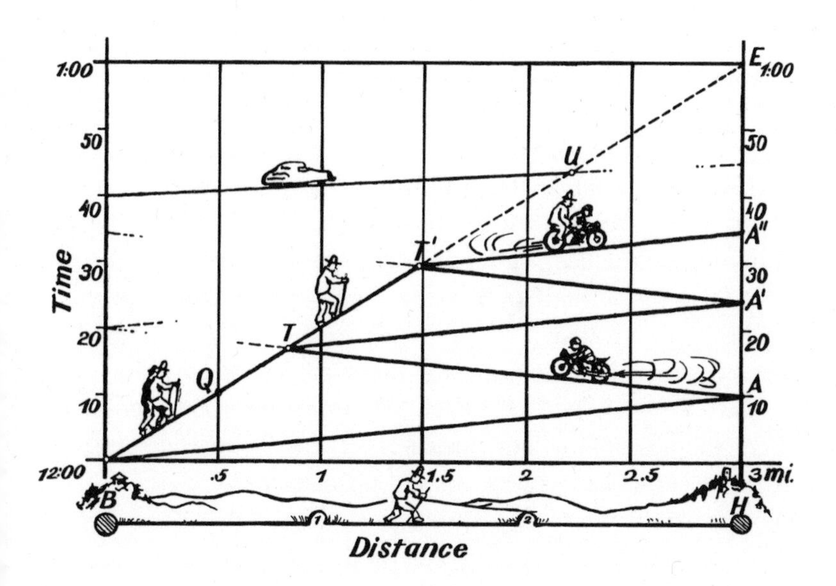

ourselves will be trudging by, followed at 12:42 by a car speeding toward *H*. All this can be seen at a glance up the perpendicular through the point 1 mi. on the distance axis. And if the pilot of an aircraft were to look down at 12:15 p.m. on this stretch of road he would see (as on the horizontal line through 12:15 on the time axis) us at .7 mi. moving toward *H*, and a motorcycle at 1.5 mi. making for *B*; otherwise the road would be clear.

Because of the convenience of a diagram of this type, railways compile their timetables by the same graphical method, using it to show the movements of all passenger and freight trains. They are called time-distance graphs, and are just like the diagram, except that the time axis is drawn downward. If it is desired to run a special train, its course is drawn with a ruler on the graph, so as not to clash with scheduled trains. Once this has been done, all necessary details of time schedules, connections, etc., can be easily and quickly read from the graph. To calculate them would be an extremely complicated and laborious task. We will solve a problem of this kind, with the help of the graph on p. 121.

A BIT OF "HITCH-HIKING." Three of us, you, John Smith, and I, are going for a walk to Heppenheim (H). A friend meets us at midday in Bensheim, with his motorcycle. He offers to take us one by one on the back riding saddle to Heppenheim, and insists that in this way we shall all be there much quicker than if we were to walk. "Get on, John," he says, "I'll have you there in 10 minutes, and then I'll come back for the next one. Meanwhile, you two start walking, and I'll meet you along the road." John is rather dubious about our prospect of being in Heppenheim before 1 o'clock, but he gets on, and off they go.

Now it would be a tricky problem to calculate when and where our friend would meet us along the road, when he would reach H for the second time, when and where he would pick up the third passenger, and so on. But it can all be solved in a flash, by drawing a graph.

First trip to H: BA, drawn from B at 12 noon ending at the destination A at 12:10. We shall reckon that mounting, dismounting, and turning around is counted in with the 10 minutes, though it would not be difficult to allow for them separately. First return journey, leaving A at 12:10, would bring our motorcyclist back to Bensheim at 12:20, but in fact he meets his second passenger at T (the intersection of his graph line with ours, BE), the time being 12:17 and the distance from B .8 mi. The second trip to Heppenheim is represented by TA' (with the same speed as before, so the line is parallel to BA). At 12:24 he reaches Heppenheim (A'). The second return trip is represented by $A'T'$, parallel to AT, meeting his last passenger at T', 12:29 and 1.45 mi. from Bensheim. The third and last journey to Heppenheim is shown by $T'A''$, parallel to TA', and it reunites us all in Heppenheim at 12:35, 25 minutes earlier than if we had walked all the way.

Allowances could be made for rests, engine trouble, varying speeds, etc., but even these would not make the puzzle much more complicated, if it were tackled by this graphical method.

So we can see the excellent properties of the time-distance graph. Its discovery has been one of the most fruitful ideas in western mathematical thought.

Why not try to sketch the time-distance graph of the two hands of a clock? The point where the two straight lines intersect will give the exact time when the hands are positioned one underneath the other.

CURVES, VISIBLE AND INVISIBLE

A FEW VISIBLE CURVES. One must develop an eye for these, for they are a curious lot. Smoothly and splendidly they can move through space, like the great ribbon of the modern thruway. Proudly they sweep through the air in the lines of a suspension bridge. Nobly and fastidiously they curve with the silhouette of a precious vase, or restlessly flutter like the beating of a bird's wing.

There are others, however, less spectatular, more homely, and still others that have no visible course at all.

The realm of the two basic curves, circle and straight line, is of primary importance: the circle is the perfect round, ever-turning; the line is the perfect straight, ever extending. We meet them both everywhere, but we also meet many other types of curve.

A car headlight in the city throws on the ground an *ellipse* of light (diagram *b*, p. 124), or on highways a *parabola* (diagram *c*), which vanishes into infinity; but if the patch of light is a *hyperbola* (diagram *d*), then there is danger for oncoming cars. These particular instances occur when the ground cuts the cone of light (ellipse; or a circle, if the axis of the cone is perpendicular to the ground); or when the upper edge of the cone is parallel to the ground (parabola); or when the upper edge lies above the parallel to the ground (hyperbola). As sections of one and the same cone, all four curves are closely related. The whole family can easily be conjured up with a flashlight on a wall, or by dipping a conical funnel into water at various angles. Of the sister of circles,

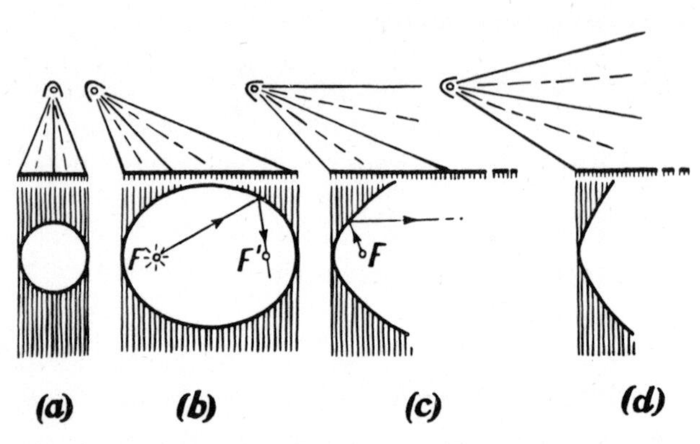

the ellipse, we will speak further on p. 130. The parabola may be seen in the curve of wheat stalks bent by ripe ears of grain; jets from a fountain, trajectories of balls in flight, a ski-jumper, and a sky rocket all describe the same type of parabolic track through the air.

We can sometimes observe a lovely double-crescent outline in an empty coffee cup, when light shines into it. The parallel rays of sunlight are reflected from the circular interior wall of the cup, but instead of returning back into space they are reflected, one on top of the other, so creating a bright concentration of light along a curve shaped like a double crescent. This is one half of a caustic curve (cf. diagram, bottom of p. 129).

We gaze with wonder at the cables of a suspension bridge or a cable railway; in imagination we too swing with them on their high and dizzy course over the broad landscape. Their curves are called catenaries, which in form are very like parabolas, but for which the principle of construction is entirely different. Every flexible cable, fastened only at both ends, and supporting only its own weight, hangs in the shape of a catenary, the mighty cables of the high-tension power system as well as a clothesline.

Every curve is specified by its own appropriate "locus" or "law of position." That which governs the circle is as follows: It is a line with all its points in one plane and equidistant from one fixed point. If the law of position which specifies a particular curve is known, its individual qualities can be deduced. For example, the beautiful mirror-like property of the ellipse (diagram *b* on p. 124): a ray of light issuing from one focus *F* would be reflected, if the curve were a mirror, through the other focus *F′*. If this second focus retreated to infinity (diagram *c* on p. 124), the rays reflected toward it would be parallel—the ideal beam for automobile headlights! To achieve such a beam, the ellipse must become a parabola. Car headlight reflectors are all parabolic. The shape is generated by rotating a parabola about its axis of symmetry, thus resulting in a three-dimensional surface. What happens when the headlight is dimmed? It is a simple matter performed by switching off the source of light at the original focal position, and substituting another differently placed. In this way the rays of light no longer are reflected parallel to the axis; instead they form a divergent beam directed toward the ground, as shown. (The lower half of the bulb is screened so that only the downward beam is reflected.)

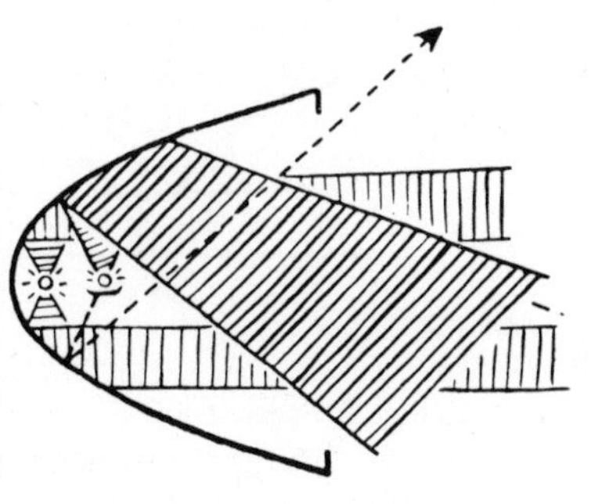

The properties of different curves cannot usually be seen merely by inspection. They are rather like human beings: many of them seem simple and unsophisticated, yet they are able to express elaborate ideas, like those which are inherent in the curve of living growth (cf. diagram b on p. 27); others come along full of their own importance, making themselves out to be, say, an ellipse, whereas they are actually only a few arcs of common circles, joined together like the fake "ellipse" seen in diagram c on p. 118. The law implicit in a particular curve is the only guide which can be trusted in these matters.

THE CYCLOID. The curves just discussed can all be seen as a whole, but there are other curves which cannot be seen at all, because only one point on them can be observed at any given instant. This is the case with curves of motion.

What is the curve described by the valve of a bicyle tire as it revolves? Consider first the valve in its initial position A on the circumference of the wheel. Now, place a penny flat on a table, and

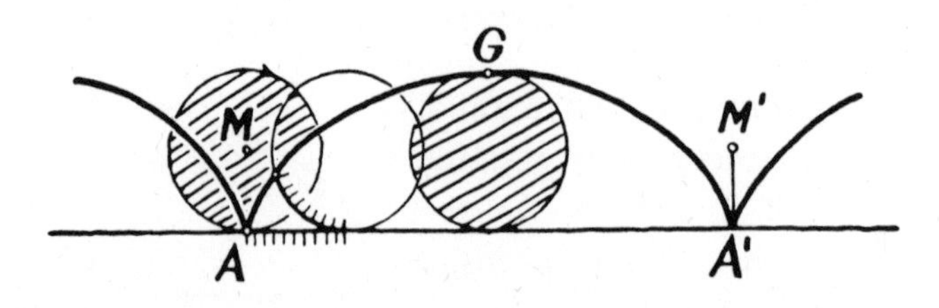

roll it along the edge of a ruler. Mark the various positions taken up by a point on the edge of the coin, starting at A. (You must be careful not to let it slide.) When the coin has been rolled completely round once, this point will have reached A'. The distance AA' is equal to the circumference of the coin. Halfway between these points, the moving point will be at the top of the coin, and it is easily seen that it describes a curve from A to A', with its ends at points on the edge of the ruler. The full title of this curve is the "cusped cycloid" (cycloid: "circle-like" from the Greek *kyklos* = circle). The variation of the point's speed is quite interesting: while the wheel moves along at a constant speed, the valve, or any other point on the circumference, comes momentarily to a stop at the ends of the curve (A, A', etc.), and subsequently accelerates, reaching its greatest speed at the points G, G', etc. Its track, AGA' is equal in length to four times the wheel's diameter (with a wheel diameter of 2 ft., the length of the cycloid is 8 ft., which is incidentally about $1\frac{1}{4}$ times as long as the distance MM', between the center of the wheel before revolving, and its position after one revolution. This distance is equal to the circumference of the wheel, given by $3.14 \times 2 = 6.28$ ft. The ratio is $4d : \pi d = 4/\pi = 1.27$. Thus for every mile covered by the wheel, the valve moves 1.27 mi.

This is a good example of the "invisible" type of curve. Its quality could be demonstrated after dark by a small light fixed to the valve of a moving cycle wheel. Alternatively, a cycloid can be traced on a smooth, sandy beach, by wheeling a bicycle along, so that a shadow of the wheel (and the valve) is cast on the sand.

LET'S TAKE ROVER. Our little terrier goes wild with delight when allowed to accompany us on a walk from M to M'. He always runs round and round us in clockwise circles, as we walk, and so his track resembles the circles of the diagrams on pp. 126 and 128. In fact, as you can see, he describes a cusped cycloid, when our distance MM' equals the perimeter u of each circle described by Rover. If he circles round us in an counter-clockwise direction, he describes a cycloid BB' upside down (diagram, p. 128), but bearing the same relationship to the length of our walk.

Now we come to something really absorbing: what sort of

curve does he describe if, every time he reaches a point on *MM'* immediately in front of us, he changes direction, thus running alternately clockwise and counter-clockwise? The answer is that he passes over from the "clockwise" cusped cycloid to the other "counter-clockwise" cycloid, which is a mirror image of the first the line *MM'*. The points at which he passes from one cycloid to the other are those where the curves cross our track *MM'*. The result is a most complicated track, impossible to visualize. (In the diagram below it is traced with the heavy line.) All we can see is Rover's course in relation to ourselves, namely, the circles which he runs round us.

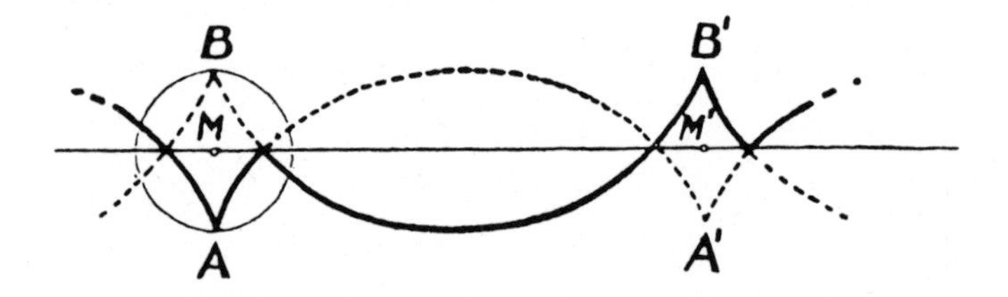

If we walk more slowly, so that *MM'* is less than the circumference of Rover's circles, the cycloid "loops the loop," and the cusps become loops. The result is called a "curtate cycloid." If we hurry our pace, so that *MM'* is greater than the circumference of the circles, the cusps are smoothed out into an arc; then we have a "prolate cycloid." These variations can be observed by studying the motion of various points on a wheel's disk (in upper diagram on p. 129—*R*, *J*, *A*). *A* is on the circumference, but *R* and *J* are inside it.

Let us suppose that the points *R*, *J*, *A* are on the wheel of a train. *R* is on the part of the wheel which is in contact with the rails, and it describes a cusped cycloid as the wheel rolls along. It is momentarily at rest (!) each time it comes into contact with the rail. The point *A* is on the extreme edge of the flange, and it describes a looped or curtate cycloid. It actually travels backward for a short distance, when it is describing half of a loop! The inner point *J*, which is where the connecting rod might be fixed,

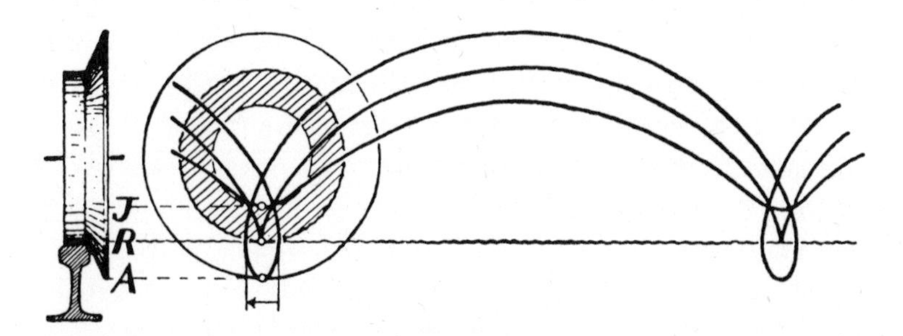

moves in a prolate cycloid, with its speed diminished at its lowest points. If at these three points were fixed red, yellow, and green lights on a night journey, we should be able to see the actual curves traced out in the dark, and an especially spectacular effect would be produced if the three points were on different radii, so that they would trace a succession of different cycloids!

All curves of movement must be considered in relation to a frame of reference. The points *R*, *J*, *A* describe, in relation to the axis of the wheel, circles, but in relation to the rail, cycloids. Relative to the earth, the moon describes a circle round it, but relative to the sun, it moves in a prolate cycloid round the elliptical course of the earth.

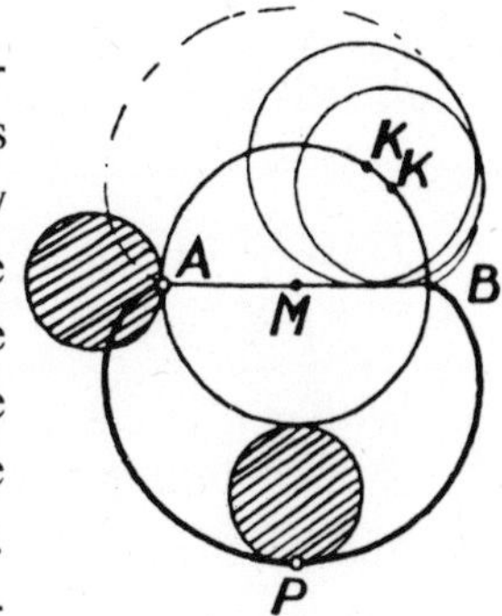

ENVELOPES. There are curves which are invisible, and there is yet another type which is not there at all—at any rate in the usual way in which a curve is described. Draw a circle with center *M* and radius *MB*. Now describe many more circles all the centers of which lie on the circumference of the first circle, and the circumferences of which touch its diameter *AB*. When this figure is carefully drawn, it is fascinating to see the fine network of circles, and one is surprised to note that they are all enclosed within a kidney-shaped curve, which has not been consciously drawn at all! If you cut through this "kidney" with a line through M perpendicular to AB, you get the caustic curve in the coffee cup, previously described (p. 125). Although it has been produced in a different way from the curve we are now discussing, it is, nevertheless, according to its law of structure the self-same curve. It can also be described by a point on the perimeter of a coin which is rolled round the perimeter of a second coin with twice the radius of the first. The "cottage-loaf" effect ABP (see diagram at bottom of p. 129) is the result, and it meets the "track," i.e., the circumference, at the points AB.

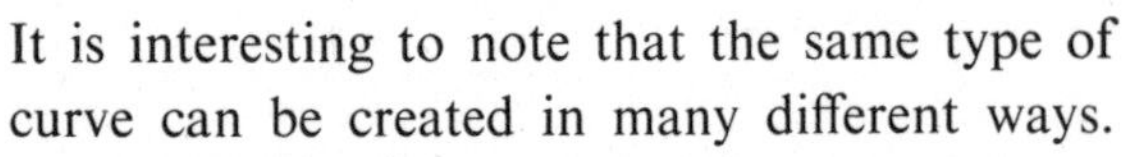

It is interesting to note that the same type of curve can be created in many different ways.

Envelopes are indeed curious members of the curve family, and among then are curves made with straight lines! Suppose you raise a ladder of length l from a position MB flat on the ground, so that its upper end M moves up the wall toward H. The many successive positions of the ladder, if drawn on paper, will frame a graceful curve, which is thus made with straight lines (cf. the double crescent in diagram on p. 125). The realm of curves has indeed many wonders to attract and reward our attention.

THE ELLIPSE: STRINGS AND PAPER STRIPS THAT THINK

With a ruler you can draw a straight line, with the compass a circle. These are the two basic curves of mathematics, the first one being the "straightest" of all, the second the roundest—in fact, it is the curve with the greatest "roundness," because it has a uniform degree of curvature at all points. If you turn the steering wheel of your car and hold it steady, you will move in a circle. The two basic curves have this much in common: both have a uniform rate of curvature. With the straight line it is zero: think of it as a circle with an infinitely large radius. All other curves have varying curvatures (cf. ellipse, diagram *b* on p. 124).

The Greek philosophers doubtless had in mind this peculiar affinity between circle and straight line when they specified that geometrical problems must be solved only with the aid of compasses or dividers, and rule. This limitation led to unexpected discoveries in the tangled field of geometrical forms. Many problems also remained unsolved as a result, such as the "squaring of the circle," i.e., the construction of a rectangle or square equal in area to a given circle.

Another close relation of the circle is the ellipse. You encounter it in everyday affairs almost as often as the circle, a few examples being a slanting section through a sausage, the elongated shadow of a wheel, and the patch of light thrown by a car headlight, but usually these are hardly noticed. The glass of a headlight is circular, and although it is often observed from a viewpoint that makes it seem an ellipse, yet the observer thinks of it as a circle because he knows that it is one. Our knowledge of facts often affects our vision in this way, and it is not only children and ancient Egyptians who would sketch a wheel seen obliquely, as a circle. Even among us "educated and sophisticated people" there are those who see as they think, and who would still say that at night trees are green.

Our picture of a circle is usually an ellipse; only if it is viewed from a point along the perpendicular to its center does it appear in its true shape. But how is an ellipse *drawn*? Here are four interesting methods:

An ellipse inside a rectangle and parallelogram (diagram *a*). A circle of wire is soldered to fit exactly inside a square of wire. The soldered points lie at the center of each side of the square. If this is held up in the sunlight, its shadow will be a rectangle or parallelogram, with the soldered points still at the middle points of the sides. The shadow of the circle is an ellipse, which can be traced on paper. With very little practice this technique can be perfected.

(a)

Diagram *b* shows a pattern of curves, which can be viewed by making a cardboard cube and cutting out the circles from each face. (If you make such a model, it is advisable to strengthen the edges of the cube with thin pieces of wire. Knitting needles glued inside would serve this purpose very well.)

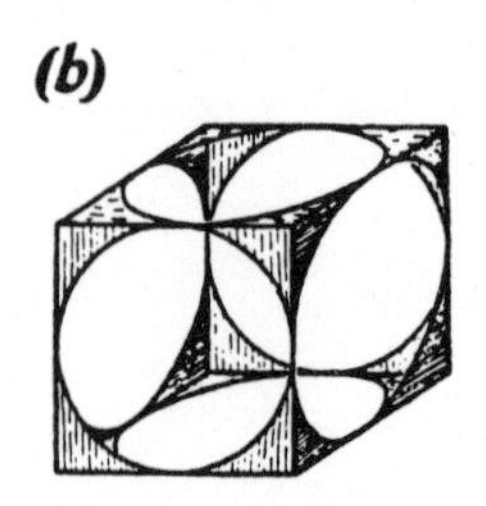

A string ellipse can be drawn in the following manner:

Fix two drawing pins through a sheet of paper on a drawing board, and loop round them a piece of string with its ends tied together. Draw this tight with a pencil point as shown, and move the pencil around, keeping the string taut: the point will trace out an ellipse. There are many such strings "that can think," in mathematics; this is only one example. The original idea was not frivolous; it arose from the ancient practice of measuring land and marking out the ground plans of temples, pyramids, and other structures with stakes and stretched ropes.

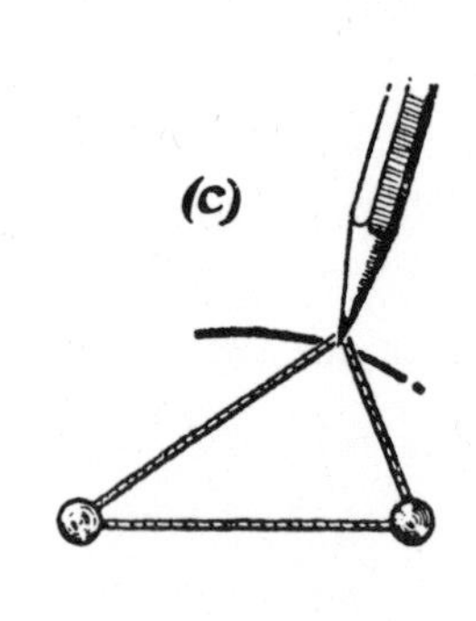

Paper-strip ellipses. An ellipse is, as it were, a squeezed circle, with a long axis AA' and a short axis BB'. Cut a strip of paper (1) from the edge of a sheet of note-paper, and mark along it half the

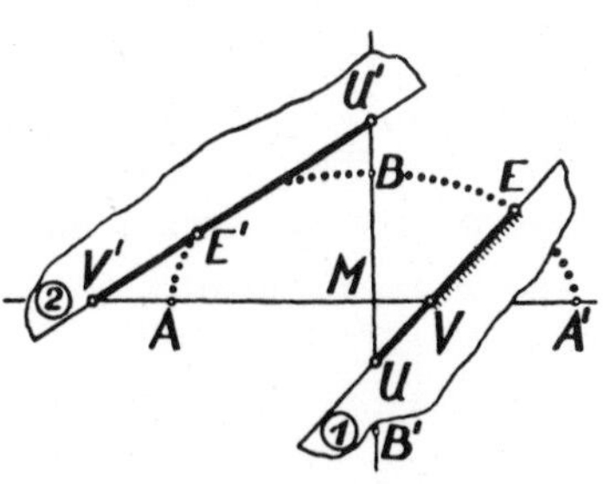

larger axis MA' (EU); then, measuring again from E, mark off half the shorter axis BM (EV). Now place the strip across the axes as shown, so that U lies on BB' and V on AA'; the section UV now lies between the axes, and E is a point on the ellipse which you are tracing. Mark its position, and move the paper strip, so that U and V take up different positions on the two axes. For each position mark the place of E. Rather more quickly than you might think, you will get a whole line of points forming an arc of your ellipse. If MA and MB differ only slightly in length, do not superimpose $MB(EV)$ upon $MA(EU)$ but place them end to end, as shown by paper strip number (2) in the diagram ($V'E'$ an extension of $E'U'$). E' is then another point on the ellipse ($E'U' = MA$ and $E'V' = MB$). And so we have paper strips that do our mathematics for us!

Contorted-circle ellipses can be drawn with compasses, i.e., with circles! Draw above the half axes MA and MB the right angle BCA, thus forming a rectangle $MACB$. Then drop from C a perpendicular to the line AB; this perpendicular, when produced, cuts the axes at K and K', as shown. Now describe a circle with center K and radius KA, and another circle with center K' and radius $K'B$. The appropriate arcs of these circles give such a close approximation to the outlines of an ellipse, that they can easily be joined freehand or with the aid of a French curve. This method is very useful, for it helps to avoid the over-pointed curve at A, which beginners often put in when drawing ellipses. Draftsmen do in fact often find this the best method, because they can work with compasses.

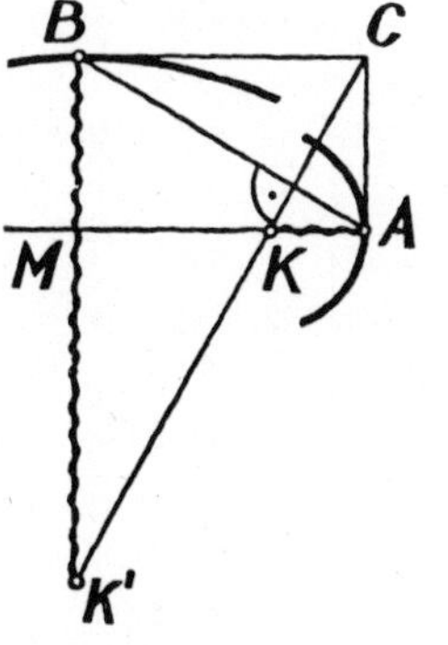

But we must here again refer back to the deceptive "circle-ellipse" (diagram *c* on p. 118), which can be drawn with compasses to look very like an ellipse. As with mankind, here we have a case where appearances are misleading and only the unseen character can reveal the truth!

Chapter 6

NORMAL AND NOT NORMAL; ELECTRIC LIGHT BULBS; THE BREAD ROLLS THAT WENT WRONG

Young John Smith shows his father the "*F*" given him for his math homework. Father is annoyed, but Johnny defends himself: "The work didn't turn out normal, Dad." "What do you mean?" "It just didn't turn out normal." Mr. Smith gives up the discussion at this. The lad might have a point if only Dad knew what on earth he meant by "not normal." Was he just making a silly excuse, or was there some sort of reasoning behind the phrase? John Smith senior decides to conceal his ignorance and find out what it all means.

CLASS PERFORMANCE SHOWN IN FIGURES. The long-suffering ninth-grade class has had to do a French and a math exercise for homework. They have come to the conclusion that the results in French have turned out "normal," for there were: one *A* (excellent), three *B*'s (good), ten *C's* (satisfactory), four *D*'s (poor), and two *F*'s (failing). The math homework, however, was in general very badly done: the pupils this time were divided among the five grades in the numbers 1, 3, 4, 7, 5. In gym they were grouped 4, 8, 6, 2, 0 which showed in general a very good achievement.

All these figures have been put together in the table below on this page. Column 1 shows the letters used for grading, Columns 2, 3, and 4 indicate the number of students placed in the different grades, the figures thus showing the "frequency" of places in each grade. In this way the facts may be conveniently summarized and an impression gained of the relative performance of the class in the individual subjects. But on what basis can this impression be expressed as "normal," "bad," or "good?" This is an interesting point: the judgment is made from a consideration of figures, which indicate numbers of pupils, but which in themselves say nothing about the quality of the work. It is not only the figures themselves, however, but their distribution among the various grades which helps to form the judgment. Note also that the judgment formed is not of John's or Frank's individual performance in specific subjects, but of the performance of an entire class.

Grade	*Frequency*		
	French	*Mathematics*	*Gymnastics*
A	1	1	4
B	3	3	8
C	10	4	6
D	4	7	2
F	2	5	0
Total	20	20	20

There is thus revealed a surprising possibility which is much used today: the use of numerical categories of parts of a group as a means of establishing judgments about the group as a whole. In many aspects of modern life it is necessary to examine the tendencies or performances of vast groups of people or things, and it is the function of statistics to supply these judgments from such mass observation based on definite figures. Examples of this kind of necessary service include, for instance, the mass production of electric light bulbs with a guaranteed life of 500 hours, the development of a species of bean with pods of a particular size, or the observation of an epidemic. Statistics are, in fact, now indispensable to industry and the public services. For instance, statistical observation of the performance of electric light bulbs will soon show the presence of inherent faults in manufacture, and these can then be quickly eradicated. How is this done?

THE GRAPH OF PERFORMANCE. Let us first consider the ninth-grade class. This group consists of twenty boys, and the yardstick against which we are measuring them is not one of weight or height, but their ability in French, mathematics, and gymnastics. The statistical information given in the table, p. 136, is now given in graphic form. The grades, *A*, *B*, *C*, *D*, *F*, are shown as points

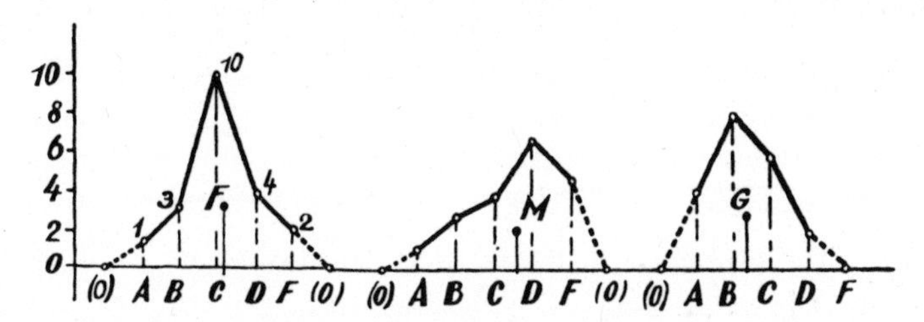

along the horizontal axis. Through these are erected perpendicular lines, the lengths of which indicate the frequency of places in each grade. In graph *F*, French, the perpendicular at *A* has a length of one unit, at *B* three units and so on. The units of vertical measurement are shown on the vertical scale on the left. If the tops of the perpendiculars are now joined with straight lines, we have the complete graph of the classification. At once we can see that in the case of French, the greatest frequency is in the center above *C*: this is the "normal" performance. With mathematics it is to the right, over *D*, tending toward "bad"; for gymnastics the peak is to the left, over *B*, tending towards "good."

FOR THE CALCULATOR. If we extend the lines on both sides of each graph so that they cross the grade axis at zero frequency, the graph encloses an area *X* (20 units of area), a number which equals the sum of the frequencies. In the case of French, the graph consists of four trapezoids and two triangles; the proof is as follows:

$$X = \tfrac{1}{2}\{f_1 + (f_1 + f_2) + \ldots + (f_4 + f_5) + f_5\} = f_1 + \ldots + f_5$$

(The f's signify the frequencies, e.g., $f_2 = 3$.)

The fact that there is an equal number of pupils in each of the three subjects is thus represented by the equality of area of the three figures, *F*, *M*, and *G*, which are enclosed by the horizontal axis and the graphs. Further consideration of this shows that the position of the center of gravity of each of these figures will indicate the average grade of achievement. In this case, for French it is 3.15, for math 3.6, and for gym 2.3. (These results are calculated by putting 1 for an *A*, 2 for a *B*, 3 for a *C*, and so on.)

For all practical purposes, the performance of a class can be termed normal when the majority of the individual performances fall into the middle grades and there is a tailing off of frequency in both the higher and lower grades. The graph for French is a fairly good representation of this, while the graphs for mathematics and gymnastics have their peaks off center, indicating divergence from normal, above normal for gym and below for math.

CLASS PERFORMANCE AND THE AVERAGE. "Won't the average of grade achievement serve as a fair indication of the class performance?" asks John Smith. "It is so much easier to find."

All right! Let us work it out by dividing the sum of the grades by their number (20). We will give to *A*, *B*, *C*, etc. the numerical values 1, 2, 3, etc.

The results are:

For French:

$$(1 \times 1 + 3 \times 2 + 10 \times 3 + 4 \times 4 + 2 \times 5)/20 = 3.15$$

For Math:

$$(1 \times 1 + 3 \times 2 + 4 \times 3 + 7 \times 4 + 5 \times 5)/20 = 3.6$$

For Gymnastics:

$$(4 \times 1 + 8 \times 2 + 6 \times 3 + 2 \times 4)/20 = 2.3$$

These figures do in fact show that the average performance in French is just a little under the normal 3.0 (which is calculated by $[1 + 2 + 3 + 4 + 5]/5$); also that the average achievement in math, 3.6, is markedly worse than normal, while for gym 2.3 is considerably better.

Nevertheless, a statistician is never content with averages, because they often convey a distorted picture of the actual state of affairs. If 10 pupils in Class X had *A*'s and 10 had *F*'s, the average achievement would be 3.0, which is exactly the same as if 20 pupils in Class Y had all obtained a *C*. In both these cases the classes would be given the same average grading for their work, but it would be nonsense to infer from this that both classes had the same distribution of ability. Class X contains both extremes, while all pupils in Class Y are of the same quality. The average value, as calculated above, is by no means a safe criterion of quality in a group; only the method of categorizing already described gives a true indication.

TESTING ELECTRIC LIGHT BULBS. To appreciate more fully the significance of frequency tables we shall now visit a factory which makes electric light bulbs. The production manager tells us that every day 2000 bulbs, each with an estimated life of 500 hours, are manufactured here. Each bulb must also undergo thirty different processes in the course of manufacture, of which some are by hand and others by machinery. If all these processes are faultlessly performed, every bulb should in theory last 500 hours. So says the production manager.

Let us now consider this on our own. Our experience in life has shown us that an action repeated 100 times does not produce each time exactly the same result. Suppose, for instance, we are cutting out ten identical stars to make Christmas decorations. At least one is bound to turn out slightly different from the others. Even a machine, stamping out holes of diameter .5 in., makes, out of 1000 stampings, some which are exactly right and others—perhaps only a few—which diverge slightly from the normal, being either larger or smaller. The reason for these variations cannot always be exactly stated. It may depend on the material, on slight variations in the power exerted by the machine, or on a thousand other things. These are chance errors, and quite unavoidable, and for this reason a machine is always given a certain "tolerance," say in this case about .005 in. above or below the required measurement. Holes, therefore, with diameters between .495 and .505 in. are all acceptable. We are all used to tolerances of this kind. For instance, a train which leaves half a minute earlier or later than its published time is still considered punctual, whereas a discrepancy of five minutes would not be considered unavoidable or an error of chance.

But even if each one of the 2000 electric bulbs were to go through all the thirty processes with negligible errors, it is still doubtful whether they would all last the prescribed time of 500 hours of continuous burning. Most of them might well last about this time, a little longer, or not quite so long, or it could happen that not a single one would last exactly 500 hours. However, there will certainly be a few of them with abnormally short or long lives. We should expect a certain number of divergencies of this kind, and they would not constitute a serious breach of normality. It is only when the number of such bulbs becomes excessive that a fault in manufacture is diagnosed. But at what figure does the number become "excessive"?

THREE "RANDOM-SAMPLE" TESTS. In order to inspect the quality of manufacture in the factory, we take from three different points on the assembly line three batches, each of 200 bulbs. These are then burned continuously to destruction, and their individual burning times recorded. For the sake of simplicity, the results are listed as follows: all bulbs with a life between 0 and 100 hours are in the category "100," those lasting between 101 and 200 hours are in category "200," etc. The table of results is as follows:

Endurance in hours	100	200	300	400	500	600	700	800	900
Batch *A*	3	4	14	45	68	45	14	4	3
Batch *B*	6	11	24	37	44	37	24	11	6
Batch *C*	15	20	35	40	45	30	10	3	2

Diagrams are drawn for each batch as follows (see below): A horizontal axis is marked off in equal division and labeled 1, 2,

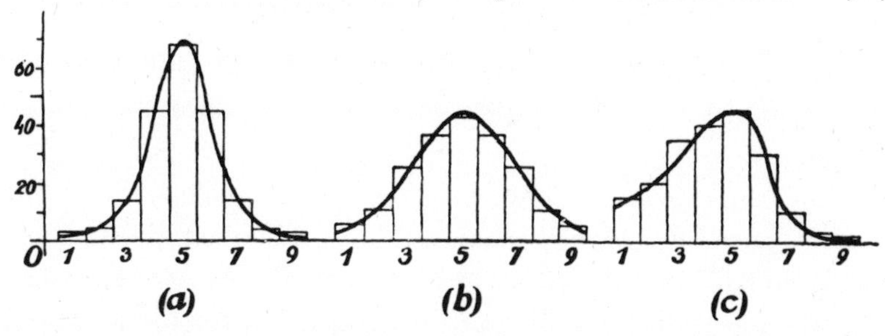

3, etc., each representing 100 burning hours. On these divisions, rectangles are drawn with their heights proportional to the number of bulbs, the life span of which comes within that particular time

division. (The vertical axis is marked in equal divisions, each representing 10 bulbs.) The resulting "frequency-rectangles" represent the numbers in the table in a form which facilitates comparison. In each diagram the total area of the figure is 200 units.

The following facts can now be seen:

Batch A. The frequency diagram, called a histogram, has its peak on, and is symmetrical around, the rectangle over the division representing 500 burning hours. This indicates a predominance of bulbs achieving the prescribed life. Moreover, the other rectangles decline sharply from the peak on either side, showing that relatively few bulbs diverge widely from the prescribed standard.

Batch B. Again the diagram is symmetrical around the rectangle for 500 hours, but its peak is much lower than in *A*. This means that far fewer bulbs attain the desired life. Moreover, the much more gradual decline on each side of the peak indicates that many more bulbs diverge widely from the prescribed standard.

Batch C. Here again the peak is not so high, and the decline from it, at any rate on the left, is not at all sharp. The "center of gravity" of the figure drawn in the graph (which is the average life span of the bulbs in this batch) lies to the left of the rectangle for 500 hours. This indicates that far too many in this batch fail to last anything like 500 hours.

Batch *A* is obviously the best of the three, but could even this be improved by insuring that more bulbs achieve the desired standard?

This can in fact be done with the aid of statistics. From the results of actual samples, such as those described above, there is formulated a theoretical ideal curve of distribution, which can then be used as a standard of comparison for the results of subsequent test samples. In this way a constant watch can be kept on the quality of production, and the proportion of unsatisfactory bulbs kept to a minimum.

The curves sketched on the graphs are approximations only. They follow very roughly the shapes of the different histograms. Greater accuracy in sketching such curves is of course possible only if the number of rectangles is increased and their width diminished, i.e., if records are kept in a much more detailed fashion of the endurance times in the sampling of a very large number of bulbs., The curves sketched on the graph enclose approximately the same area as the respective diagrams (200 units).

Another method of constructing a theoretical ideal curve of this kind to serve as a standard is to consider how a given number of bulbs is subdivided into groups, when undergoing a series of manufacturing processes, each of which may be either well or badly carried out. The stages of manufacture are represented as a lattice diagram (cf. diagram on p. 146); bulbs passing satisfactorily through a given process are shown as moving to the left, marked *n*: "no fault." Those which do not pass without flaw move to the right (*f*: faulty). This sub-grouping eventually covers all possible combinations of values of *n* and *f*, which altogether make a total equal to that of the number of processes in manufacture. For example, if this is 30 there would be 30 *n*, 0 *f*; 29 *n*, 1 *f*, and so on to 1 *n*, 29 *f* and 0 *n*, 30 *f*. The total number of possible combinations can be calculated exactly. If a graph is now constructed with these numbers, it portrays a "curve of error" (or an ideal, standard curve), which is bell-shaped, with a broad peak and sides dipping down steeply at first, then more and more gently, and finally flattening out and merging into the horizontal axis.

From all this now emerges a most significant fact: if it is not possible to construct an ideal, standard curve of distribution, which conforms reasonably well to the curves resulting from actual sampling, it can be concluded that faults are inherent in the scheme of production: not unavoidable faults due to chance, but errors which can be tracked down and eradicated.

The curve of distribution can therefore act as a detective, relentlessly exposing the presence of faults in manufacture. It does not, of course, show which of the thirty stages in manufacture have produced the faults, but only that faults are present. Further checking can identify the actual stages which are faulty: distribution graphs for each process can be compared for normality with the appropriate ideal standard curves. This is now common practice in large industrial concerns, especially in the United States. For each stage in manufacture an ideal curve is calculated, and identified by a code number. All batches passing through the machine are numbered and tested (e.g., for weight); the results are passed to a computing machine, which quickly converts them into an index number for their actual distribution, and compares it with the ideal standard. In this way every process, down to the final stage of assembly, is carefully watched, and any unwelcome deviations which may occur can be dealt with immediately.

After plodding through all this, John Smith feels rather more familiar with the idea of normality. The detective aspect particularly appeals to him, and one day he has the opportunity of applying the method to his baker, whom he has long suspected of supplying short weight.

FAULTY ROLLS. Mr. Bunn, the baker, sends round some rolls, each of which is supposed to weigh 2 ounces. Smith goes to the shop and says "Now look here, Bunn, you're baking too many faulty rolls. They're underweight!" Bunn vehemently denies the charge, but afterward he is rather cross that John Smith should have found him out.

Time passes, and Smith calls on Mr. Bunn again. Bunn gets his word in first: "Well, Mr. Smith, you can't complain now that you are getting light weight!" "No," says Smith, "my rolls all weigh 2 ounces." "That's right, none of my rolls is too light now." "Well, Mr. Bunn,

I'm not too sure of that. You've probably selected and weighed mine specially, because I complained." At this, Mr. Bunn storms off into his bakery, slamming the door behind him, and, surely, he is right to be annoyed. John Smith's suspicions have been carried a bit too far. What grounds has he for saying what he did?

It's quite simple, really. If Bunn is baking rolls with a prescribed weight of 2 oz., the inevitable incidence of chance errors will cause the weight to vary slightly round this standard. (A sample graph would show a bell-shaped curve of distribution.) John Smith actually weighed his rolls over a period of several days, and sketched their distribution curve: its peak was only 1.5 oz., showing that Mr. Bunn had taken as his standard a weight .5 oz. too light. When John Smith complained, he was then sent only selected non-standard rolls, all weighing 2 oz. The inevitable demons of chance error would never permit such accuracy. A batch of rolls, or of anything else, with a distribution curve showing no spread at all is highly suspicious: somebody with a bad conscience has undoubtedly been doing some special selecting! And so when John Smith tackled his baker, he knew that Mr. Bunn was in the wrong—and so did Mr. Bunn!

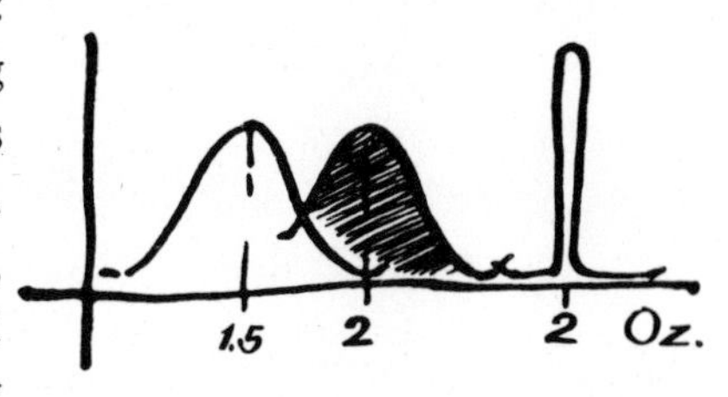

THE CROWD DIVIDES

LATTICE TOWN. This is the story of a most curious town in the kingdom of Mathematics, a town built in the form of a triangle and containing a lattice-work arrangement of streets. When you step out of the railway station S (see diagram on p. 146), you find yourself at a corner A, from which lead two long perimeter-roads, one to the left, the other to the right. A short way

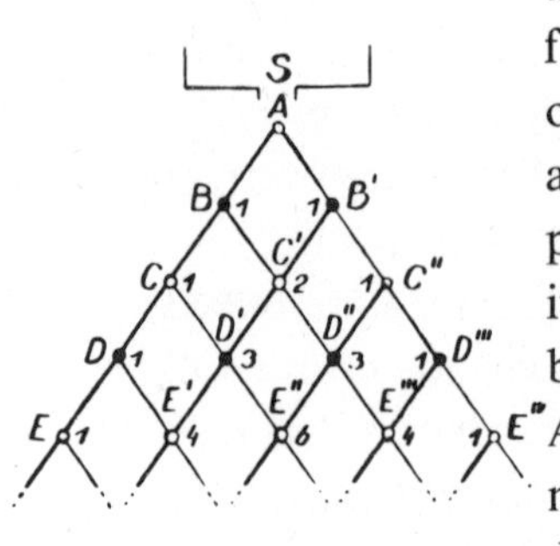

along each of these is another corner B, B', from each of which lead other streets. From our approach the one from B goes to the right, and from B' to the left, and each of them is parallel to one of the roads from A. And so it goes on: this is Lattice Town, crisscrossed by two systems of parallel, equidistant streets. As shown in the diagram, the two systems do not cross at right angles, but they might well do so, as do the lines outlining the square on a chess board. There are no other streets at all, and so none directly connecting the points C, C', C''', etc.

Lattice Town stands by the sea, and the beach is situated along a line joining the 25th turning on each of the perimeter roads ($Z \ldots Z_1$). Every Sunday in summer an excursion train arrives at the station with 1600 people, and the passengers stream out joyfully from the station, heading for the beach. None of them bothers about whether he should turn left or right at the various intersections, so by and large the streets to the right have the same chance of being used as those to the left.

THE POLICE UNDER ATTACK. One Sunday the police receive information that a wanted criminal is on the train, which has just arrived at the station. Inspector Jones decides to throw a cordon across the town, through all the D's, and to post his 200 men, in squads of 50, at these four points. "For I should expect," reasons Jones, "that roughly a quarter of the crowd—400 people—will pass each point, and so each of my men will have to scrutinize 8 people. If each scrutiny takes one minute, the whole affair will be over in 8 minutes—a nice, neat piece of work."

But unfortunately not quite neat enough! When the plan is put to work, there is absolute chaos: long after the people at the outer points D and D''' are through, there are still great crowds at points D' and D''.

Next day the newspapers are howling: "Surely the police should have known what would happen!" Inspector Jones defends himself: "How could we possible have known that the crowd would divide as it did, without any rhyme or reason?" But the papers still insist that the police should have foreseen what would happen and planned accordingly. They should have realized that D would only be used by those moving left through A, B, C, D; and D''' by those moving right, through A, B', C'', D''' (see the diagram; the terms left and right are used from the reader's viewpoint). On the other hand, D' would be passed by all those who had moved twice to the left and once to the right ($ABCD'$); by those who had moved once to the left, once right, once left ($ABC'D'$); and in addition by those who had moved once right and twice left ($AB'C'D'$).

Providing that there was no special preference for any particular course, it seems likely that 3 distinct groups of people would come by D', three times as many as would come by D or D''', because only one group of people, the exclusively left-moving or right-moving, would pass through these outer points. The same reasoning would apply in the case of the point D'', as Inspector Jones ought to have realized. Thus, the division of the crowd at the four points was not, as the police expected:

1, 1, 1, 1 or 400, 400, 400, 400

but

1, 3, 3, 1 or 200, 600, 600, 200

The Inspector should therefore have divided his men thus:

1, 3, 3, 1 or 25, 75, 75, 25.

At a person a minute, the whole scrutiny at each point would still take eight minutes and no longer ($200/25 = 600/75 = 8$). But if the police were stationed 50 at each point, at D and D''', it would take 4, while at D' and D'' 12 minutes ($600/50 = 12$). Such injustice might well be likely to inflame people's tempers.

THE PINBALL MACHINE. If the police could not accept this reasoning about the way the crowd would divide, they could easily have tried out the whole affair by taking a board and fixing nails upright on it, in the style of a pinball machine, each pin representing a road junction in Lattice Town. If such a board is tilted slightly, and if balls are rolled down it from S to A, the balls being of such a size that, on striking any one nail, they would have to move to the left or right, just as did the crowd at the station, quite at random. In this way the police could observe that at every line of check points a distinctive pattern of distribution of the balls results; e.g., along the line of E's it is $1:4:6:4:1$. This order of numbers is given by the so-called law of probability governing the divisions of a group. The editor of the *Lattice Town Clarion* had in fact urged the police to familiarize themselves with it.

And so the police actually made a pinball machine of this kind. To their astonishment they found that the balls divided at the various points in accordance with the figures shown in the diagram on p. 146. Each of them indicates the number of routes by which anyone can reach that particular point, for instance four different routes to E', six to E''. Furthermore, when the police realized that they could even calculate from the groupings at one line of check points the groupings at the next line, they thereupon committed the board ceremoniously to the fire. Henceforth, they would feel much more confident with their new-found mathematical insight.

So ends the story of Lattice Town. It is such a striking one that there is a need to emphasize it with yet another, this time from real life.

FAMILIES WITH SEVERAL CHILDREN. This law of probable distribution operates in all cases where a large number of individual items is split up into smaller groups, with each individual item having the choice between only two possible courses, as for instance, the choice of moving left or right. If the "strength" of this urge to left or right (in mathematical terms its probability) is known, then predictions can be made which to the uninitiated seem quite incredible.

One case of great interest concerns the sexes in families of 4 children. Let us consider 120,000 families of this kind. How many will have 4 boys, or 3 boys and 1 girl, or 2 boys and 2 girls, or 1 boy and 3 girls, or 4 girls? In considering this we shall pay no regard to the order of birth, but only to the final constitution of the family.

You might say that such things just cannot be predicted: only fate can determine the sexes of the children. But the law of distribution states that, because mankind cannot influence the sex of children, families of 4 will be distributed among the 5 different combinations in the ratios $1:4:6:4:1$, on the assumption that in a very large number of births there will be equal numbers of both boys and girls (but see below!).

What is the explanation of this? It is very simple with the help of our diagram on p. 146: to reach the E-line, 4 streets must be traversed (e.g., to reach E', $AB - BC - CD - DE'$). For our purpose each "street" represents the birth of a child, one to the left signifying a boy b, and one to the right a girl g. The journey to E' mentioned above thus represents $b - b - b - g$. The diagram shows that this proud achievement of parenthood can occur in four different ways:

$$
\begin{aligned}
ABCDE' &\quad (bbbg = 3b1g)\\
ABC'D'E' &\quad (bgbb = 3b1g)\\
ABCD'E' &\quad (bbgb = 3b1g)\\
AB'C'D'E' &\quad (gbbb = 3b1g).
\end{aligned}
$$

Thus, there are four different "sequences" for family groups of four children which consist of three boys and one girl, while there is only one possible "sequence" for a family of four boys, and that is *ABCDE*. If the sex of a birth is chosen at random, just as the crowd going to the beach moved at random to left or right, then it must be expected that the division at the *E*-line would be the same as with the beach-goers:

$$4b0g : 3b1g : 2b2g : 1b3g : 0b4g = 1 : 4 : 6 : 4 : 1.$$

This is all very well in theory—but what happens in real life?

An investigation was made in Saxony involving 120,137 families with four children, and the actual distribution was determined. This is shown in the table below, but the totals have been adjusted proportionately so as to give a total of 120,000 families. Line *A* gives the predicted distribution according to theory, the second line the actual figures counted. Line *B* will be referred to later.

	$4b0g$	$3b1g$	$2b2g$	$1b3g$	$0b4g$	TOTAL
A	7500	30,000	45,000	30,000	7500	(120,000)
Actual	8640	31,560	44,760	28,080	6960	(120,000)
B	8440	31,800	44,910	28,210	6640	(120,000)

As percentages:

A	6.25	25	37.5	25	6.25	(100%)
Actual	7.2	26.3	37.3	23.4	5.8	(100%)
B	7.0	26.5	37.4	23.5	5.5	(99.9%)

As can be seen, the actual results are extremely close to those predicted. The diagrammatic representation on the next page is especially impressive. (The shaded portions show the deviations from the predicted results.)

Even better is to come. The distribution on line *B* corresponds even more closely to the observed results, especially in the cases of $4b0g$ and $0b4g$. The numbers on line *A* were calculated on the assumption that the stork would bring equal numbers of boys and girls (in mathematical terms the probabilities of male or female birth is equal). In reality, however, the stork shows a slight preference for boys, as the figures of the actual distribution show, for he brought, in every thousand babies, 515 boys and 485 girls, instead of 500 of each.

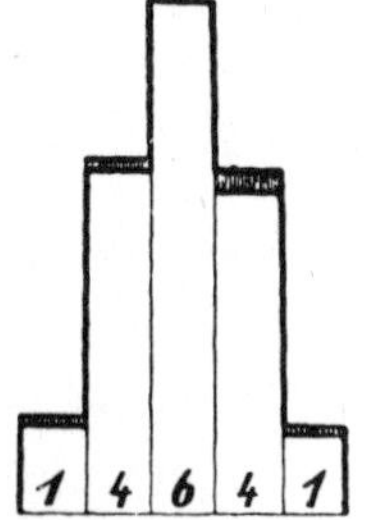

This state of affairs can also be reproduced experimentally with a pinball table. The table is given a slight inclination toward the left, and the distribution of line *B* is recorded. The degree of correspondence between the middle line and *B* is remarkable: in no case does the discrepancy exceed .3%!

Thus we see that by and large there is no element of fate in all this. The law of distribution is followed so closely that accurate predictions can be made: such is the mysterious organizing power of the "triangle" of distribution.

FOR THE CALCULATOR, the determination of the distribution in line *B*: The law of distribution mentioned above is sometimes called the binomial distribution, because it is calculated by the successive multiplications of a binomial, i.e., a two-part number. In this case the two parts are the probability of a male birth (p) and of a female birth (p'). For families of n children, the distribution is given by the coefficients of the terms in the expansion of $(p + p')^n$. Thus for families with four children,

$$(p + p')^4 = p^4 + 4p^3p' + 6p^2p'^2 + 4pp'^3 + p'^4$$

Taking $p = p' = .5$, the distribution of line *A* can be calculated; with $p = .515$ and $p' = .485$ we should get line *B*.

Distribution *B* starts as follows:

$$p^4 = .515^4 \approx .0703 \quad \text{or} \quad 7.03\%$$
$$4p^3p' = 4 \times .515^3 \times .485 \approx .265 \quad \text{or} \quad 26.5\%$$

and so on, as the percentages in the table indicate.

Consult p. 141 *et seq.* for the nature of distributions: small marginal values (4*b* and 4*g*), high "middle" values (2*b*2*g*), and the part they play in technology.

The more rows of nails there are on the pinball table, and the greater the number of balls rolled down, each one having only the choice of moving to left or right, the more will the stepped distribution diagram on p. 151 resemble the bell-shaped frequency curve of diagram *a* on page 141.

A PICTURE THAT CAN CALCULATE

Everyone must have seen the automatic scales used in food markets. A moving pointer (*I*, *II*) moves over a triangular dial. With the pivot *M* of this pointer as center, an arc is described at the top of the dial, and is marked off in division of pounds from 0 to 10. Below this there are nine price scales, 0–10, 0–9, etc. down to 02–, and each of them is subdivided into as many parts as its upper figure (e.g., price scale 0–7 into seven parts). These divisions are colored alternately in two different shades, so that they can be easily distinguished. The whole contraption is in fact a picture which can calculate. With the smooth accuracy of an elaborate computing machine, it performs two tasks simultaneously. If the unit price is known (e.g., so much per pound), it will indicate: (*a*) the cost of any quantity weighed, (*b*) the quantity that can be bought for a given sum of money.

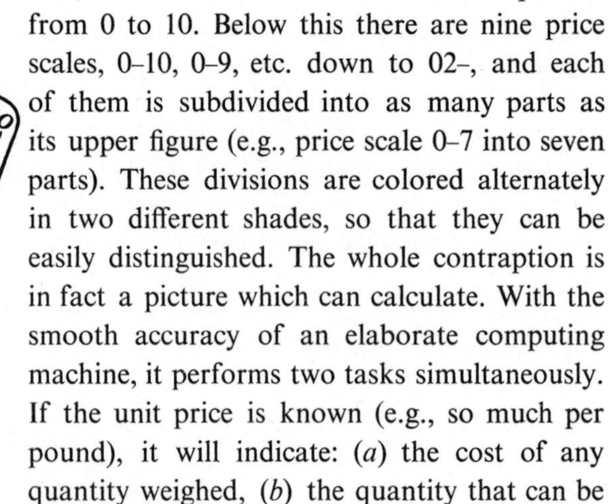

EXAMPLES

(*a*) 1 lb. of steak costs $1.00. If we buy 8 lb., the pointer *II* shows 8 lb. at *A* on the top scale, and $8.00 at *B* on price scale No. 10. But if 1 lb. costs only $.70, *C* on price scale No. 7 will show the cost $5.60 for 8 lb.; for hamburger costing $.40 per pound, the total for 8 lb. can be found at D on scale No. 4, \$3.20. If the meat costs \$.74 per lb., then we read off for 8 lb. on price scale No. 7 at C \$5.60, and on price scale No. 4 at D \$.32, making a total of \$5.92.

(*b*) You wish to spend \$3.00 on sliced salame at a price of \$.70 a pound. How much do you get? The butcher merely adds slices on the scale pan, until pointer I is at 3 on price scale No. 7 (Q). You can then read off the weight (4.28 lb.), at P on the top scale.

THE MATHEMATICS BEHIND IT? Number and scale are cleverly combined to make a "calculating diagram," which is called a nomogram ("picture for a law," from the Greek *nomos* = law). With this device a shopkeeper is saved from the trouble of making such tedius calculations as this:

$$\$\ .70 = 1 \text{ lb.}$$
$$\$3.00 = x \text{ lb.}$$

$$x = 1 \times 3.00/.70 = 4.28 \text{ lb.}$$

Nomograms play an important part in industry, and indeed in every branch of applied science in which it is necessary to calculate by a single method quantities, the values of which change frequently because of changes in their associated conditions.

Consider, for example, how the electrical resistance of metal wires varies with their cross-sections or their temperatures; or how the angle of an emerging beam of light, refracted through a series of different media, varies with the different angles of incidence.

The advantages of nomograms are obvious: results can be rapidly ascertained, even by operators who need be skilled only in the reading of their particular nomogram; it is not necessary for them to understand in full the mathematical principles on which the nomogram is based. A very important branch of mathematical theory is concerned with the construction of such calculating devices; it is called nomography.

The pointer of the automatic scales, connected directly to the weighing mechanism, moves across the dial. (The slide rule, the use of which is taught in engineering schools, is another example of the "moving" calculator.) All calculations of the "rule of three" type (cf. p. 153) can be solved at a glance, even without making a weighing. The pointer can be replaced by a thread, or a narrow beam of light which emerges from the point M, and passes through the known values.

Mathematically speaking, a calculator of this type is the representation of a multi-valued function (cf. p. 50). In the case of the automatic scales the variables are the weight W, the price per pound p, and the machine will determine the cost by performing the calculation:

$$C = pW.$$

FOR THE CALCULATOR. The calculation of example (*a*) on p. 153.

As the cost and the weight vary proportionately, the statement of their relative proportions, or ratios, is:

$$\begin{array}{lcl} \text{Cost : Weight} & = & \text{Unit price : Unit weight} \\ 5.60 : 8 & = & .70 : 1 \end{array}$$

Chapter 7

THE REALM OF LADY LUCK

What Is Probability?

LADY LUCK. Between "impossible" and "certain" lies the great gulf of probability. It is certain that a stone leaving my hand will fall to the ground, and it is impossible for a stream to flow uphill. But it is neither impossible nor certain that John Smith will win first prize in a raffle, or that his car will break down when next he goes for a drive. There is a degree of probability about these events, but even that degree of probability is uncertain: when you look at his car you might say that it is very probable he will have a breakdown, or it might seem very improbable that he will win the raffle.

Probability is, for the ordinary man, hedged round with imprecision; it is subject to the incalculable vagaries of chance, and chance rules our very lives. There may be a friendly element in it—good luck in games or in love—but there may also be a less pleasant, almost malicious aspect. John Smith sometimes finds himself crossing his fingers, avoiding walking under ladders, and the like, seeking, as it were, to propitiate the mighty gods of chance and to keep them well disposed toward him. For, as we all feel, chance can at any time intervene in the system of cause and effect in which we and the whole of nature are involved.

It might be said that there is no such thing as chance, but only cause and effect. We are not going to consider here either religion or the nature of things; rather let us examine chance or probability on the assumption that the law of cause and effect is at all times valid. On this basis, it could be asserted that if John Smith knew all possible causes of a breakdown of his car, right down to the smallest detail, and knew also the exact state of reliability of all its innumerable components and of his own state of mind, the condition of the roads upon which he will travel (exactly similar, by the way, for all other road users), not forgetting the state of the weather during his journey—if, in short, he could survey every single link in the complex chain of possible causes of a breakdown, then he would be able to state with certainty whether or not one will occur. But clearly all these things cannot be known in advance, and so the most prudent view would be one between complete denial and complete acceptance of the existence of chance. Let us say that, whenever it is impracticable to investigate the possible causes of an event, we must admit the influence of chance. This compromise helps to some extent to rob the giant Fate of his exaggerated reputation.

A mathematician, however, is not really worried by such considerations: he is much more interested in one particular aspect of chance,—measuring the actual degrees of probability. That a good marksman will hit the target is highly probable; that he will hit the bull's-eye is probable, but that he should score five successive bulls is improbable. Is it, in fact, possible? Yes, possible but not probable. But if it is possible and not probable, then it must surely be certain? It is certainly a very confusing matter, this business of assessing the degrees of probability!

The mathematician intervenes to say, "Even though probability cannot be defined with complete philosophical clarity, is it not possible to comprehend its nature sufficiently well by the medium of numbers, so that the influence of confused, subjective, or prejudiced thinking can be banished from our contemplation of the gulf between *certain* and *impossible?* Then we might be able to state by *how much* five successive bull's-eyes are less probable than one."

If a numerical yardstick could be devised for probability, an immense number of concerns in which it takes a hand could be lifted clear of the morass of confused speculation. They could be classified, with symbols to give easy reference to the degrees of probability involved, whether they be greater or less (cf. p. 160). If this were done, it is even probable that certain underlying laws might be revealed which govern the probability of, let us say, outwitting Lady Luck at Monte Carlo (cf. p. 190), or in our tip on the football pools (p. 178). Let us now follow the mathematician's explorations in the mysterious twilight world of chance: just think of the advantage of knowing exactly how the dice are loaded for or against us!

FAVORABLE AND POSSIBLE CASES. John Smith can remember from his fair-going days the old-fashioned lottery, complete with betting drum. In this were contained numbered coupons, and the drum could be rotated to mix them all up, before the customers "drew lots." "Three draws for a dime! Beautiful prizes if you pick the winning numbers!"

Let us first suppose that the "lots" are red and white balls, the white ones being winners and the red ones losers. One important condition, however, there must be: after each draw the ball must be returned to the drum, and the drum rotated to mix them anew before the next draw. This insures like conditions for each draw.

Let us consider two drums, *A* and *B*. In each there is 1 white ball (the winner!), together with 9 red losers in *A*, and 19 in *B*. These facts are known only to the fair-ground operator, and not by the customers. If the customers knew, they would of course draw from drum *A*, assuming that the stake or prize would be the same for both drums, and they would realize that their prospects of winning from *A* would be greater than from *B*, seeing that *A* has 1 winner in 10 balls, while *B* has 1 in 20. It is quite easy, therefore, to express in numbers the prospects of making a winning draw from the drums: for *A* 1 : 10 and for *B* 1 : 20. The mathematical probability *P* of winning is expressed by the ratio of favorable cases to the number of all possible cases:

$$P = f/p$$

f = number of favorable cases
p = total number of possible cases

In *A* there is 1 white in a total of 10 balls, so that the probability of drawing a winner is $1/10 = .10$. In *B* it is $1/20 = .05$. If there were a third drum *C*, with 4 white balls and 46 reds, the probability of a win would be $4/50 = .08$, which is greater than is the case with *B*, but less than with *A*.

Probability can also be expressed as a percentage, e.g., $1/10 = 10/100$ or 10%. This transformation of a fraction, much used by calculators but really only an increasing of the denominator to 100 with a proportional adjustment to the numerator, is a convenient way of saying, "Whether we have 1 white in 10 balls, or 10 in 100, the probability of drawing a white ball remains the same." It is often said, "It is 90% certain that we shall have rain today." Usually, however, common or decimal fractions are employed for expressing probabilities.

A pack of cards is in effect a betting drum with 52 "lots";

the probability of drawing, say, the king of hearts is therefore 1/52; that of drawing a red card is 26/52 or 1/2; for an ace it is 4/52 or 1/13; and for a picture card 12/52 or 3/13.

If we can express in numerical terms the probability of an event, there arises the interesting possibility of comparing the probabilities of quite different events. Thus, the probability of winning a first prize on the "10 forecasts" of a football pool (see p. 178) is about the same as that of picking out at random 1 white lead shot from a barrel containing it and 59,999 black ones! Also, the probability (2/3), that a 60-year-old man will live to be 70 (cf. p. 176), is the same as that of not throwing either 5 or 6 with a single throw of the dice (see p. 169).

A STEP-LADDER OF PROBABILITY. As the total number of "favorable cases" is always less than, or at most equal to, the number of possible cases ($f \leqq p$), the probability is always a proper fraction, and so lies between 0 and 1. If an event has zero probability, that is a way of saying that it is impossible; if its probability is 1, it is certain to take place. If there is no white ball ($f = 0$) among the 10 in the drum, then $p = 0/10 = 0$, i.e., a white ball cannot be drawn. Further, it would be as good as impossible, if there were one white ball among a very large total number (expressed in algebraic symbols as $p \rightarrow \infty$). If only white balls were in the drum, then the number of "winners" would equal the total number of balls ($f = p$), and the probability of drawing a white ball is obviously certainty: $P = p/p = 1$. In this case we are, as race-goers express it, "a hundred per cent sure."

Between 0 and 1 lies the tantalizing range of probabilities, and these can be categorized as follows:

Uncertain. An event can be called uncertain when its probability is 1/2 (on the knife edge between impossible and certain). Consider for example the tossing of a coin: it will fall either heads or tails. The probability of either heads or tails is

1/2 (i.e., one favorable in two possible), but it is uncertain as to which it will be.

Probable and improbable. An event the probability of which lies "in the upper half" ($P > 1/2$) may be termed probable; "in the lower half" ($P < 1/2$) it would be termed improbable.

Thus we get this scale of probability:

Probability	0	. . . . . .	1/2	. . . . . .	1
Event	impossible	improbable	uncertain	probable	certain

To some extent, therefore, words can be used to indicate various degrees of probability; numbers give a much more precise method.

PROBABILITY AND ANTI-PROBABILITY. With figures, moreover, we can appreciate another important relationship stated in the title to this paragraph. If we have the possibility of two events, the probability P of the first combined with the probability Q of the second will together represent the certainty of an occurrence of one of the two events: in algebraic notation $P + Q = 1$.

For example, if one event is the drawing of a white ball from drum A, with a probability of $P = 1/10$, then the "anti-probability" (i.e., the likelihood of *not* drawing a white ball), is:

$$Q = 9/10 = 1 - 1/10 = 1 - P.$$

This complementary nature of probabilities in the range between 0 and 1 gives a useful way of checking calculations; but it also gives a method (sometimes the only one) for calculating the probability of a win, by considering the probability of not winning. For instance, "How great is the degree of safety for traveling by rail?" can be rendered as "what is the probability of not being involved fatally in a railway accident?" In practice this can be calculated only by the figures for the "anti-probability of not being involved fatally in a railway accident," i.e., by our knowledge of the actual number of fatal accidents which have occurred. It might be, for instance,

$$Q = 1/500{,}000{,}000 = .000000002.$$

From this our chance of surviving a rail journey is

$$P = 1 - Q = \cdot 999999998,$$

which is comfortably near to certainty.

Railway authorities record the number of fatal accidents against the number of passengers carried and the number of miles traveled. Thus it reckons on, say, one fatality in 500 million "passenger-miles." Thus, if 500,000 people are transported 1000 mi., they would expect one fatal accident.

In the case of drum *A* the ratio of probability to anti-probability, i.e., the ratio of winning to losing draws, is 1 : 9. John Smith expresses this in everyday language thus: "It's a one to nine chance of drawing a winner," or "After nine losers comes the winner." If the ratio is 1 : 1, then the outcome is uncertain, for probability and anti-probability both stand at 1/2.

To sum up, it is clear that a numerical approach to probability is a considerable help to understanding it, and it reveals quite a few valuable facts. Before we introduce more examples to help you to understand the subject better, we must first discuss two important topics: the nature and scope of mathematical probability and the two forms in which probability comes to our notice.

TWO KINDS OF PROBABILITY. If I were to know that drum *A* held 1 white and 9 red balls, I should have a complete picture of the number of winners and losers, and would thus be able to predict the probability of a win, 1/10. As a mere player, however, trying my luck at the drums, I would not know these facts, and so could make no reliable predictions.

In real life we are in the same position as the player, and life itself is the lottery. Within it are the lucky and unlucky lots, and no man knows how many of each kind fate has in store for him.

PROBABILITY AND LENGTH OF LIFE. A child is soon to be born. Will it be a boy or a girl? Can we say anything about the probability of its being a male birth? The human life span is 70 years, but many die at a much younger age. Our John Smith is 40 years old: can anything be said about the probability of dying at the age of 40? Some people travel by train: is anything known about the degree of safety of rail travel? There is a whole series of such questions touching on probability in real life. Can they all be answered with reliable numerical predictions?

The answer is yes, but only on the basis of past experience. For example, in a total number of registered live births N, the number of boy babies B is counted; the ratio $R = B/N$ gives the relative frequency of male births. Suppose that in a certain town, which we will call A, 14 boys were born out of a total of 20 babies. The relative frequency for boys is thus $14/20 = .7$. This figure must not be taken as an infallible guide, for in town X there may be during the same period 480 boys in 1000 births, with a relative frequency of .48. And in the city of Y, R might well be .56, whereas over the whole county of Z it could be .515. Finally, the figures for the whole country might give a result .515.

PROBABILITY FROM EXPERIENCE. In the example given above, the larger the number of events recorded the more does the figure for relative frequency tend to become steady at a certain value.

Births	20	1000	10,000	100,000	1,000,000
Relative frequency	.700	.480	.516	.515	.515

If, over a large number of events, there is observed a similar steadying of frequencies, then this steady value can be taken as a guide to the probability of future events. For the birth of a boy baby the probability .515 might be called "probability based on experience," to distinguish it from a gambler's assessment of chances, with which he tries to predict without any reference to previous experience, as is commonly done in most games of chance.

In a similar way, the probability of a man's dying at the age of 40 can be assessed at .535%, based on these figures: out of 76,313 people aged 40, 408 died in the ensuing year. The relative frequency was thus 408/76,313 = .535% (cf. extract from mortality tables on p. 249).

Again, in this way, a man gambling on that lottery drum *A* could find out from experience the chances of winning. He would have to draw 1000 or 5000 or many more times, replacing the ball each time, of course, and noting the number of times he drew a white ball.

Number of draws	10	100	1000	2000	5000
Frequency of whites	0	8	92	190	499
Relative frequency	0	.08	.092	.095	.0998

He would then see the values for P approaching .100, which we know to be the correct assessment. This value he might call the "probability based on experience" (its learned title is "probability *a posteriori*"). Thus do the results of practical experience usually agree with the theoretical probability (probability *a priori*): this is indeed the astonishing feature about the whole theory of probability. It seems that behind the scenes a mysterious law is at work, fulfilling in practice what is predicted by theory as being probable.

To sum up, if the order of probability of an event can be calculated in advance, from the details of the attendant conditions (e.g., the number of "winning" balls and the total in the drum), the validity of this figure for probability can be confirmed by experiment, provided that the number of events is large enough. In theory at least, such an experiment is always possible, though few people would relish the job of drawing lots 10,000 times or more! But of course in the last analysis all this talk about probability will not help us to probe into the future, and see what life has in store for each of us. We cannot really say with confidence that our next child will be a boy, or that Mr. So-and-so will die at 40. The laws that govern such events are too complex for our understanding.

THE MEANING OF PROBABILITY. These last few remarks bring us back to a consideration of the real nature of probability. What does it do? What is the significance of the statement that the probability of drawing a white ball from drum *A* is 1/10? There are two points to note:

(*a*) We shall establish what it does *not* mean, to emphasize what probability *cannot* indicate. The statement above tells us nothing about the outcome of any individual draw. It does not say that John Smith must draw one white ball in every 10 draws, or 2 in 20, or 10 in 100.

(*b*) It is correct to say that the validity of a probability is confirmed with greater exactitude, the greater the number of events recorded.

This holds good for probability based on experience. Let us consider the embarrassing experience of John Smith. He knew that with a probability .515 for boy babies there would be a probability of .485 for girls. Now Mrs. Robinson was expecting a happy event, and she hoped so much it would be a boy. "I'll get the figures for this neighborhood," says John Smith, "and then I can work out what you will have." He then ascertained that for the current period the local births so far numbered 30, with 13 boys. "So the frequency for boys is now 13/30, well below one half," said he, "but there ought to be more than one half. The stork has not yet made up his quota of boys." Accordingly, he told Mrs. Robinson that "by the strictest mathematical reasoning" she would without doubt have a boy. When later a girl was born, John Smith and his mathematics came in for a candid piece of Mrs. Robinson's mind! Ever since then he has given a very wide berth to the Robinson baby carriage with its pink-clad passenger, while Mrs. Robinson mutters darkly "Him and his mathematics! He doesn't know the first thing about having babies!"

THE LAW OF LARGE NUMBERS. What went wrong with our friend's calculations? Was the figure .515 at fault? No, the figure was all right, but John Smith's use of it was quite wrong in that he related the probability .515 to the individual case of Mrs. Robinson. He failed to realize that probability is a concept valid only for a large number of events, and quite inapplicable to a single case or even a small number of cases. In relation to a large number of events it makes a positive statement, which is fulfilled more and more precisely, the larger the number grows. Conversely, the law becomes less dependable, the smaller the number of cases recorded, until with very small numbers it is quite unreliable. This is the "law of large numbers," which is fundamental to the study of probability: large numbers obey the laws of probability, but small numbers are subject to sheer chance.

"By and *large*" the probability of male births is .515; "by and *large*" you will draw from drum *A* a winner one-tenth of the total number of tries; but over a small number of events, and especially for a single event, Lady Luck presides, and mathematics cannot help.

What is a large number? Or shall we say, when is a number large enough for the law to become effective? Indeed, the law itself seems to be a mixture of precision and uncertainty, for its degree of certainty increases with the number of events. A subtle-minded person once described this state of affairs as follows:

"I am not surprised that God makes laws, nor indeed that He rolls dice, and allows chance to take a hand in events. But I am surprised that He rolls His dice in accordance with laws!"

We must not forget this duplicity in the law of probability: "*Chance* for the *single* event, *law* for the *many*." Only thus can we understand what this concept can do, and what it cannot. Let us now work out a further example.

THROWING THE DICE. A die is, so to speak, a betting drum with six balls or lots, numbered 1 to 6. The probability of throwing a 3 is the same as that of drawing a lot numbered 3 from a drum containing six. Note well that this does *not* mean that if you cast the die six times you are certain to throw a 3, but only that if you throw a large number of times, the ratio of 3's thrown to the total number of throws will approximate to 1/6. The approximation is all the closer, the more throws you make. This has been the subject of an experiment: a number of people, throwing in turn with a single die, made a total of 2920 throws. The 1's and 2's, etc. were recorded, giving the following results:

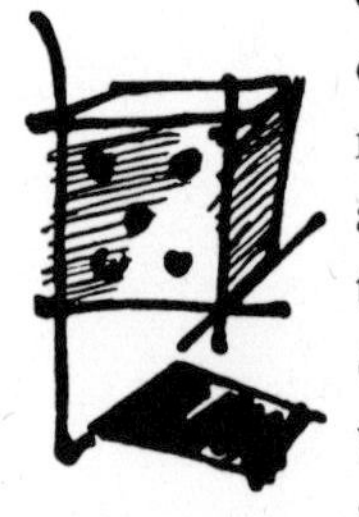

Scores	1	2	3	4	5	6	*Total*
Throws	467	469	512	493	504	475	2920
Probability	.160	.161	.175	.169	.173	.163	1.001
Deviation from 487	— 20	— 18	+ 25	+ 6	+ 17	— 12	—

It is surprising how close is the agreement between the calculated probability and probability based on experience, which is set down in the third line. All numbers recorded from the experiment, e.g., 467/2920 = .160, are very close to the predicted 1/6 = .167; and of course the numbers of throws for each score approximate closely to the predicted number 2920/6 = 487. The number of throws of any particular score w is equal to the product of the total number of throws by the probability P. In algebraic symbols $w = pP$ or $P = w/p$.

One might think that the agreement should be even better than it is, considering the large number of throws recorded. The deviations + 25 (for the 3's) and — 20 (for the 1's) seem too large and too varied to be dismissed as chance effects. They seem to indicate the slight preference by the die for 3's, and a reluctance to score 1's, which means that the die used might not be properly balanced, and therefore does not give the same chance to each score. It might in fact be said that the large number of throws has revealed this flaw in the die, small though it may be. This is quite true: the large number of throws has in fact performed this feat of detection. (Cf. use of large numbers in control of industrial production, p. 141).

Other examples demonstrating the law of large numbers at work are given on p. 178 (football pools), p. 190 (the gaming table), p. 145 (probable division of a crowd).

Diminished and Increased Probability

THE SOLDIER AND THE DEVIL. Have you heard the tale about the soldier, who bartered his soul to the Devil in exchange for good fortune in battle, love, and gambling? When his time came, the Devil appeared, to carry him off. "Hello, my friend," said the soldier, "What about one last throw of the dice, to see if I can win just one more year of life? You surely won't grudge that to an honest man!" The Devil, not wishing to seem churlish, agreed, and they sat down beside the upturned drum, which was to serve them as a dicing table.

The soldier shook his die in its cup. "What is to win, Father of Hades?" "Two." "Only that? Let's have a double throw: a two or a five." "Agreed." And so the soldier shook and rolled, mumbling foul incantations over his die: "Six!" The Devil smiled. Then came the second throw, with even more violent shaking and fouler imprecations: "A five! A five, and another year of life!" The soldier capered around with joy. "What do you mean?" roared the Devil. "You lost! It should have been a two and a five in two throws, and you scored a six and a five!" "A two *or* a five, my friend, not *and*." The Devil realized that he had been tricked, and slunk off to Hell. When the year had passed, he came forth again, muttering to himself "And, and, and . . . *not* or!" Again they sat beside the drum to throw dice, for again the Devil could hardly refuse this last request without seeming unsportsmanlike. "Two throws," said the soldier, "just as before, and a two or a five to win." "And, and, and," screamed the Devil, "two *and* five!" "Why *and?* Why not *or?*" asked the soldier. In his rage the Devil belched forth blue flames and hammered on the drum—and the soldier knew what the drumbeat meant for him, for the *and* is harder to throw than the *or*.

But he rattled the die in the cup, and swore, and rattled again, then rolled it out: two! "Hurrah! half won!" Then all those present watched with bated breath, as the soldier rattled the die, and swore, and rolled again—one! Beaten at last. But like a true soldier he hid his feelings, tightened his belt, bade farewell to his comrades, and marched off to Hell.

OR—AND. "The *and* is harder to throw than the *or*." We shall now put on our mathematical spectacles, and examine this statement. The soldier had to make two throws. In the first game (let us call it Case *A*), he had to throw according to his own rules 2 *or* 5. In the second game (Case *B*), played under the Devil's rules, he had to throw 2 *and* 5. We will calculate the probability of each of these cases. Now we known that the probability of throwing any prescribed number is 1/6, and this holds for a 2 as well as for a 5. The probability in a double throw must be determined from a combination of these two single probabilities, but how are they to be combined? The diagram here will help you to see this. The two rectangles each contain 6 squares of equal size, numbered 1 to 6. Each square is 1/6th of the total area of the rectangle, and so each square can represent the probability of throwing its number with a single throw of the die.

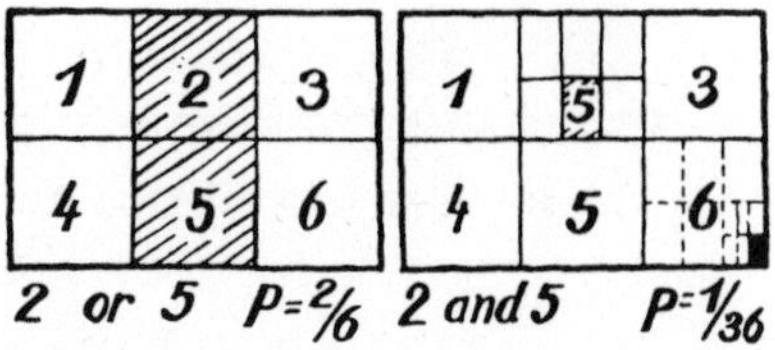

2 or 5 $P=2/6$ 2 and 5 $P=1/36$

When a small coin is thrown at random into the rectangle, it will fall into one or another of the squares, if we ignore throws in which the coin falls on a line. Supposing the coin were to fall on square 2, then we can take it to represent a throw of the die with a score of 2. Now for Case *A*: the coin may fall on square 2 *or* square 5, and the permitted area consists of two squares which make up 1/3rd of the total area of the rectangle. Thus it is clear that the probability is equal to the sum of the separate probabilities. Expressing this in symbols:

$$P(2 \text{ or } 5) = P(2) + P(5) = 1/6 + 1/6 = 1/3.$$

Thus the probability of throwing 2 *or* 5 is greater than the probability of throwing one of these numbers. This we shall term "increased probability."

In Case *B* we must divide each constituent square into six smaller areas, just as we divided the original rectangle into six. Now, for 2 and 5 the permitted area is much smaller, in fact only the small area marked 5 in square 2, which is 1/36th of the large rectangle. Thus it can be seen that the probability of throwing 2 *and* 5 is given by the product of the two individual probabilities. In symbols:

$$P(2 \text{ and } 5) = P(2) \times P(5) = 1/6 \times 1/6 = 1/36.$$

Thus the probability of throwing 2 and 5 is considerably smaller than that of throwing one number. This we shall call "diminished probability."

THE WHEEL OF FORTUNE. This offers another chance of investigating increased and diminished probability.

A circular turntable is divided into six equal sectors, numbered 1 to 6. Each sector has in turn six smaller equal divisions, marked 1′ to 6′. A fixed arrow near the perimeter of the circle indicates the winning spot when the wheel ceases to spin. This toy will enable us to review the soldier's prospects from another angle.

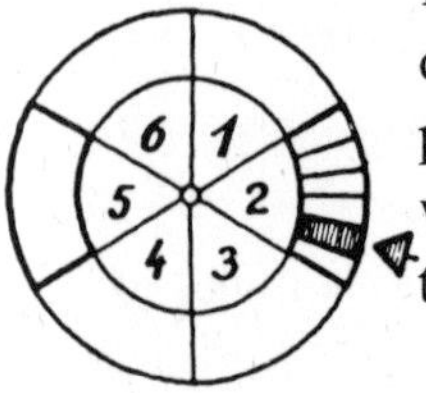

If he had had only one throw, 2 for example (the wheel stopping at sector 2), the probability of this would have been $1/6 = .17$. For a throw of 2 or 5 (i.e., the wheel stopping at 2 or 5) the probability would clearly be $2/6 = 1/3 = .33$. But for a result of 2 followed by 5 the probability would be 1/6th of that for a single throw, or spin of the wheel. In the case of the wheel, it would have to stop at sub-division 5 of sector 2, and this would be only 1/12th of the probability in the 2 or 5 result, or $1/36 \approx .03$.

Thus in every 100 throws or spins the player may expect to turn up a specified number (2 for instance) 17 times; one of a specified pair (2 *or* 5) 33 times; and two numbers consecutively (2 *and* 5) only 3 times.

It is not surprising, therefore, that the soldier won his year's grace at the first game, only to be soundly beaten in the second. To sum up, both compound probabilities, the "and" and the "or," can be exactly calculated by a combination of the individual probabilities. Here are some more examples, which lend themselves to calculations of probabilities, often in quite complicated cases.

THE CARD LOTTERY. In this we have to draw certain cards from a well-shuffled pack. The probability of drawing a king will be $4/52 = 1/13$. The probability of drawing a queen (or jack, 10, or any other) is the same. In order to understand even more clearly the working out of compound probability of either the increased or diminished type, let us make a draw of two cards, returning each time the card first drawn, so as to keep the same conditions for the second draw.

Let the conditions of the draw specify either a king or a queen. Then $P = 1/13 + 1/13 = 2/13$. If we must draw first a king and then a queen, $P = 1/13 \times 1/13 = 1/169$.

If in this second case the order of drawing is not specified, $P = 1/169 + 1/169 = 2/169$.

If we must draw first a king and then a queen, without replacing the first card, then $P = 1/13 \times 4/51 = 4/663$; but if here again the order is not specified, then again the probability is doubled.

The probability of drawing the king of hearts is $1/52$; king of hearts or queen of hearts $2/52$; king and queen of hearts $1/52 \times 1/52 = 1/2704$. Thus, in the course of 2704 draws, cards being replaced after drawing, we should expect to draw the hearts pair only once.

Finally, what is the probability of drawing three red cards in succession? The probability of drawing one red is clearly $1/2$, since there are as many reds as blacks. The probability for a succession of three reds is therefore $1/2 \times 1/2 \times 1/2 = 1/8$. Thus, in 100 separate draws of three cards one may expect to draw 13 all-red groups. Why not put some of these predictions to the test?

A RUN OF GOOD (OR MAYBE BAD) LUCK. If John Smith were to cut his finger on Monday, lose his wallet on Tuesday, miss his train on Wednesday, he would, quite rightly, regard this as a run of bad luck, a series of quite unconnected but unpleasant incidents.

Smith would be uneasy and might think that Fate had marked him down for special attention.

Supposing, however, he had fallen from his bicycle, cut his finger in so doing, and lost his wallet down a drain, all of this causing him to miss his train. This would not be a run of bad luck, but a chain of mishaps, because the various events are causally connected. This sort of thing is more likely to annoy the subject than make him feel uneasy. If John Smith buys tickets in three separate raffles, and wins them all, this would constitute a run of good luck, a pleasant series of independent if similar events, each one possessing a similar degree of probability.

Other instances of this type of "chains of events" are: drawing 3 successive red cards, or 4 successive aces from a pack; scoring bulls-eyes with 5 successive shots; being the proud father of 3 successive baby boys; or throwing a 6 with a die twice running.

If a single event has a probability measured by P, then the "diminished" probability for n successive similar events is calculated by, in algebraic symbols, P^n. As P is always less than 1, the probability of the compound event diminishes as the number of events increases, and its value decreases much more rapidly than the value of P.

EXAMPLES

The probability of drawing a red card from a pack is 1/2, but for a series of 3 red cards (the card drawn being replaced in the pack each time) it is $(1/2)^3 = 1/8 = .125$.

The expectation of drawing a set of 4 successive aces is only once in 28,000 sets of 4 draws. Each card drawn is returned to the pack before the next is taken, so that there is a possibility of, for example, drawing the ace of hearts each time. The probability of drawing one ace is 1/13, of drawing 4 successive aces $(1/13)^4 = 1/28,561$—a most unlikely happening!

Clearly there is a very high probability that the successful progress of such a draw will be interrupted by the drawing of a card other than an ace. The probability of this P' is what we have called the anti-probability of the other, i.e., $P' = 1 - P = 28{,}560/28{,}561$, which is very close to 1. It is practically certain that the series of aces will be interrupted by the drawing of one or more other cards.

We all have a certain inborn perception of this notion of diminishing probability, when a series of events is under consideration, and so we feel somewhat uneasy when a person, having drawn or played three aces, produces the fourth. We would realize that this is a highly unlikely event, and suspect cheating. Conversely, the rapid increase of the probability of a series of rare but unpleasant events makes the sufferer hope with confidence for better luck: "Sunshine always follows the rain," or "Every cloud has a silver lining."

The shooting match. If with 10 shots John Smith hits the bull's-eye 3 times, then the probability based on experience of scoring a bull's-eye is $3/10 = .3$. The probability therefore of scoring a succession of 2, 3, or 5 bull's-eyes in succession will be respectively $.3^2 = .09$, $.3^3 = .027$, and $.3^5 = .00243$.

Proud father. The probability based on experience of a male birth is .515. Accordingly, the probability of a woman producing 3 boys in succession (not of course triplets) is $.515^3$, which is .136; whereas for 3 girls it is $(1 - .515)^3 = (.485)^3 = .114$. Out of 100 families with 3 children, chosen at random, we should expect to find about 14 with 3 boys and 11 with 3 girls.

Throwing pairs at dice. The probability of throwing the same number twice running with a single die is $(1/6)^2 = 1/36$, and for throwing the same score three times running 1/216. (Cf. diagram on p. 169, with the small black square in square 6 of the right-hand rectangle.)

THE RAINY SUNDAY. John Smith has a friend who runs a small hotel in the country. According to the weather records they can expect to have 73 sunny days every year, and the proprietor has mentioned this in the prospectus, which he sends to people all over the country, not forgetting John Smith. The latter starts wondering, as is his wont: "73 sunny days each year? I wonder how often Sunday is spoiled by rain?" He then makes a table with the following numbers:

Relative frequency of rainy days r
Relative frequency of sunny days s
Probability of rainy Sundays rS
Probability of sunny Sundays sS
No. of Sundays as a fraction of the year S
No. of weekdays as a fraction of the year W
Probability of rainy weekdays rW
Probability of sunny weekdays sW

There are 52 Sundays in a year, and so the probability that a day chosen at random from the calendar will be a Sunday, $P(S)$, is 52/365, which is approximately 1/7. Think of a rectangle divided into 365 equal parts, and the chance of throwing a coin into a selected part.

The probability of a weekday is the anti-probability of a Sunday: $P(W) = 1 - 1/7 = 6/7$. Now sunshine may be expected on 73 days per year, in symbols $P(s) = 73/365 = 1/5$, and the probability of a rainy day is therefore 4/5.

	rS	rW	sS	sW
Probabilities	$4/5 \times 1/7$ 11% (app.)	$4/5 \times 6/7$ 69% (app.)	$1/5 \times 1/7$ 3% (app.)	$1/5 \times 6/7$ 17% (app.)
Number of days per year	42	250	10	63
So, during a vacation of one month (30 days) one may expect	3.4 Rainy Sundays	20.6 Rainy weekdays	.9 Sunny Sundays	5.1 Sunny weekdays

For convenience in calculating, John Smith divides all days into two categories, rainy or sunny. Presumably overcast days are ranked as rainy. Now for the calculation: are the probabilities "and" or "or" cases? If Sunday and sunshine are to go together, it is clearly a case of "and," and the probabilities must therefore be multiplied by one another. The results of the calculations are clearly shown in the table appearing at the bottom of the opposite page.

Faced with the prospect of only one fine Sunday out of four in his vacation, John Smith, naturally enough, decided to go elsewhere.

This example shows how it is possible to estimate the probability of a combination of circumstances, provided that the separate probabilities are known. The method has an important application in the field of genetics (e.g., the laws of heredity), to name only one.

PHILEMON AND BAUCIS were a couple in Greek legend, who had grown old together through long years of love and piety. Despite their poverty they gladly gave hospitality to Zeus, who came in disguise to their hovel.

When he took leave of them the visitor asked what he could do in return. They replied that they could think of no finer gift than to be allowed to die together, and, as the Roman poet Ovid tells the tale, Zeus granted their request by turning them into trees, an oak and a lime tree.

Nowadays Zeus no longer walks on earth, and man has learned how to estimate the probabilities, or expectancy, of both life and death, so that one can say more or less how it will fare with old people. Let us suppose that Philemon is 60, and Baucis 50. What is the probability of their being alive together in ten years' time?

Referring to the table of expectation of life on p. 249, we can see that, out of 60,883 people aged 60, 41,906 will still be alive ten years later; accordingly, the probability is 41,906/60,883, which is approximately $4/6 = 2/3$. Similarly, out of 71,006 people aged 50, 60,883 survive after ten years, the probability being $60{,}833/70{,}006 \approx 6/7$. Thus the probability of Philemon's dying before the age of 70 is the anti-probability of 2/3, i.e., 1/3; for Baucis the figure will be 1/7. Let us tabulate as follows:

	Probability of 10 more years of life	*Probability of death within 10 years*
Philemon	2/3	1/3
Baucis	6/7	1/7

This can be symbolized by two jars, one (*P*) for Philemon containing two white balls for continued life, and one black ball, denoting death; the second jar (*B*) for Baucis contains six whites and one black. Fate draws one ball from each, and these are the possible results:

P (white), *B* (white): both will be alive in ten year's time, and the probability is $2/3 \times 6/7 = 12/21$.

P (black), *B* (black): both will be dead in ten years' time. Probability $1/3 \times 1/7 = 1/21$.

P (white), *B* (black): Philemon will be alive, Baucis dead. Probability: $2/3 \times 1/7 = 2/21$.

P (black), *B* (white): Philemon will die, Baucis will live. Probability: $6/7 \times 1/3 = 6/21$.

This means that if, after ten years' absence, John Smith were to return to his home town, where formerly 21 old couples of comparable ages to Philemon and Baucis had been living, he might now find only 12 of these couples alive together, whereas there would be 2 widowers and 6 widows, and one couple gone completely. The word "might" is used deliberately, because the numbers are not large enough to fulfill adequately the conditions for the law of large numbers, and to make the values for the probabilities dependable.

Chapter 8

A TIP ON THE FOOTBALL POOLS*

John Smith has been clutching his coupon for some time: should he take a flier? On it groups of ten and twelve football teams are set out in opposing pairs, Club 1 *v* Club 2, etc. He doesn't know any of these teams or their capabilities, but he is going to bet on the results of the games, e.g., a win for Club 1, a win for Club 2, or a draw. He indicates his choice by putting 1, 2, or X in the appropriate squares on the coupon. A sample line for ten games might read:

10 Games			Forecasts		
No.	Club 1	Club 2	(1)	(2)	
1	A	A'	1	2	
2	B	B'	2	X	
3	C	C'	X	1	
⋮	⋮	⋮	⋮	⋮	
10	K	K'	1	2	

1 2 X 2 1 2 X X 2 1

The coupon when filled in must be sent to the pools firm, with a postal order for the amount of the stake. Now this is all very clear and simple, but who wins? This appears on the back of the coupon, where is printed:

* Throughout this chapter the author refers to the German football-pool system.

First prize. The client or clients submitting a completely correct line of results.

Second prize. Those submitting a line containing only one incorrect result.

Third prize. Those submitting a line with only two incorrect results.

Note. If no completely correct result is submitted by any client, those lines containing the highest number of correct results shall qualify for first prize, those with the second highest number for second prize, and those with the third highest number for the third prize. If, however, no line is submitted by any client with at least six correct results, no prizes will be paid, and the entire sum set aside for prizes on that particular coupon shall be held over, and added to the prizes for the following week.

It is therefore quite clear who wins, but how much does he win? This is reckoned on the basis of the total stake money received for a particular set of games. It is thus quite different from a lottery, in which the prizes are stated beforehand.

BETTING WITH A HAT. John Smith understands all this quite well, but he knows hardly anything about football. Still, he decides to bet, and chooses the list for a series of ten games. He decides to let chance rule the whole venture, and intends to write down on slips of paper all the possible combinations of results that he can think of; then he will fold each slip, toss them all into a hat, shake them up, and draw out several at random to enter on his coupon.

THE NUMBER OF POSSIBLE "TEN FORECASTS." How many slips of paper must John Smith write out? Without doubt, a very large number: three of them quite obviously would consist respectively of all 1's, all 2's, and all X's, but there would be many more containing mixtures or arrangements of 1's, 2's, and X's. Although John Smith realizes that counting up all these possibilities is no mean task, he embarks upon it bravely. "I won't start right off with the ten games," he says to himself; "First I'll find the number of possible arrangements for a small number of games, and perhaps, while I'm doing this, I'll hit upon some rule governing the whole process, which will help me to calculate the number of possible lists with the ten forecasts."

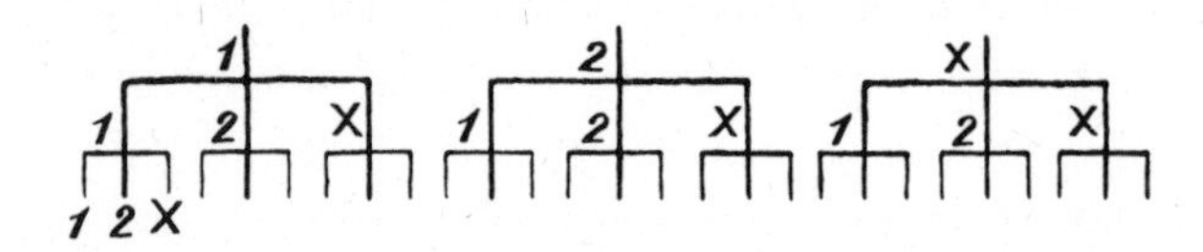

He names the paired teams A v A' : B v B', etc., and sets out the possible arrangements of results in a diagram like a "family tree" (above). Where only two teams are concerned there are three possibilities, 1, 2, or X. For these he would need a number of slips to go into the hat, and to represent this John Smith makes three vertical lines and labels them 1, 2, X. This shows him the number of possibilities (diagram above, top row). With two pairs of teams, a "three-pronged fork" is attached to each of the vertical columns, each representing three possibilities, 1, 2, X (diagram, second row). The total possible number of arrangements is now $3 \times 3 = 9$, namely, 11 12 1X and 21 22 2X and X1 X2 XX. So into the hat would go nine slips.

For the case of three results, he would attach to each prong of the second row a three-pronged fork, and the total number of possible arrangements thus becomes $9 \times 3 = 3 \times 3 \times 3 = 3^3 = 27$ slips of paper for the hat. Each possible arrangement is represented in the "family tree" by its pattern of branches (the two diagrams at left show the pattern for the three-forecast combinations 1 1 1 and 1 X 1).

The rule is now clear: in the case of four forecasts, there will be $3 \times 3 \times 3 \times 3$ or 81 possible arrangements or permutations.

For ten forecasts — $3^{10} = 59{,}049$
For eleven forecasts — $3^{11} = 177{,}147$
For twelve forecasts — $3^{12} = 531{,}441$

There is a formula for calculating the total number of possible arrangements. A ten-forecast list such as:

1 1 2 X 1 1 X 2 1 2

is a grouping of the three symbols, each appearing several times, to fill a total of ten places. According to the law of arrangement (cf. "combination," p. 9), it can be described as a permutation of three symbols, grouped in tens, with repetitions. Denoting the number of symbols by n, and the number in each group by k, the total number of permutations is described algebraically by:

$$G'(n; k) = n^k; \qquad \text{here} \qquad G'(3; 10) = 3^{10} = 59{,}049.$$

The $'$ of G' indicates that repetition of the constituent symbols is reckoned with. Knowledge of this formula saves one from having to proceed from first principles, as did John Smith.

To take another example, let us calculate the number of possible arrangements of dots and dashes as used in the Morse alphabet: in this code the letter *m* is represented by a group of 2 (— —), *r* is a group of 3 (· — ·), and *b* a group of 4 (— · · ·). Only two symbols are used, a dot and a dash. Considering the code as a whole, the arrangements are of 1, 2, 3, or 4 places for letters of the alphabet and 5 places for numerals. The total number of possible arrangements is therefore:

$$G'(2; k) = 2^k; \quad \text{so} \quad 2^1 = 2,\ 2^2 = 4,\ 2^3 = 8,\ 2^4 = 16, \text{ and } 2^5 = 32.$$

Thus there are 2 single-symbol letters, 4 made with 2 symbols, 8 with 3 symbols, 16 with 4, and 32 with 5. For instance, the 8 possible arrangements of dot and dash using 3 places are as follows:

s · · ·   u · · –   r · – ·   d – · ·   w · – –   k – · –   g – – ·   o – – –

Thus, the total number of arrangements available for the Morse alphabet and numerals is:

$$2 + 4 + 8 + 16 + 32 = 62.$$

THE FIRST PRIZE. John Smith is astonished at the enormous number of different arrangements possible in the ten-forecast list: 59,049. Out of these only one line is going to be the one without a single error. The probability of his selecting this slip from his hat is only 1 in nearly 60,000! Still, he muses, "Nothing ventured, nothing won." It doesn't have to be the correct line: a line with one mistake would bring in the second prize, and perhaps there is more chance of picking out one of these, as there should be more of them. How many lines with one mistake will there be? He again tackles the problem with the easier three-forecast calculation, and takes the line consisting of three 1's as the correct one (column 3 of the table below):

1	2	3	4	5
Row	*Games*	*First prize*	*One error*	
			With 2	*With* X
1	A v A'	1	2 1 1	X 1 1
2	B v B'	1	1 2 1	1 X 1
3	C v C'	1	1 1 2	1 1 X

Thus there are two kinds of error:

(*a*) 2 standing in place of a 1, which can occur in 3 positions, thus giving 3 possibilities (column 4).

(*b*) X standing in place of a 1; again possible in 3 ways (column 5).

Altogether, there are 2 × 3, i.e., 6 possible lines with one mistake. Working on this basis, a set of ten-forecast entries will contain a possible 2 × 10 lines with one mistake, so that John Smith's hat contains, among the 59,049 slips, 20 which qualify for a second prize. The probability of selecting one of these is therefore about 20 in 60,000, or 1 : 3000 (cf. law of probability, p. 160). If a coupon comprising 60,000 lines were to be filled in, every 3000 lines would contain one qualifying for a second prize—still not a very rosy prospect for John Smith.

WHAT ARE THE POSSIBILITIES OF WINNING THE THIRD PRIZE? It is rather more difficult to work this out, but John Smith eventually manages to compile the following specimen table:

1	2	3	4	5	6	7
Row	*Game*	*First prize*	*Two errors*			
			With 2, 2	*With* X, X	*With* 2, X	*With* X, 2
1	*A* v *A′*	1	2 1	X 1	2 1	X 1
2	*B* v *B′*	1	2 2	X X	X 2	2 X
3	*C* v *C′*	1	1 1	1 1	1 1	1 1
4	*D* v *D′*	1	1 1	1 1	1 1	1 1
⋮	⋮	⋮	⋮	⋮	⋮	⋮
10	*K* v *K′*	1	1 2	1 X	1 X	1 2

The correct first prize line is taken as that which consists of ten 1's (column 3). The third prize lines each contain two errors, and the table shows that these can occur in 4 ways:

The incorrect 2 or X may occur in two positions in each arrangement (column 4: 2 arrangements each having 2 twice in place of 1; column 5: each with two X's; column 6 and 7:

each with 2, X or X, 2 appearing in place of two 1's. Note that the pairs of arrangements in each of these columns have both errors in rows 1 and 2, and 2 and 10 respectively).

The actual positions in each line can of course vary. In how many places are the errors (2, 2) possible? There are 10 places to each arrangement, and the two errors can therefore be placed in rows 1 and 2, 1 and 3, etc., as is shown below:

	1 2					
	1 3	2 3				
	1 4	2 4	3 4			
	⋮	⋮	⋮			
	1 9	2 9	3 9	...	8 9	
	1 10	2 10	3 10	...	8 10	9 10
Total	9	+ 8	+ 7	+ ... +	2	+ 1 = 45

(A formula for calculating such a total with any number of places is given on p. 188.)

Thus 45 arrangements each with (2, 2), and an equivalent number for each of the pairs of errors (X, X), (2, X) and (X, 2), in all $4 \times 45 = 180$, would qualify for third prize. With 180 of these in the hat, the probability of drawing one is about 180 in 60,000, i.e., 3 : 1000. For every 1000 arrangements there will be 3 third-prize winners.

The chances of winning some sort of prize are:

First prize	1
Second prize	20
Third prize	180
Total	201 out of 59,049

This works out at about 200 : 60,000, or 1 : 300, as the probability of winning a prize.

THE PRIZE. How is the prize calculated for the different kinds of winning line? John Smith is very concerned about this: assuming that the pools firm receives from its clients the exact number of 59,049 entries, which represent all the possible arrangements of ten results, then at 10 cents per line the sum received represents a "model" stake of $5904.90.

Out of this, in Germany, half is allocated as prize money, and the rest goes toward administrative expenses, taxes, and donations to charities. (The state always wins on the pools, and wins well, in the form of taxes.)

The details of what is done with the cash might look something like this:

Stake money (59,049 × 10 cents)	= $5904.90
50% of this for prize money	= $2952.45
1/3rd of the prize money for each prize	= $984.15

The prizes are actually distributed as follows:

First prize	1 winner receiving	$984.15
Second prize	20 winners each receiving	$49.21
Third prize	180 winners each receiving	$5.47

This would be the division of prize money in the case of the "ideal" list of entries, i.e., one of each arrangement of the game results. In this case it is possible to say that there will be the exact number of winners in the three prize groups, but in reality considerably more lines are submitted by the public: 4 or 5 millions would not be unusual. The total number of lines entered for any particular list of games can in fact be easily ascertained by making the following calculation in respect of one of the prize groups:

Number of lines = 60 × number of winners × amount of prize.

E.g., Entries for "Ten Forecasts." First-prize winners numbered 124, each receiving $626.14. Therefore the number of entries was $60 \times 124 \times 626.14 = 4{,}658{,}481$.

(Why is this so? The number of winners × amount of individual prize = total prize in the particular group. This is 1/3 of 1/2 (or 1/6) of the total stake money reckoned in dollars. But for one dollar, ten lines can be submitted, so that the number of entries is 60 times the total prize money in any of the winning groups.)

LAW AND CHANCE. More than $4\frac{1}{2}$ million entries! That is indeed a very large number, even for the size of numbers required by the law of probability (p. 165). In this case the proportionate values, calculated for the "model" entry, would indeed hold good; in particular the proportion of winners in the three classes should be 1 : 20 : 180. In fact, the figures were in this example 124; 2244; 19,001, which have the ratios 1 : 18 : 153, which is quite a good approximation to the predicted results. Who would have thought this possible in a gamble involving so many people submitting so many lines? In such a case as this the precision and power of the law of probability is really marvelous.

Nevertheless, there is one important condition which must be fulfilled: the lines must be submitted entirely at random, without any special bias, just as if they were drawn from John Smith's hat. If the entries are sent in on some planned system, evolved from the study of the form of individual teams, the ideal distribution, which results from chance, will be given a certain bias, and may in fact differ markedly from predicted values. In May 1953, the ratios for prize winners in the three groups of a competition was: 1 : 55 : 790 instead of 1 : 20 : 180!

Putting it the other way, it could be said that the more the actual ratios of the numbers of winners correspond to the predicted values, the less has the entry list been influenced by "system." It is curious that the more pure chance is allowed to take effect, the more closely does the actual distribution of results fit the predicted values.

For those interested in calculations, here is an interesting table, listing the possible numbers of ten-forecast lines with 0, 1, . . . , 10 errors:

1	2	3	4
Errors	*Number of possible lines calculated by the formula*		*Probability*
0	1 × 1	1	1 : 60,000 or .000017
1	10 × 2	20	1 : 3000 or .00034
2	45 × 4	180	1 : 330 or .003
3	120 × 8	960	1 : 60 or .016
4	210 × 16	3360	1 : 18 or .057
5	252 × 32	8064	1 : 7.3 or .137
6	210 × 64	13,440	1 : 4.4 or .228
7	120 × 128	15,360	1 : 3.8 or .260
8	45 × 256	11,520	1 : 5.1 or .195
9	10 × 512	5120	1 : 12 or .087
10	1 × 1024	1024	1 : 58 or .017
		59,049	1.000(357)

Thus there are 8064 possible ways of constructing a line with 5 errors, but most frequent are the lines with 7 errors: they account for more than a quarter of the total. In every 100 lines of the "model" entry, therefore, we might expect about 26 lines with 7 errors. The degrees of probability in column 4 give the ratio of lines with the various numbers of errors to the total number of lines in the complete entry list (e.g., 15,360/59,049 = .260).

Lines containing 10 errors, that is, with no correct results forecast, number 1024, not just one or two. John Smith is quite wrong in assuming that it is as rare to get a line completely wrong as one completely right. The reason for this is as follows: if the row consisting entirely of 1's is taken as the correct one, then one completely wrong line is that consisting entirely of 2's, while another is that containing only X's—so far two lines in all. But to these must be added all those lines which are arrangements of 2's and X's, for instance with nine 2's and one X, or eight 2's with two X's, etc.

The derivation of the total from the two factors in column 2 is very interesting. The first factors consist of the so-called binomial coefficients, obtained from multiplying out $(a + b)^{10}$, and the second consists of powers of 2 ($2^0 = 1$; $2^1 = 2$; $2^2 = 4$, etc.)

THE GENERAL FORMULA. The number T of lines with f errors (f from 0 to k) in a "k results" competition is:

$$T(k;f) = \frac{k\,(k-1)\,(k-2)\ldots(k-f+1)}{1 \times 2 \times 3 \ldots f} \times 2^f$$

The total number of lines with 3 errors in a ten-forecast competition can be calculated from this formula by putting $f = 3$ and $k = 10$:

$$T(10;3) = \frac{10 \times 9 \times 8}{1 \times 2 \times 3} \times 2^3 = 120 \times 8 = 960$$

This formula, which is expressed in abbreviated form by mathematicians as $\binom{k}{f}$, is easily remembered: the denominator is the product of whole numbers from 1 upward to f, and is called "factorial f," while the numerator is the product of whole numbers, from k downward. It is deduced as follows: The f errors can occur in f of the k places in a particular line. There are as many possibilities as there are combinations of f in k terms, i.e. $\binom{k}{f}$, or in our example $\binom{10}{3}$. If the completely correct line is taken as that consisting only of 1's, then 2 and X, wherever they occur, are errors. The number of groupings of f errors, including both 2 and X counting repetitions, is $G'(2;f) = 2^f$, as has already been described (cf. p. 181).

TEN, ELEVEN, OR TWELVE GAMES? Which type of competition offers the best chance of winning? If the figures are calculated for the eleven- and the twelve-game coupons, as they have been for the ten-game one, the following table can be compiled. The total number of possible lines for each competition is listed in the first line, and the numbers of lines qualifying for prizes are listed in the 2nd, 3rd, and 4th lines.

	Ten Games	*Eleven Games*	*Twelve Games*
Total Lines	59,049	177,147	531,441
1st prize	1	1	1
2nd prize	20	22	24
3rd prize	180	220	264

The surprising feature is the very small rise in the number of lines which qualify for prizes in the eleven- and twelve-game series, in contrast to the enormous increase in the number of possible lines. This shows that the probability of winning on the ten forecasts is far greater than on the others. The relative probabilities, in round figures, are as follows:

Probability	*Ten Games*	*Eleven Games*	*Twelve Games*
1st prize	9	3	1
2nd prize	7.5	3	1
3rd prize	6	2.5	1

Thus the chances of winning a first prize on the ten or eleven forecasts are respectively 9 and 3 times greater than on the twelve forecasts. These ratios are derived from the figures in the previous table. It is indeed a shock to learn that the chances of winning on the ten forecasts are 9, 7.5, and 6 times more favorable than on the twelve forecasts, but the figures cannot be denied, and John Smith resolves that henceforward he will bet only on the ten-game forecasts.

Chapter 9

MONTE CARLO AND THE TWO BIRDS IN THE BUSH

A LITTLE GAME. John Smith is sitting forlorn on the hotel veranda, for the rain is pouring in torrents. "Don't be downhearted," says a fellow guest, "Let's have a game of something. I tell you what: I'll be banker and pay odds of 3 to 1 every time you throw a 4 with the die. Before each throw you stake a quarter, and if you don't throw a 4, the quarter is mine. Agreed?"

"Better have a bird in the hand than two in the bush," as the old saying goes. But there is another one: "If you don't speculate, you can't accumulate," and John Smith stands irresolute between a bird in hand and two in the bush. "A bird in hand": he does not play, and so loses nothing; or rather, he wins all the quarters that he does not wager. "Two birds in the bush": suppose he bets one quarter. He could win three quarters, a welcome profit, but, of course, there is a change of losing! Suppose he goes on playing —and losing? What is the probable outcome? Would gains and losses cancel one another out in time? From the player's point of view does the game offer a "fifty-fifty" chance? He cannot see how to assess his chances before beginning to play, for the game is ruled by chance, and who can possibly know whether banker or player will be favored in the outcome?

In point of fact it is possible to assess the chances, for the probability of throwing a 4 is 1/6 (cf. p. 166). A player, therefore, cannot be certain of winning three quarters, because his chance of a win is only once in six throws. At this point we will bring in what shall be called the "expectation of prize" E, and define it as the product of winnings W, and the probability of winning P. Algebraically, $E = WP$. Applying this to John Smith's little flier: $E = 3 \times 1/6 = 3/6$ of a quarter, or 12.5 cents. Similarly, expectation of loss E' can be calculated by the product of the stake B and the probability of losing P'. Therefore, John Smith's expectation of loss is $1 \times 5/6 = 5/6$ of a quarter, or 20.83 cents, for the probability of losing is the anti-probability of winning, $1 - 1/6$, i.e., 5/6 (cf. p. 160).

Thus his gambling expectation G is equal to the difference between E and E'. In this case it is 12.5 cents — 20.83 cents, or — 8.33 cents. This is *negative*, and implies that if John Smith plays a large number of times—say 120—he may expect to lose 8.33 cents, or 1/3 of a quarter on every throw, making a total loss of $120 \times 1/3 = 40$ quarters = \$10. The law of probability becomes more inexorably certain as the number of throws increases (cf. p. 165). So if the rain keeps on and the game continues the banker will gradually take one-third of all John Smith's bets—not a very rosy prospect for our friend. His chances would be what are commonly called "even" if the gambling expectation were nil. Winnings would then equal losses; neither party would have won—or lost—anything. This would be the case if, with a loss expectation $E' = B \times 5/6$, the banker were to pay for a win five times the stake B. Then we should have: $E = 5 \times B \times 1/6 = 5B/6$.

The conditions of play would be favorable for John if the bank paid out six times the stake for a win. In this case the gambling expectation $G = 6 \times B \times 1/6 - 5B/6 = +\ 1/6B$.

It is the old story of a bird in the hand being worth two in the bush. If you want to be sure of winning ($P = 1$), and therefore lose nothing ($P' = 0$ — "a bird in hand"), then you must not expect a gain of two birds from the bush, but only to keep your bird in the hand, i.e., your stake. In algebraic symbolism the gambling expectation is in this case $B \times 1 - B \times 0 = B$. To win anything from the bush the winnings must be greater than the stake; the player must take a risk, and be prepared for the possibility of losing:

$$G = WP - BP'.$$

When does a risk become sheer speculation? It is when the probability of winning in the case of a large bet is very small, and the probability of losing correspondingly large. It would be a wild speculation on John Smith's part, if he placed a bet of $10 on throwing two fours in succession, the prize for winning being $100. In this case (cf. p. 173), $P = 1/36$, and his gambling expectation would be calculated as follows:

$$G = 100 \times 1/36 - 10 \times 35/36 = 2.78 - 9.72 = -6.94 \text{ dollars.}$$

This is downright speculation, for in the long run he is certain to lose, though initially it is possible that he might win by sheer chance in throwing two fours in succession.

MONTE CARLO! This magic name reverberates in John Smith's mind, as he reads a poster advertising the casino in a holiday resort a few miles from where he is staying. Since his little game with the dice on that rainy afternoon he has been suffering from a slight touch of gambling fever, and so he decides to visit the casino. The two birds in the bush are busily flapping their wings: he is tempted to try to become rich overnight—or bankrupt! Roulette, moreover, is so much more exciting than football pools or rolling dice.

So there he is in the roulette salon of the casino. The wheel is concave, like a dish sunk into the table surface. The French word "roulette" refers to the little ball that rolls round and round on the wheel. Marked on the inner rotating part of the wheel there are 37 divisions, colored alternately red and black, and they are numbered from 1 to 36, but not in correct arithmetical sequence. The 37th, which is numbered 0, is in a special color. A specimen group of consecutive sections might be numbered, for instance, 0, 32, 15, 19. . . . The croupier in charge of the game spins the inner section of the wheel, and throws in a little ball, which bounces round and about until the wheel slows down, when it settles in a recess adjacent to one or another of the numbers.

On either side of the roulette wheel, the baize table top is divided into squares, numbered from 0 to 36. Other squares are marked to indicate certain groupings of these numbers: "Red" (all the red numbers), "Black" (all the black numbers), "Even," "Uneven," "Manque" (numbers 1 to 18), "Passe" (19 to 36); still more squares are reserved for the number groups 1–12, 13–24, 25–36, and also three lines, each of 12 numbers, as arranged upon the table (see diagram at right). The players place their bets on one or more of these squares, in the form of "chips" (or counters), representing various sums of money, which are bought from a cashier, and there is an upper limit to the amount that may be staked at any one time. The odds on the different ways of winning are listed as follows:

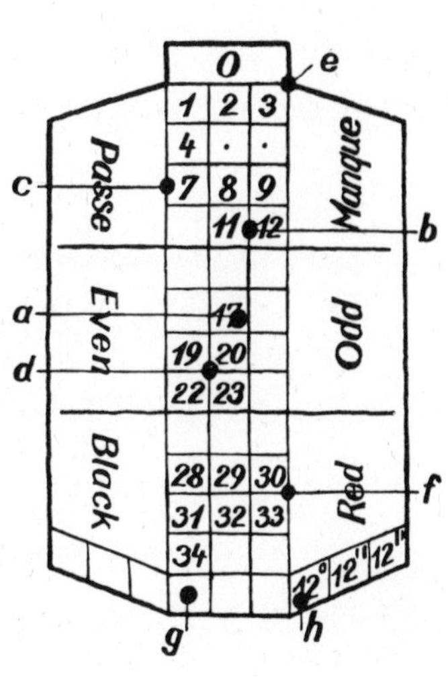

(*a*) A single number (*plein*) wins 35 times stake.
(*b*) Two consecutive numbers (*cheval*), e.g., 11 and 12, wins 17 times stake.
(*c*) A transverse line of 3 numbers (*transversale pleine*), e.g., 7, 8, 9, wins 11 times stake.

(*d*) A square of 4 numbers (*carré*) wins 8 times stake.

(*e*) The first 4 numbers (*les quatre premiers*), 0 to 3, wins 8 times stake.

(*f*) Two consecutive transverse lines (*transversale simple*) wins 5 times stake.

(*g*) A column (*colonne*), e.g., 1, 4, 7 . . . 34, wins 2 times stake.

(*h*) One of the three groups of 12 (*premier 1 . . . 12; deuxième 13 . . . 24; dernier 25 . . . 36*) wins 2 times stake.

(*i*) Red or black—even or odd (*manque 1 . . . 18; passe 19 . . . 36*) wins the stake.

These are the odds (*les chances*) or, as we have called them, the prize expectations. The French terms are used in all countries.

To start the game the croupier spins the wheel and throws in the ball, which at first runs round and round the outer edge, passing over the numbers. Then he calls "*Faites vos jeux, messieurs.*" (Please place your bets.) The players place their chips on one or more of the different sections (*a* to *i*), the positioning indicating the method of betting. When the ball begins to slow down, the croupier calls "*Rien ne va plus.*" (No more bets.) All eyes are riveted on the little ball, which gradually slows and finally settles, shall we say, on number 17. The croupier calls out the winning numbers: "17—black—odd number—*manque!*" rakes in the losing chips for the bank, and pays out the winnings in chips, according to the indicated scale. All this takes place in a very short space of time.

John Smith stands watching for a time. He feels strongly tempted to play, but has yet to summon up a little more courage. If only he knew, he thinks, whether his chances of winning were favorable or just even. Let us try to put him wise.

A PLAYER'S CHANCES of winning at roulette are *unfavorable*, being 1/37th of his stake, no matter how he places his bet.

John Smith has in mind a bet of $10 on No. 21. Now, a single number has one chance in 37 of winning, and therefore the probability of losing is 36/37. A win would bring in 35 × stake, i.e., $350, while a loss would mean forfeiture of the stake money. The prize expectation E would be $350 \times 1/37$ dollars, and the loss expectation E' $10 \times 36/37$ dollars. Hence, Smith's gambling expectation $G = 350/37 - 360/37 = -10/37$, or $1/37 \times \$10$, which is 1/37th of the stake. The chances of winning are therefore unfavorable, and exactly the same circumstances prevail for all other methods of betting. These are set out below:

1 *Mode of betting*	2 *Total individual nos. involved*	3 *Value of P for a win*	4 *Odds*	5 *E*	6 *E′*	7 *G* ($E - E'$)
a	1	1/37	35	35/37	36/37	— 1/37
b	2	2/37	17	34/37	35/37	”
c	3	3/37	11	33/37	34/37	”
d, e	4	4/37	8	32/37	33/37	”
f	6	6/37	5	30/37	31/37	”
g, h	12	12/37	2	24/37	25/37	”
i	18	18/37	1	18/37	19/37	”

As can be seen, the casino authorities have fixed the odds in such a way that the players' chances of winning remain the same (and unfavorable!), however they make their bet.

Another fact also emerges: while an individual may well be smiled on by Lady Luck, and win a handsome prize (for if it were otherwise, nobody would play), yet with a large number of players and games the law of probability exerts its full effect, and the gambling expectation settles down more and more closely to — 1/37th of the total stakes. If in the course of one day's play the wheel is spun 250 times, and 20 players take part in each game, each making two bets of $1 each, this means that there is a total stake of $250 \times 20 \times 2 \times 1 =$ $10,000. Let us think of this as being staked by one player (for it does not matter to the bank whether one bets $10,000, or one thousand bet $1 ten times), at the end our imaginary gambler will have lost about 1/37th or .027 of his total stake to the bank, and this amounts to $10{,}000 \times .027 =$ $270.

When John Smith has duly heard and considered all this, he abandons his plans to trap the two birds in the bush, and, clutching his one bird firmly in his hand, returns to his hotel. We will stay on, however, to watch another game being played.

THEORY AND PRACTICE. The casino authorities make a note each day of all winning numbers in their order of occurrence. These lists are closely studied by the gambling clientele, who can thus ponder on the caprices of fortune as demonstrated in them, and try to establish whether there is perhaps some law which rules the erratic course of the ball, and to derive from it some expectation of its future behavior in accordance with the law of probability. It is most exciting to see, for example, how suddenly a color or a group of numbers starts to turn up more frequently than usual, and reigns supreme for a while, before reverting to its usual frequency. In such a way does Lady Luck beckon to the gambler, enticing him to seize his opportunity. Were he to hesitate, all might be lost. In a German casino, on April Fools' Day, 1953, the following winning numbers were recorded:

31 35 13 26 33 29 29 36 19 10

This meant that in ten successive games No. 29 won twice running, four numbers were above 30, black numbers won seven times running (only 36 and 19 are red); and there might have been some subtle significance in 26 following 13! Whereas, in actual fact, there could hardly have been a more spectacular example of pure chance confounding theoretical expectations.

But of course, as we know, the law of probability is effective only over a large number of games. Is there, even in such circumstances, any record of strange deviations? Well, in the same casino, between March 1 and 15, 1951, a total of 7143 games were played, and there were therefore that number of winning numbers. As the probability of any single number is 1/37, theory predicts that each of the 37 numbers should have occurred $7143 \times 1/37 = 193$ times. Only one number, the zero, did this precisely. The deviations of the others from their expected frequency were within the following limits:

Actual deviation *Deviation in %*	0 0	1 . . . 10 to 5%	11 . . . 20 to 10%	+ 24 12%	— 20 15%	
Numbers	1	19	14	2	1	(= 37)

So 19 numbers occurred with a frequency of $193 \pm 10 = 183 \ldots 203$, and so on; only three numbers deviated in a large way from the expected frequency.

Where combinations of numbers are concerned (e.g., *b* to *i*, p. 194), the total number of winning numbers is greater, and values are therefore closer to expected frequencies. In the case of *transversale simple* (two consecutive transverse lines), the following table of results was obtained:

Transversale simple—nos.	1–6	7–12	13–18	19–24	25–30	31–36
Frequency of winning nos.	1142	1157	1160	1163	1124	1204
Deviation from expected frequency	— 18	— 3	0	+ 3	— 36	+ 44

The expected frequency of one of these six numbers is calculated as follows: the total of winning numbers excluding 0 is 7143 — 193 = 6950; this multiplied by the probability 6/36 gives 1160. (Alternatively, total of winning numbers including 0 is 7143; multiply this by 6/37.) The greatest deviation from the expected frequency is 44/1160 = 4%!

It is astonishing also to note the almost complete accord between prediction by theory and actual practice; in the case of *red* the actual number of wins was 3478, and for *black*, 3472 wins; the expected frequency is in each case 7143 × 18/37 = 3475. The maximum deviation here is ± 3, as a ratio, 3/3475 or .00086, or approximately .09%.

According to theory, the deviation could be as much as 42, or 42/3475 = .01% of "normal," and still qualify as a reasonable figure by the laws of chance. The "normal" deviation is calculated by the formula $\sqrt{nPP'}$, where n is the total of winning numbers, P the probability of winning, and P' the probability of losing. In this case, therefore, the possible deviation is $\sqrt{1780}$, with $n = 7143$, $P = 18/37$, and $P' = 19/37$. This gives as the answer approximately 42.

It is extraordinary how, in games of chance, the law of probability is justified whenever the number of games played is sufficiently high. Now we shall remove our mathematical spectacles and, following in John Smith's footsteps, depart from the casino.

OUR PERCEPTION OF SPACE

The comprehension of space is a wonderful part of our intellectual equipment, and is the basis of all geometry, if not of all mathematics. It leads not only to the perception with the mind's eye of such familiar shapes as cube, sphere, or straight line, but also to the comprehension of purely abstract relationships, which are devoid of all actual shape. For the thinking mind is often helped by this kind of imagination; it is an intuitive faculty, which is highly developed in some people. We often talk of "insight." What can be seen can be thought about, and many people can think only about things that can actually be seen.

The ability to perceive or comprehend space and spatial relationships is a help in visualizing many kinds of abstractions. It is latent in all of us, and can be developed by careful training.

A simple but most effective way of helping the "inner eye" to function is to practice "air geometry." Outline a cube in the air with your hand: there are left and right sides, front and back, top and bottom. Now extend both forefingers so that they point toward each other along the straight line which joins the rear upper left-hand corner to the front lower right-hand corner. Can you visualize this line, and the whole cube around it?

Now in imagination let us make a flight from London to Buenos Aires. Scoop out the shape of the earth in mid-air, set in it the axis with your forefingers, and then describe the line of the equator round it: there is your world. Now, remembering your geography, trace out the course from London to Buenos Aires, and try to think of the positions of Tokyo and Moscow.

The inner eye—the mind's eye—can see things and the relationships between them that the physical eye can never perceive. A straight line is defined as the shortest distance between two points, but the mind's eye alone can comprehend the meaning of "point," which has no area, and "straight line," which has only length but not breadth. The mind's eye too can realize that there is only one type of straight line.

The image of a perfect circle is so firmly fixed in our minds that when we contemplate the elliptical outline of the rim of a bucket viewed obliquely, we still think of it as a circle.

SEEING IS NOT ALWAYS EASY. One goose goes in front of two, one behind two and one between two. How many geese are there? Once you have pictured in your mind's eye geese waddling along in line, the whole thing is clear. A hundred people walk in front, and a hundred people follow—but there are only a hundred people altogether! How on earth can this be? If you cannot picture it, just think of them moving round a circle, and there you are! Can you make four equilateral triangles, each made of three matches, with a total of six matches? After many fruitless efforts you will probably admit defeat. Well, you have failed only because your mind's eye has not fully perceived three-dimensional space. Set out three matches on the table to form a triangle, and then set up the other three at its corners to form a three-sided pyramid. The third dimension is so often neglected. How many lines can be drawn parallel to a fixed straight line at a distance of 5 in.? If you think in terms of two dimensions you will give the answer as two, one on each side, but the correct answer is "an infinite number," and this can be understood only if you think in terms of three-dimensional space.

Two highways, each with two lanes of traffic—we will denote them by $A\,(r, l)$ and $B\,(r, l)$—cross each other's path, B passing under A. Can you visualize, without making a sketch, how a driver can change from $(A\ r)$ to $(B\ r)$ without crossing over any other lane on the same level? It is only when you have drawn the crossing layout and added the loop-roads which lead the traffic from one level to another—e.g., $(A\ r)$ to $(B\ r)$—that you can really picture the situation.

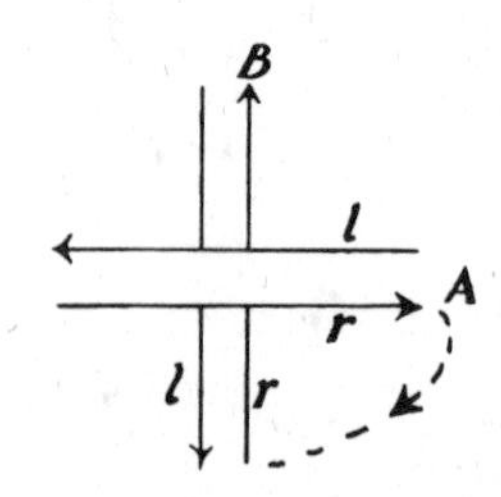

To be able to visualize, to picture such things, whether in the mind or on paper, is a great help in all mathematical thinking. Even relationships between pure numbers can often be expressed in geometrical form. How complicated seemed the clock problem

on p. 78, yet how simple it was once a diagram had b
(See p. 81.) What a tedious job it would have been to
all the figures for the trips made by the motorcyclist on p. 121,
yet how simple they were to read from the graph on that page!
A curve in a graphical diagram is the visual representation of a relationship between two sets of numbers (cf. Function, p. 50); there are even diagrams that can calculate (cf. p. 152). There can be no doubt that visualization is a major preoccupation in mathematics.

But appearances can sometimes deceive: imagine a road encircling Vesuvius, which we shall consider for our purpose here to be a perfect cone. This road rises with constant gradient from the valley on one side of the mountain, passes round the peak,

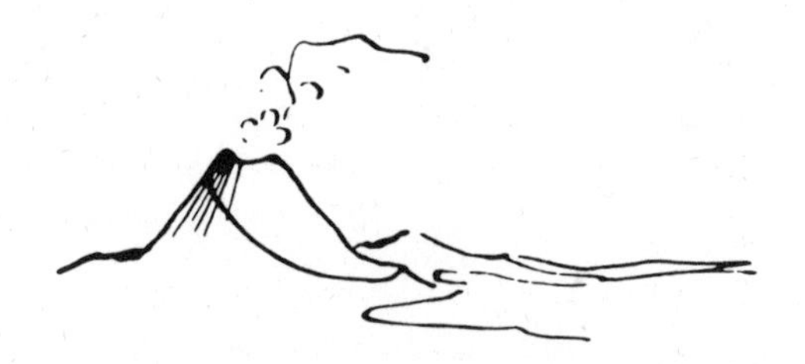

and then descends on the other side, still with a constant gradient, back to the same valley below. Where does it bend most, at the peak or in the valley? At the peak, surely, for in the valley the perimeter of the cone is greater!

Our eyes suggest that the line of the road is egg-shaped, but we are deceived: the curve is an ellipse, and the curvature at the peak is exactly the same as it is at the foot. This can be seen in another way: hold up a cone-shaped wine glass which is half full and tilt it. The outline of the liquid surface represents the line followed by the road round Vesuvius (except that in this case Vesuvius is upside down). The liquid surface also reproduces a section of the cone, and it is elliptical (cf. diagram *b*, p. 124).

Our eyes, therefore, can err, but they are often helped by our intuition, our inner eye. We shall shortly see the same thing happening when we consider a section of a sphere ("the Earth's corset," below). Observation by itself is not considered reliable as a proof in mathematics; proof must be securely based on reasoning, though of course physical observation must have a hand in the matter. In such a complicated instance as that of the twisted belt (p. 75) the limitations of actual observation are very clear. Who could have predicted, simply by looking at the belt, what would happen when it was cut in two along its center line, and also when further cuts were made? There is no doubt that where curves are concerned the whole business of visualization is much more difficult than in the case of plane figures or solid shapes outlined by straight lines. Here is a further example.

MOTHER EARTH'S CORSET. Mother Earth has an immense stomach, and the circumference of her corset (the equator) is 25,000 mi. long. Suppose she wanted to loosen her corset, say by 10 ft., and breathe a little more easily. If she did this, there would be a small gap of x ft. between her stomach and the corset. Let us call it "x, the breathing space."

It is readily doubted whether such a small increase—only 10 ft. in a distance of 25,000 mi.—about 1 in. per 200 mi.— would have any significant effect on her comfort, but a simple calculation will show that x is actually 1.59 ft.!

The diagram on the next page will help us to visualize the problem and so calculate x. The circumference of the corset is given by the formula $C = 2\pi r$, and the loosening, l, increases this by 10 feet, thus giving a breathing space x. The loosened corset will therefore have radius $r + x$, and circumference $C' = 2\pi (r + x) = 2\pi r + 2\pi x$. It is now clear that the increase in the circumference ($l = 10$ ft.) is equal to $2\pi x$. Hence,

$$x = 10/2\pi = 10/6.28 = 1.59.$$

The breathing space is about 1/6 of the *increase* in the circumference!

Let us consider this matter from another angle and in a different context. A telegraph wire is erected round the equator on poles 15 ft. high. How much longer will the wire be than the equator? In this case x, the distance between wire and earth, is 15 ft., and therefore the increase in length $l = 2\pi \times 15 = 94.2$, only 94 ft.!

These two calculations prove that there is a distinct limit to our powers of visualizing a situation: we should never have expected the truth to be what it is, and what now follows is even more startling.

The breathing space is quite independent of the size of the circumference of the corset! Whether the increase in girth of 10 ft. is distributed around a circumference of 25,000 mi. or of only 3 ft., the breathing space will still be 1.59 ft. This is quite contrary to our natural expectation, for surely it is reasonable to suppose that with the same increase in circumference, a *long* belt would afford less breathing space than a *short* one. And yet it is not the case!

It is curious that we can understand this phenomenon much more easily if we consider straight lines instead of curves. Imagine a square house with sides of 10 yd., and that we wish to surround it with a fence at a distance of 1 yd. It is easy to see that the fence perimeter will exceed that of the house by the 8 yd. that have to be added to make the corners. Clearly, the same amount would be needed for the corners, even if the side of the original square were 100 yards.

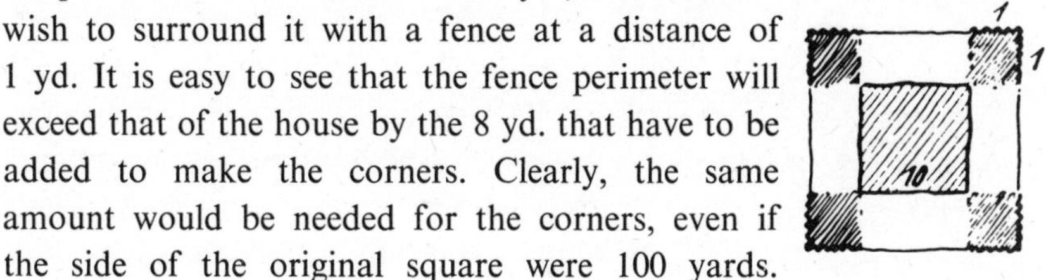

The "breathing space" remains the same, and is quite independent of the perimeter of the house, just as in the first example it was independent of the girth of the stomach. It depends only on the increase in length of the fence.

In the case of the square house the increase in the length of the fence is eight times the distance of the fence from the walls, while with Mother Earth's ample stomach the increase in circumference is 6.28 (2π) times the breathing space. The relationship seems obvious in the case of the square, but we have great difficulty in visualizing it in the case of the circle.

There is another very common application of this "breathing space" idea, in that source of discomfort for men—the shirt collar. What rather portly gentleman has never on occasion roundly cursed his tight collar? Suppose the collar that is strangling him is size 16 (circumference 16 in.). Choking with breathless rage, he dashes to the store, and to be really sure of relief he buys size 17, only to find later that this one is impossibly slack. The breathing space is much more than he had reckoned on, for it is nearly 1/6 the increase in circumference, and there is therefore an extra gap of 1/6 in. all around his neck.

An increase in the circumference of your collar of just one inch gives you, then, an extra clearance of 1/6 in.: and an identical increase in the circumference of Mother Earth's gigantic corset would give her exactly the same amount of breathing space.

Now for another case, this time a matter of moving circles.

THE ROLLING PENNY. Place a penny on the table with another one beside it. Now roll the second one around the circumference of the first. How many times has the rolling penny rotated round its own center? Try it first with the mind's eye. This is no easy matter, so perhaps a little bit of calculating is needed.

Both coins have the same circumference, so surely the second coin will rotate only once in rolling its entire circumference round that of the first? But it is not so: the coin rotates twice.

How often will it rotate, if it rolls round the inside of a ring, with a circumference twice that of the coin? In this case one would certainly say twice, because of the double circumference, but in fact the answer is—once only! Try these two experiments, and see for yourself.

How is this to be explained? A drunken reveler was once found staggering around a circular pillar, and shouting "Help! Help! I'm locked in!" Ignoring his predicament, we will just ask whether, as he walked around from point *A* to point *A′* (diagram *a*), he has rotated his body. He has in fact done this, describing one complete turn, just as the moon rotates round its own axis while revolving round the earth. Now let us straighten out the circular wall of the pillar, and so make a straight line *AA′* (diagram *b*). If our friend walks along this, he is not turning at all, but if we now bend it round the other way (diagram *c*), then again the man rotates as he walks, but in the opposite sense to that of diagram *a*. Although he is not conscious of turning, the very fact that he is following the curve of the pillar box causes him to change direction and therefore to turn as he walks.

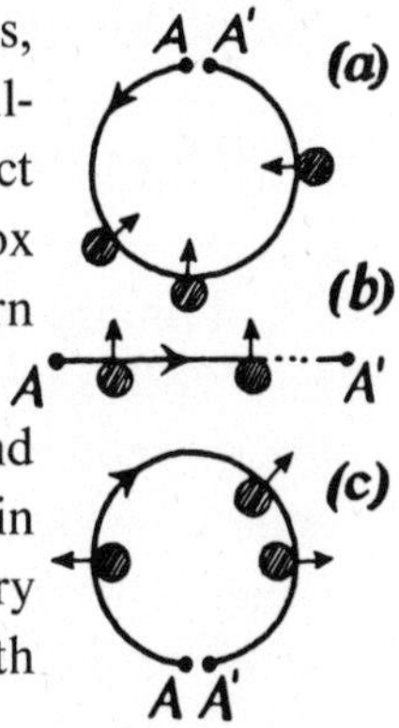

A A′ (a)
(b)
A A′
(c)
A A′

Come back now to our penny. If we slide it round its stationary partner, keeping the same point in contact with the circumference of the stationary coin, we have the same situation that we had with the drunken man.

How could he work out for himself that he is not in some kind of prison? He spreads out his arms to touch the wall of the pillar, and finds, as he walks round it, that the wall continually recedes from him. In a cell with rounded walls, it would curve toward him. It is just the same with the rolling penny: when it rolls round the outside of a circle, its track continually recedes, and, in order to keep in contact, the rolling penny must roll still more, and as we have seen, it rotates twice in moving round once. Whereas, rolling round the inside of a ring, its track continually curves toward it, and so it has to rotate less. To sum up, a person walking round the outside or the inside of a circular track, rotates once only; but a coin rolling round the outside of a circular track, rotates twice in rolling a distance equal to its own circumference; but rolling the same distance inside it would make only half a rotation. Try it out for yourself.

Now try to visualize another aspect of the rolling penny. What sort of curve is described by a point on the circumference of the penny as it rolls round the inside of a ring with twice its circumference? (See the diagram on page 204—the point under the 1.) Can you visualize it? It is not an easy matter, even with a diagram; the point swings to and fro along a diameter of the ring.

THE LIMITATIONS OF VISUALIZATION. It is quite impossible to visualize situations which bring in the concept of infinity. We might perhaps visualize infinity itself thus: the number sequence 1, 2, 3, etc. is never ending, i.e., it extends to infinity. You can see it in the mind's eye always extending, ever increasing by one more term at a time. Similarly you can visualize a straight line extending to infinity. But, inasmuch as our powers of visualization include only objects or concepts in three dimensions (length, breadth, depth), any ideas or concepts of four-dimensional or multi-dimensional space are beyond the average man's comprehension. It is, however, sometimes possible to transform concepts of higher spaces into terms that can be visualized, and so partially understood (cf. p. 243).

SEEING SHAPES. This is another aspect of visualization, and is important in analyzing all manner of problems (e.g., locating positions, calculating, etc.). The diagram shows a pattern of nine dots, arranged in three rows of three. You can think of them as being arranged in three rows or in three columns, or as a square with a dot in the middle, and so on. One way is to see them as follows: One dot in the upper left corner, combined with a corner of three dots round the first dot, and then a final corner of five dots to make up the square. If you can see it this way you will understand an important fact of arithmetic, viz., $1 + 3 = 2^2$; $1 + 3 + 5 = 3^2$. Subsequent corners (7, 9, 11, etc.) can be continually fitted round each square to produce the next larger square. In other words, the sum of any number of consecutive odd numbers, starting with 1, is always a square.

With mental arithmetic it often helps to be able to visualize the construction of numbers. It is not easy, perhaps, to work out mentally 437 — 243, but it makes it much easier to see it as 43′7 — 24′3 = 19′4.

In this diagram we have a square, on each side of which is a crescent-moon shape. Can you see how the areas of these crescents can be calculated? Just think for a moment, and it becomes clear that the sum of their areas is equal to the area of the square, plus the areas of the semicircles on the four sides of the square, less the area of the circle drawn round the square. A short calculation then shows that their total area is equal to that of the square. For if a is the side of the square, the area of the crescents is

$$a^2 + 4\pi a^2/8 - 2\pi a^2/4 = a^2.$$

Another problem is to devise a peg shaped so that it will pass through each of the three holes illustrated on p. 208 while filling them completely. The peg is shown at right below: viewed from the front, it is square; from the side, triangular; and circular when viewed from below beneath it.

WORDS CAN BE BOTH A HELP AND A HINDRANCE TO VISUALIZATION. A speaker or a writer has a certain picture in his mind, and what he says or writes is intended to reproduce it in the minds of listeners or readers. We are not interested in those people who seek to impress by the deliberate use of long words and unnecessarily technical expressions. We shall discuss instead various words which completely fail to express the meaning they should convey, words which fail to invoke any visualization of the principle involved. It is a great pity that quite often there are no existing words which can do the job better. Consider the symbolic statements $10^2 = 100$ and $10^3 = 1000$. These are usually expressed in words as: "ten squared equals one hundred and ten cubed equals one thousand." There are other ways of expressing them, viz., "ten to the power of two and ten to the power of three"; "two powers of ten with indices respectively 2 and 3." This is all easily understood by any junior scholar: 10^2 means "multiply one by ten twice in succession to obtain 100; 10^3 means multiply one by ten three successive times to get 1000." It is also easy to realize that the indices provide a rapid means of multiplying large numbers together, merely by simple addition of the indices; e.g. $100 \times 1000 = 10^2 \times 10^3 = 10^5 = 100{,}000$.

But a sixteenth-century scholar used instead of index the word "exponent," and another in the seventeenth century invented the word "logarithm," having in mind the use of indices as aids to multiplication, as described above. (Logarithm is derived from the Greek, and means "the number of the ratio.") Both these terms are still used, and constitute a great hindrance to the student who is struggling to understand the principles involved. Any youngster soon learns the meaning of index, or even exponent, but many a senior pupil has only a hazy notion of what is implied by the term logarithm. Even a knowledge of Greek will not help, for the words in that language give very little clue to enable us to grasp what the composite word means. It is entirely the fault of such unfortunate terminology that many quite simple concepts have been transformed into obscure topics of so-called "higher knowledge."

Words, therefore, play an important role. They can obscure what is clear and kill any interest in topics that might have had a lively appeal. Fortunately, of course, they can do the exact opposite: every branch of knowledge has its share of technical terms which are splendidly apt and immediately conjure up in the mind's eye what they seek to convey. But alas, there are less praiseworthy terms which must be laboriously explained by a teacher before they can be used with understanding. Students are advised to make due allowance for these bits of pedantic lumber, which endure only because tradition has preserved them. It should always be our aim to establish exactly what a term means, not to allow it to confuse our minds and sap our interest.

THE LOST DIMENSION

SUPPOSE YOU WANT TO MAKE A DRAWING OF A DIE. It has length, breadth, and depth, but your paper has only length and breadth. The third dimension is missing, and this presents a problem.

A child can always get round this difficulty, even though nobody else could recognize his drawing for what it is supposed to portray. In this sketch we can see all six faces of the die, but the trouble is that it no longer looks like a die. The child's mind hardly realizes the loss of the third dimension; blithely he produces a drawing which ignores all the measurements and proportions of the object, and by adult standards he has not visualized it correctly.

Accurate representation of measurements and appearance is essential to a drawing, if it is to be acceptable for technical purposes, but it is not possible to combine both these qualities in one drawing, because of the lack of a third dimension. Technical drawing, as it is called, seeks to effect a useful compromise and has developed three different methods of representation, which are called orthogonal (or orthographic), oblique, and perspective. In this sequence the three are in ascending order of fidelity in representation, but in descending order of fidelity to actual measurements.

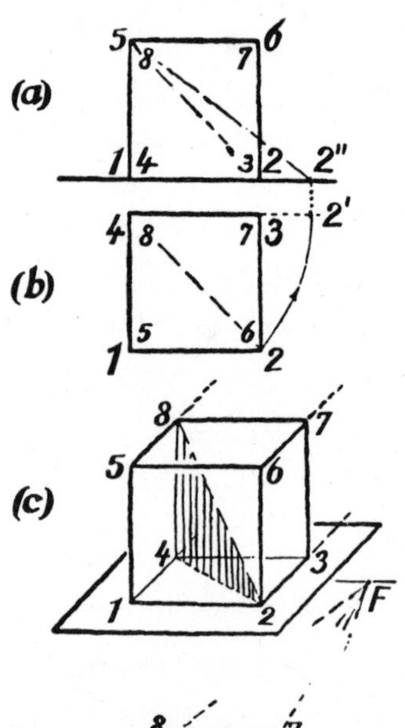

ORTHOGONAL PROJECTION. Consider a cube standing on a sheet of paper, which lies flat on the table (diagram *c*). If you look down on the cube from a position directly above the centers of its base and upper surface, you see what is called its "plan" (diagram *b*); if you view from one side, your eye in line with the centers of sides 1265 and 4378, you see an "elevation" (diagram *a*). In both cases the cube is telescoped into a square: the plan is square 5678; the elevation, square 1265. The edges 14, 23, 67, 58 which, as diagram *c* shows, lie parallel to the plane of the base and provide depth for the three-dimensional cube, are omitted from the elevation (diagram *a*), but appear in the plan (diagram *b*). Similarly, the sides 51, 62, 73, 84, suppressed in the plan, are shown in the elevation. In this way the drawings of plan and elevation each supplement the information given in the other, and enable anyone with good powers of visualization and some experience with such drawings to visualize clearly the solid object. A layman, however, who knows nothing about them, might well find them beyond his powers of interpretation, especially if the object is of complicated shape or elaborate construction.

In this respect oblique projection has an advantage, for objects portrayed in this way can be visualized without any difficulty. Diagram *c* is drawn in oblique projection, and you can see that the sides giving depth to the cube are not suppressed, but are fully visible. The method has certain peculiarities, in that the lines of depth are drawn parallel to one another, at a fixed angle (usually 45° or its supplement 135°) to the horizontal. This distorts the rectangles framed by the "depth" edges and the horizontal, and makes the faces 5678, 2376, 1234, 1458 appear as parallelograms; but to the eye this convention is quite acceptable and we can visualize the object as a cube. Another curious fact is that the "depth" edges, 23, 67, 14, 58, are all shortened, in this case to half the length of 12, 34, 56, 78. Even so, we can still "see" the parallelograms as squares.

In perspective drawing an even more natural method of portrayal is used. The difference between it and oblique projection is that the lines of depth are no longer drawn parallel, but all converge on a "vanishing point" *F*. This is a perfect representation of what we see: you have only to look down a long, straight stretch of railway track to realize this. An express train hurtling away from you would disappear from view at such a vanishing point. This perspective style of drawing is used by artists (at least, by the "traditional" ones). It is curious that such an elaborate distortion of the correct relationships—right angles changed to acute or obtuse, square faces becoming trapezoidal—should present to the eye what it sees as a faithful portrait of a cube!

These three methods of representation are, as was stated, in ascending order of fidelity to appearance, but in descending order of fidelity to actual measurements. No craftsman who wishes to construct an object would be able to take his angles from an oblique projection or a drawing in perspective (diagrams *c* and *d* on p. 210). Taken from the orthogonal projection (diagrams *a* and *b*), such measurements would be accurate.

In practice, all building plans and drawings used for the actual construction of things are drawn in orthogonal projection; on the other hand, a picture of a piece of furniture for a catalogue would probably be in oblique projection, while pictures of houses and other large objects would be drawn in perspective. The oblique method is easier than perspective, and offers a convenient compromise between accurate measurements and true appearance. It is sometimes impossible to take certain measurements from any type of drawing (e.g., the diagonal 28 of the diagrams on p. 210), but in such instances orthogonal projection is likely to be the most helpful.

For the amateur draftsman: Imagine the triangle 842 in diagram *c* to be hinged along the line 84; turn it until it lies in the same plane as the face 4378. This can be easily represented in orthogonal projection: 842′ is its plan (diagram *b*), from which the elevation 82″ (diagram *a*) can be drawn to show the actual size and shape of the triangle. Such faithful representation of size and shape can be obtained for any line or surface, once it is visualized as lying in the surface of the paper.

Restoration of the lost third dimension, by showing the lines of depth in oblique projection, is a rather curious solution to the problem. In this way we are able to view a two-dimensional distortion as if it were an actual three-dimensional object. In the early development of drawing techniques, such distortion was for a long time considered an inaccurate and deceptive practice. It is indeed strange that no child, young enough to be uninfluenced by his elders' ideas of perspective, will use the oblique method in his drawings. The invention of this technique and its development from an initial vague idea to a state of practical utility are due entirely to the questing intellect of the Western world, with its profound awareness of spatial relationships.

The three types of projection can be reproduced as follows: Hold a wire framework, made in the shape of a cube, in a shaft of light (e.g., sunlight, p. 215). The shadow thrown on a screen is an orthogonal projection, if the parallel beams or rays of light are at right angles to the screen; it is oblique if the beam is at an angle to the screen. If the beam is not parallel but diverging from a small hole in a screen placed in front of the light source, then a shadow image in perspective will be thrown on the screen (cf. a motion-picture projector).

Finally there is another method, interesting, yet simple enough: it is a variation of the oblique method. It was once the practice in Germany to draw up plans of military installations in this way. The "plan" view is drawn as in orthogonal projection, i.e., a square is drawn as a square, a circle as a circle. The perpendicular sides are then erected on the plan, and they also are drawn in orthogonal projection. This method is especially useful in the case of such shapes as cylinders or cones, because figures are recorded as they actually are, instead of, for instance, circles being drawn as ellipses.

CHANGE IN SHAPE IS RELATIVE

RELATIONSHIP. Look in the mirror: is it exactly like you, or not? Your body has changed somewhat, for when you move your right arm, the figure in the mirror moves its left. Look at the reflection of your face in a silver spoon: once again it is your face—and yet it isn't. This time all your features are much smaller and ridiculously distorted. Your eyes seem right, but your nose juts out like a strawberry. If you walk out into the sunshine, your shadow accompanies you: distorted it may be, but it is your shadow, an image that has something of you about it. Bearing all this in mind, let us now state that there are many shapes which seem to have no possible relationship with others, but which can in fact be classified as "projections" of an original "parent shape."

A new and fertile development took place when mathematicians began to consider various shapes not merely as individual specimens—a circle, for instance, as a circle in its own right—but as members, however distantly related, of certain families. From this broader point of view it was possible to see distinct relationships between various different shapes. Laws were formulated, based on these relationships, showing how one could be transformed into another: a circle into an ellipse, or a hyperbola, and so on.

Such changes are made possible by an essential relationship between classes of shapes, i.e., by those qualities which they have in common: in the case of the circle and ellipse there is the fact that both are closed curves.

Following such lines of thought, mathematicians have been able in the last few centuries to investigate and analyze the whole structure of geometry, arranging and classifying the results for us. Two examples will typify this mode of thought: in the first we shall easily recognize the essential relationship but in the second it is not so evident.

THE SUNLIT WINDOW. Sunlight shines on your window, and projects its rectangular shape (1234) on the floor. This projected shape (1′2′3′4′) is in some ways like your window, but in others not. The shape has been changed. The physical laws which govern this situation provide for the projection, point by point, of the rectangular window on the floor by parallel rays of light which make up the beam of sunlight (in the diagram, 1 projects into 1′, etc.). We could think of it as a translation of every point of the window down a bundle of rails leading to the floor. In the process, however, the original shape and dimensions are lost: the length of the sides are altered, and right angles become acute or obtuse, and what appears on the floor is a parallelogram.

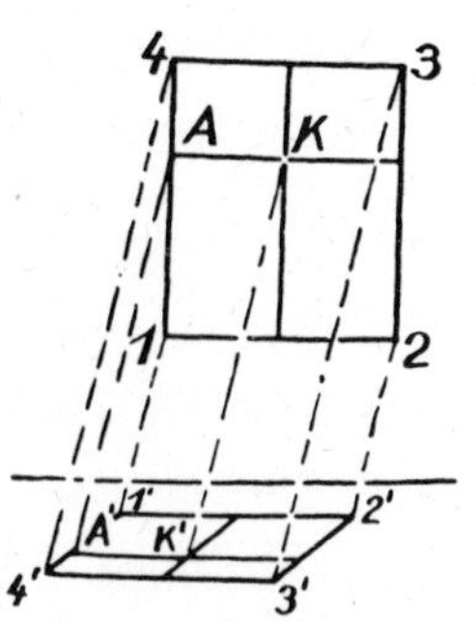

The four-sided, four-cornered character of the window still exists in the shape on the floor: it has not become circular! Another feature unchanged is that the two pairs of opposite sides are still parallel (12 and 43 parallel, as also 1′2′ and 4′3′); furthermore, ratios of corresponding lengths are unaltered. For instance, *K* on the window is halfway across, and so is its projection *K′* on the floor. Also, if the distance *A*1 on the window is three quarters of the length 14, then *A′*1′ is three quarters of 1′4′. These are the invariant qualities which the two shapes have in common.

The parallelogram is a projection of the rectangle, but it is also clear that we may regard the rectangle as a projection of the parallelogram. In the interests of generality so essential to the abstractions of mathematics, both of them must enjoy equal status as embodiments of their common properties: four-sided, four-cornered, and having opposite sides parallel. Each of them can be projected into the other. You may, for instance, perform an experiment similar to the preceding one by letting the sun shine through a parallelogram-shaped hole, cut out of a piece of card. If the card is held in a suitable position the projection will be a rectangle: it could even be a square! Point for point, there is a correspondence between the two. Relationship, correspondence, projection—these are all terms implying a rearrangement; all are closely connected, and indeed partially synonymous.

Now follows the example in which the relationship between two shapes is not at first evident.

THE SQUASHED HAT. The wind has blown your hat off, and a truck has run over it. What a sorry wreck you now hold in your hand! It is still your hat, and yet it is hardly a hat at all, for it has undergone, to put it mildly, a change of shape.

Now let us consider what has altered, and what if anything remains unaltered. A lot of it, we fear, has been altered: the once shapely, domed crown is now a dirty, squashed, flat pancake, no sort of a hat for a man, though it is possible your wife might see in it a new style for herself. Is anything unchanged? The crown is ruined, the measurements have changed, the stylish curves of the brim have disappeared, but one thing remains: the hat is still intact, in that it is still in one piece! The crown is still fastened to the brim, and the band to the crown.

This is small consolation indeed, though your wife might regard it as important, for if there are no holes or tears, the hat can be restored—reblocked, as it is called. This means that all points and parts can be restored to (or "projected into") their old positions relative to one another. Of course, it will be a tricky process: just imagine the complicated twisted paths described by the different points on the hat's surface, as they undergo steaming, pressing, stretching and straining, on their way back to their former positions. Yet there is a basic relationship between that new hat and its poor, squashed, downtrodden other self: the new can be converted into the squashed, which can be reconverted to its original shape.

It may be that you regard the haphazard deformation of the hat as a most inappropriate example for our purpose: it is not possible, as it was in the case of the window, to consider the situation with mathematical precision. But there are times when you would accept as a mathematical process a very similar case of deformation. To make a segment of a hollow rubber ball lie flat on a table you must press it down and deform it. Now a map is essentially the same thing—a segment of the earth's spherical surface, stretched and deformed so that it lies flat on a sheet of paper; moreover, all the bumps and hollows, hills and dales have been squashed flat. How else could the land be represented on paper, if it were not squashed as flat as your hat (or flatter than that)?

Those little "route and distance plans" on the tourist leaflets are also projections, although the only essential relationship between them and the actual terrain is that of the distances marked between the names of the towns. No uniform scale of distance is used, and no attempt is made to indicate the bends and twists of the roads, but the places marked are spaced out in their approximate relative positions, and the straight lines between them represent the roads, with actual distances marked. In this way essential information is conveyed by reducing all necessary details to the absolute minimum, and it is this minimum which constitutes the essential relationship between plan and terrain.

There is a cynical comment on mathematics, that it is the science of drawing the right conclusions from the wrong assumptions. Actually, this is correct, provided always that the "wrong" assumptions show the "right" relationships. From a curve with the unsightly bulging contours of a potato, the mathematician can make most ingenious projections, for he looks on the matter with the eyes of one familiar with the mathematical primeval "world" (cf. p. 236), and a few bumps or dents do not matter at all.

When a child makes a drawing of you—head, eyes, nose,

ears, mouth—even though his portrait may not resemble you at all, yet the correspondence between the parts will be there. They will all be more or less in the right place, except possibly in the case of a very young artist. This being so, it is possible to refashion the portrait until it resembles you exactly. If, however, a surrealist were to draw you with nose on stomach and ears on knees, the essential correspondence between your various parts would be upset, and only extensive rearrangement would make the picture into a true likeness. These examples should help you to understand the meaning of correspondence and projection. The organizing power of man's intellect, which conceived these ideas and gave them these names, has gone on to reveal further associations which were not foreseen initially.

Many well-known phenomena can indeed be described in terms of the essential relationships which they embody. A film projector, for example, throws on a screen an enlarged image of a smaller object, the film, in such a way that all the shapes and spatial relationships on the object remain unaltered on the image. As another instance, the relationship between the sections of a cone has been described already (see page 124). In conclusion we can truly say that geometry embarked upon a whole new unexplored ocean, quite undreamed of by earlier mathematicians, when it changed its point of emphasis from individual shapes and began to consider the correspondences between them.

Chapter 10

THE STRANGE INTERPLAY OF VOLUME AND SURFACE

Why We Grind Coffee

Why do we grind coffee beans, those of us who do? For we don't get any more coffee that way. One reason is that freshly ground coffee has a better aroma; a more important reason is that if we tried to make coffee from whole beans, we should have to wait forever, because the boiling water cannot get at the coffee. A coffee bean is like a curled-up hedgehog, with its vulnerable surfaces concealed as far as is possible. Uncurl the hedgehog, and you expose the whole of its vulnerable underside; grind a coffee bean, and you do the same, presenting as large an area possible to the boiling water.

In order to understand how it is that grinding the bean exposes a greater area of surface, let us think of it as a cube, and the grinding as a division of the cube into many smaller ones.

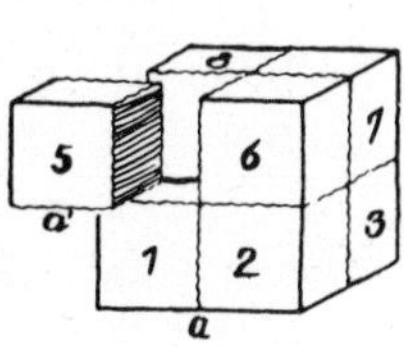

Suppose that a large cube is divided into eight smaller cubes by three cuts, as shown. The original cube, with side a, has volume a^3, so that if a is 2 in., the volume is 8 cu. in. If you wish to cover this cube with paper, you would need an area equal to the complete surface, consisting of six faces. The surface area is therefore $6a^2$, in this case 24 sq. in.

Now what about the volume and surface area of the eight small cubes? The volume is unchanged at 8 cu. in., but the total surface area is greater, since the eight small cubes are all separate, like No. 5 in the diagram on p. 219. When placed together to form the original cube, each smaller one contributes only three of its faces to form the surface area, but when the smaller cubes are separated, each one has three more faces laid bare—as much again! The total surface area of the eight separate cubes is therefore twice the surface area of the original cube, and is in this case 48 sq. in.

Suppose we now continue the process, dividing each of the eight small cubes into eight even smaller ones. The total volume of these 64 tiny cubes is the same as that of the original cube, but the total surface area has again been doubled, or, in relation to the original, quadrupled, and is now 96 sq. in.

Summing up, the original cube was first divided into eight smaller ones with edges half those of the original; then each of these was further subdivided into eight with edges a quarter of the original. The surface area has been quadrupled.

We can now tabulate as follows:

Decrease-factor in edge length (k)	1	1/2	1/4	1/8 . . . $1/n$
Surface area	A	$2A$	$4A$	$8A$ . . . nA
Number of cubes (N)	1	8	64	512 . . . n^3

With this table in mind, we can now generalize as follows: When a solid object is divided into n^3 identical parts, each having the same shape as the original, the total surface area of all these smaller parts increases to n times the surface area of the original, and the length of the edge of any one constituent part is diminished by the factor $k = 1/n$.

This holds good for any kind of shape, which is divided into similarly shaped constituent parts, a sphere for instance. A sphere of diameter 10 in. can be reshaped into eight smaller spheres, each of diameter 5 in.

If we could take a wooden cube with edge one foot, and cut it into tiny dice with edge .001 ft., or .012 in., the decrease factor k would be 1/1000. The total surface area of the tiny dice would be 1000 times that of the parent block, so that the new area A would be 6000 sq. ft. And how many tiny dice would there be? According to the rules set out above $N = n^3 = 1000^3$, i.e., 1000 million!

Putting this another way, if a cube of 1^3 ft. is divided into 1000 small cubes, by how much has the surface area been increased? The answer is tenfold; if $N = n^3$, then $n = \sqrt[3]{N} = \sqrt[3]{1000} = 10$. Now let us make a general statement. If a solid body with surface area A is divided into N similar constituent parts with total surface area S, the proportional increase in surface area S/A is the cube-root of N.

This enlargement of surface area by subdivision of volume plays an important part in natural processes and in technology.

FUEL VAPORIZATION. Nearly everyone has had the experience of lighting a gas jet. You only have to hold a lighted match and turn on the gas, which immediately ignites and burns with a steady flame; but if the gas is allowed to escape for some time before the match is applied, it mingles with the air and on being ignited probably explodes. A lump of coal in your home is a safe source of warmth and comfort, but the distribution in the air of fine particles of coal dust in a mine shaft constitutes a potentially very dangerous source of explosion, which is rightly feared.

In a car engine liquid gasoline is divided by the carburetor into a fine mist or spray, which is mixed with air. The diameter of a single droplet of this mist is about one ten-millionth of an inch (10^{-7} in.). Thus the surface area of a drop of gasoline with volume .06 cu. in. is increased to 4.85 million times the original value (the ratio is that of .738 sq. in. to 25,000 sq. ft.!) This vaporization exposes to the oxygen of the air an immense, vulnerable surface area, and the mixture becomes highly explosive.

Let us consider an unvaporized drop of gasoline as being a sphere of volume .06 cu. in., and having therefore diameter $d = .485$ in. and surface area .738 sq. in. (These figures are calculated from the formulas for volume and surface of a sphere which are respectively $\pi d^3/6$ and πd^2. After vaporization the diameter of a droplet is 10^{-7} in., or .0000001 in.; the decrease factor in dimensions, i.e., the ratio of the diameters, is 1/4,850,000. Hence the surface area is increased by the factor 4,850,000, and becomes $.738 \times 4.85 \times 10^6 = 3.58 \times 10^6$ sq. in., or about 25,000 sq. ft.

The whole purpose of crushing, milling, grinding, or any other form of subdividing is to increase the surface area of substances and thereby assist the processes to which they are subjected. We grind coffee to help the boiling water extract the flavor from it. We break up a lump of sugar in a cup of tea to make the grains smaller, and so expose a larger surface area to speed up the process of solution. For the same reason nature divides many substances into very small particles, for instance, the blood in our own cells.

THE BLOOD CORPUSCLES. Every adult body contains about 10 pints of blood, holding 25 million million red corpuscles and 34 billions of white. The red corpuscles, which we will consider, are tiny drum-shaped objects with diameter about 3/10,000 in. and height 8/100,000 in., with slightly concave ends. Their function is to pick up a coating of oxygen in the lungs (their surface area is therefore important) and convey it to all parts of the body, where it is transferred to the tissues which need it, taking up carbonic acid in return. They then return to the lungs, deposit the acid, and take up more oxygen. In order to carry as much oxygen as possible, a very large number indeed of these willing helpers is needed.

Suppose Mother Nature kept a stock of spherical containers, each holding 143 cu. in. of blood corpuscles, which is enough for one person. Each ball of corpuscles would have a diameter of about 6.5 in., and a surface area of 129 sq. in. (about the same as that of the seat of a chair). This area is much too small to act as a carrying area for the oxygen needed in the body, so nature splits the ball up into 25 million million corpuscles. If these were also spherical their total surface area would increase, according to the principles explained above, by a factor of approximately 30,000, to something like 26,400 sq. ft., which is much larger than the average tennis court! But in fact, the corpuscles are drum-shaped, and each one has a surface area a third as large again as a sphere with equal volume. Hence the total surface area of the corpuscles is still greater, actually 35,000 sq. ft., slightly larger than the area of a square with sides 185 ft. long.

For those who like doing sums:

(*a*) A drum-shaped blood corpuscle with radius 15/100,000 in. and height 8/100,000 has a volume calculated by the formula $\pi r^2 h$, which gives in this case $\pi \times 1800 \times 10^{-15} \approx 5.7 \times 10^{-12}$ cu. in. (we ignore the slight concavity of the ends).

(*b*) The spherical "parent group" of corpuscles has a volume given by $25 \times 10^{12} \times 5.7 \times 10^{-12} = 143$ cu. in. (The total number of corpuscles is taken as 25×10^{12}.) A sphere of volume 143 cu. in. has a radius of 3.25 in. From this the surface area can be calculated by the formula $4\pi r^2$, and is $4 \times 3.14 \times 3.25^2 = 129$ sq. in., which is roughly equivalent to a square with 11-in. sides.

(*c*) The increase factor for surface area, as has been explained, is the cube root of 25×10^{12}, which is 29,240.

When the sphere of corpuscles is split up into its constituent parts, the surface area is enlarged from 129 sq. in. to $129 \times 29{,}240$ sq. in. $\approx$ 3,772,000 sq. in., or 26,400 sq. ft. ($\approx 162 \times 162$ ft.). It is assumed here that the corpuscles are spherical, which is of course not the case. The surface area of a corpuscle is given by the formula $2\pi r(r + h)$, and is $2 \times 10^{-7} = .0000002$ sq. in. The corpuscles together have a surface area given by $25 \times 10^{12} \times 2 \times 10^{-7} = 50 \times 10^{5} = 5{,}000{,}000$ sq. in. $\approx$ 35,000 sq. ft. Compare this with the 26,400 sq. ft., had the corpuscles been spheres. The figure is $1\frac{1}{3}$ times as large. If we transform a sphere into a drum or cylinder with the shape of a blood corpuscle, then the drum will have a surface area 1.33 times that of the original sphere. A sphere has the smallest surface of all bodies with the same volume.

HOLLOW BODIES. So far we have considered only solid objects, but will now turn to hollow ones, such as footballs or rooms, which consist of a shell enclosing an empty space. Suppose the wall surface of the local art gallery is insufficient to accommodate a special display of paintings. Extra partition walls would solve the problem, for they would increase the available wall area. But in what ratio would the area be increased? Consider again the cube on p. 219, and think of it as hollow. Instead of the three cuts, think of them as partitions of negligible thickness. The original cube is now divided into eight smaller ones, and it can be seen that the total internal surface area is twice that of the original cube. Three square, double-sided partitions have been added to the original six squares of the surface area. It can thus be seen that the same principle holds for hollow bodies as for solid ones, provided that the thickness of the partitions is ignored, for otherwise they would occupy a proportion of the original internal volume.

There are many examples in nature of the enlargement of the surface area of hollow objects. A mushroom is the visible, spore-producing part of a stringy, fungoid growth which is hidden in the soil. Since only a few of the spores succeed in creating new growth, the mushroom must produce an immense number of them. A hollow canopy would have far too small an area to cultivate sufficient spores, so it is divided into a large number of vertical platelike structures. Some varieties have an arrangement of tubular structures beneath the canopy. In this way the restricted space under the canopy is utilized to the full.

Our lungs use a similar device. It is their function to supply fresh oxygen to, and absorb carbonic acid from, the blood, and in order to provide a large enough area for the exchange (in humans from 1000 to 1500 sq. ft.), the lung is not just a plain sack, fed by a windpipe and with flat internal surfaces with an area between 10 and 20 sq. ft.; it has a dense, spongy texture, containing about 300 million tiny, bubble-like cavities, to provide the requisite area. The olfactory (or smelling) zone inside a dog's nose has a wrinkled mucus membrane, which provides a greatly increased surface area. In the case of a medium-size dog the area available is about 10 sq. in., which is fifteen times as large as the similar membrane in the human nose!

Compact and Diffuse Bodies

COMPACT AND DIFFUSE. There are fat people and thin—"tubs and beanpoles." The former roll genially through life, while the others stalk nervously through it on ungainly spindle-shanks. You can see examples of these extremes everywhere, and once your attention has been drawn to degrees of corpulence and leanness, you will constantly notice the contrasts between the two opposites. In the animal world, for instance, we have the massive yet compact elephant, and the spindly giraffe, all legs and neck; the round hedgehog and the slender weasel; the compact cockroach and the spidery daddy longlegs.

In architecture there is the broad, solidly based Norman

church, with heavy, square-set towers, small windows, and thick walls; in contrast there is the slender perpendicular (Gothic) style, with soaring pinnacles, spires of delicate stone tracery, and slim walls pierced by immense windows and tall archways.

As examples from civil engineering, there are bulky, weighty stone bridges, set heavily on piles across a river, contrasted with the airy, sweeping arcs of graceful suspension bridges.

In everyday life the waitress in a restaurant may place on your table dumpy rolls or slender sticks of bread. A beech tree, soaring slender and majestic in the forest, is cut down and sawn into bulky logs.

There is no doubt that we distinguish in our minds between the bulky, concentrated massiveness of some objects and the slender extensiveness of others. Can this perception of degrees of compactness be rationalized, and expressed in terms of the dimensions of a body, by some sort of mathematical expression?

If we put on our mathematical spectacles we soon realize that what decides whether a body appears fat or thin is the ratio C of its volume V to its surface area A. Thus we will define $C = V/A$ as the degree of compactness.

Suppose that two men, one short and fat and the other tall and thin, have the same weight and therefore approximately the same volume. Of these two, the tall thin man obviously has more skin to cover a greater surface area than that of his portly companion. Thus we can say that he is less compact than the fat man. To give another example, a telescopic camera tripod has, when closed, a greater degree of compactness than when it is fully open.

DEGREE OF COMPACTNESS. Let us consider three bodies of equal volume, 1000 cu. in.: they are a long stick, measuring 1000 in. by 2 in. by $\frac{1}{2}$ in.; a cube with edge 10 in.; and a ball with diameter 12.4 in. These all have different degrees of compactness, for their surface areas are respectively 5002, 600, and 483 in square inches.

Here are the details of the calculations. The surface area A of the stick is: $2\,(1000 \times 2 + 1000 \times \frac{1}{2} + 2 \times \frac{1}{2}) = 5002$; that of the cube is $6 \times 10^2 = 600$; that of the ball is $3.14 \times 12.4^2 = 483$.

Note how much these areas vary, a fact which may well surprise most people, for many seem to think that bodies of equal volume must also have equal surface areas. From these figures we can compile the following table:

Description	*Surface area A in sq. in. compared with* (3)		*Degree of compactness in in.^{3}/in.^{2} compared with* (1)	
(1) Stick	5002	10.4	.2	1
(2) Cube	600	1.24	1.7	8.5
(3) Ball	483	1	2.1	10.4

It can be seen that the cube is nearly nine times, and the ball more than ten times as compact as the stick (column 5). The ball is 1.2 times as compact as the cube ($2.1 : 1.7 = 1.2$).

DIAGRAMMATIC REPRESENTATION OF COMPACTNESS. Let us think of the surface areas of these three objects as spread out flat, the result of being rolled out just like pastry, so that the whole volume of each object is a uniform sheet. The quantity of "pastry" is the same in each case, viz. 1000 cu. in., but the areas when rolled out are different. That of the cube is 1.24 times as large as that of the ball; the stick's area is 10.4 times that of the ball (cf. third column of table, and diagram *a*). The thickness of the pastry must therefore vary in each case. That from the ball will be thickest at about 2.1 in.; next from the cube, about 1.7 in., and finally from the stick, as thin as .2 in. (cf. fourth column of table, and diagram *b*).

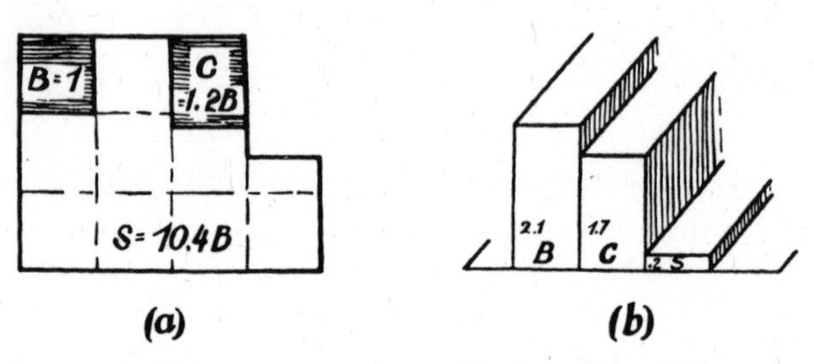

(a) (b)

To sum up, the compactness of three-dimensional objects varies according to their shape. The most compact of all is the sphere, for there is no body that, for the same volume, has a smaller surface area. Contrariwise, there is no body which, for the same surface area, encloses more volume.

DEGREE OF COMPACTNESS AND SIZE. We now come to an important point. As has been seen, for bodies of equal volume, compactness depends upon shape. If, however, we increase or decrease the volume of an object, keeping its shape the same, the degree of compactness will alter, becoming greater with increased size, and vice versa!

A cube, with volume 1000 cu. in. and surface area 600 sq. in., with edge 10 in., has a degree of compactness measured by $1000/600 = 1.7$ in.^{3}/in.^{2} Now suppose that its edge grows to 100 in. Its volume in cu. in. is 1,000,000 and its surface area 60,000 sq. in. Its compactness is now $1{,}000{,}000/60{,}000 = 17$, which is ten times what it was before. Similarly, were we to investigate what happens when its edge is reduced to 1 in., we should find that the compactness would now be .17.

Thus, strangely enough, bodies of different shape can have the same degree of compactness. In our first example, the ball of volume 1000 cu. in. had a value of 2 for compactness; for the cube with the same volume it was 1.7. If the cube were enlarged so that its edge were 12 in. instead of 10, it would then have the same degree of compactness as the ball, for its volume is now 1728 cu. in. and its surface area 864 sq. in., from which the compactness is $1728/864 = 2$.

It is easily established in the case of a cube that the degree of compactness varies with the dimension. Let a represent length of the edge, then the volume V is a^3 and the surface area A is $6a^2$. Thus the compactness V/A is $a^3/6a^2 = a/6$, and thus increases or decreases with a. For a sphere of radius r, a similar calculation would give a result of approximately $r/3$.

The fact that compactness decreases with reduction in size has been put to good use by nature. Dandelion seeds are attached to small, feathery parachutes, so that the wind will blow them far and wide. Without their parachutes the seeds would fall directly to the ground, as they are too small and have too little surface area for the wind to carry them. There are also certain types of plants which are fertilized not by pollen-bearing insects but by wind-blown pollen that does not have a parachute attached to every particle. Such pollen is made on the principle of maximum volume in smallest shape, i.e., maximum compactness. However, the particles are so tiny that their degree of compactness is very small (the radius of a pollen sphere is approximately 1/10,000 in.). Nevertheless, the surface area per cu. in. is immense, and so the wind seizes on the tiny particles just as vigorously as it does with the dandelion parachutes. Other instances are the ability of tiny specks of dust to dance in midair (see them in a sunlit room), and the drops of moisture carried along in a cloud until they grow too big and fall to the earth as rain.

Bridges and Penguins

COMPACTNESS IN THE TECHNICAL WORLD. An old stone bridge looms, weighty and massive, above the river. Comparing it with the delicate, curving steel cables of a modern suspension bridge—the one, for instance, which spans the Golden Gate in

San Francisco—the latter seems almost frightening in its loftiness and lack of massiveness. Here are some of its measurements: it is 2 mi. long and 220 ft. above the water; the piers which carry cables 3 ft. thick are 746 ft. high; the central span between these piers is 4200 ft. in length.

If the ratios of volume to surface area for each of these bridges were compared, then the stone bridge would give a greater figure

than the suspension bridge. If they had both to be painted and both were of equal volume, the suspension bridge would need much more paint than the other, for the total area of cables, piers, etc. would be greater than the surfaces of the squat stone pillars of the other.

A well-known bridge in Germany, the Müngsten railway bridge, crosses the valley of the River Wupper (the Wuppertal). With a height of 340 ft. it is the highest bridge in the country. It is made of about 6700 tons of steel, presenting a surface area for painting of 810,000 sq. ft. This quantity of steel has a volume of 27,200 cu. ft., equivalent to a solid cube of steel with edge 30 ft. The degree of compactness of the bridge is 27,200/810,000 = .034 cu. ft./sq. ft. This is 150 times less compact than the cube, for which the degree of compactness is 5 cu. ft./sq. ft. (= 30/6 $ft.^3/ft.^2$).

In our times we build sometimes with greater massiveness, sometimes with less, than did previous generations. An old locomotive used to stretch its smokestack high in the air, and carried a crude open platform on which the driver and fireman stood. A modern locomotive is a veritable colossus, with hardly any protruding parts. The modern principle is to cram as much mass as possible inside the smallest surface area. This aim is pursued in many spheres of design: the streamlining of cars, such machines as typewriters, houses in stark contrast to earlier designs. On the other hand the load-bearing frame work of a modern bridge is made as lightly as safety considerations will permit, with an outstanding lack of massiveness. There could hardly be any structure lighter and more spindly than the steel framework of a modern block of apartments or offices. In such instances there is an undoubted move toward less compactness in loaded frameworks.

What is the reason for this? There are two: the desire for economy in materials, and the consequent need for new structural arrangements, in order to preserve essential stability.

THE SAGGING BRIDGE. Here is an example to show the applications of these two techniques. A bridge is to carry a footpath from pier A to pier B over the gap C. For convenience in calculating, let C measure $1 \times 1 \times 1$ yd., with volume therefore 1 cu. yd.

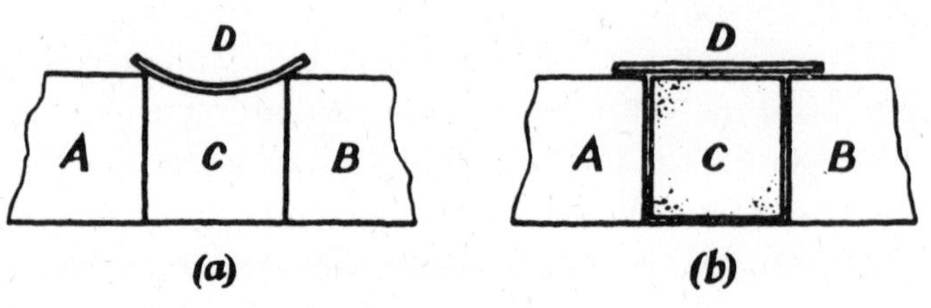

Across the gap is placed a plank D (diagram a), which is, however, so thin that it sags dangerously under our weight. What can be done to support it?

One method would be to fill in the gap with concrete (diagram b). The volume needed would be 1 yd.^{3}, with surface area 6×1 yd.^{2}, and compactness $1/6 = .17$. But this would be an obvious waste of materials: such a massive support is not necessary.

A second possibility would be (diagram c) to erect a pillar R with half the volume of the gap, $V' = .5$ yd.^{3} It thus leaves two smaller gaps, each .25 yd. on each side. This would need only half

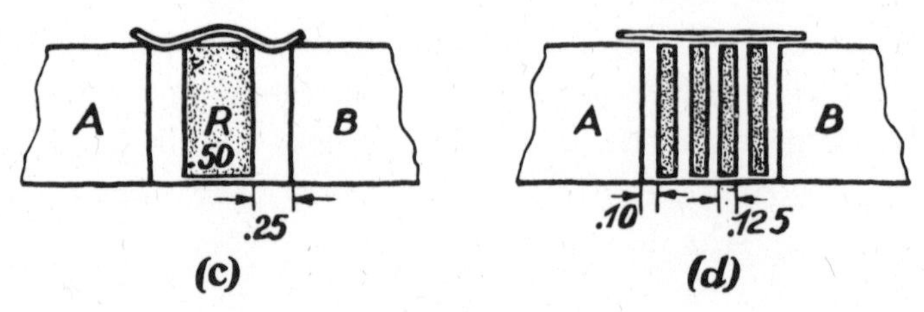

the former amount of concrete (economy of materials!), and with a surface area $A' = 2(1 \times 1) + 4(1 \times .5) = 4$ yd.^{2}, its compactness $C' = V'/A' = .5/4 = .125$, which is less than before. But suppose that the plank still bends dangerously under our weight, as we cross the gaps. We must think again.

The third and best method is to "replace" the single pillar with four narrower pillars, each 1/8 yd. in width, placed at equal distances across the gap of 1 yd., as shown in diagram *d.* Each pillar is now .125 yd. wide; the gaps, .1 yd. What is the degree of compactness now? The total volume of the four pillars is $V'' = .5$ yd.^{3}—the same as that of the single pillar of diagram *c*; the total surface area is greater, as $A'' = 4\,(2 + 1/8) =$ 10 yd.^{2} Hence the compactness $C'' = V''/A'' = .5/10 = .05$, which is much less than the previous figure (.125).

It can be assumed that the gaps of .1 yd. between the pillars are now narrow enough for the plank to span them and bear our weight without bending.

To sum up, the compactness, V/A, of the bridge supports was reduced, first by the reduction in volume which was desirable in the interests of economy of material, and then by increasing the surface area by a redistribution of the supports, in order to overcome completely the plank's tendency to bend. From an original value of .17. the compactness has been successively decreased to .125 and then to .05 (yd.^{3}/yd.^{2}), $\frac{1}{3}$ of the original value.

This example is a help in appreciating how it is that new building materials, such as prestressed concrete, are in increasing demand these days. Such materials lend themselves far more easily than stone to modern techniques, which exact maximum strength from an economical use of materials.

COMPACTNESS IN NATURE. In winter we heat our rooms, and wear overcoats out of doors, but trees, which are also living organisms, do not need such aids to comfort. If the temperature around them sinks to 14° F., their "body temperature" also sinks to the same level, while in spring a rise in air temperature to 50° F. results in a similar rise in the case of the trees. For they possess the ability to endure a variable body temperature.

Humans (and other mammals and birds) are not like this: if a man's temperature rises above or falls below normal, he feels "out of sorts," for human beings must have a constant body temperature, and to maintain this we must produce heat within our bodies to replace what is radiated to the surrounding air. In wintertime we take steps to minimize this loss, by keeping our windows closed, excluding drafts, insulating walls, and so on. The production of heat depends on the size of the "stove," i.e., upon the volume of the body, whereas the heat which it radiates, depends upon the surface area (cf. pp. 18–19). Surprisingly enough, then, we ourselves are subject to the same relationship between volume and surface area which has been discussed throughout the last few pages.

If the body temperature is to remain constant, the heat produced in the body must equal that which is radiated. Let e represent the heat produced per cu. in. then eV represents the heat produced in a body of volume V; further, let a represent the heat given off per sq. in. of body surface, so that aA represents the total heat lost from a body with surface area A. As heat production is to equal heat loss, $eV = aA$.

A HARE IN SUMMER IS STILL THE SAME HARE IN WINTER. In winter its heat loss is greater than in summer, because its surroundings are colder. But nature has several ways of helping it to make good this increased loss of warmth.

(*a*) The hare grows a thicker winter coat of fur, which insulates the body more efficiently and helps it to retain heat. We humans insulate ourselves in a similar way by wearing scarves, overcoats, winter underwear, etc.

(*b*) The radiating surface area is decreased when the hare curls up in sleep (cf. p. 227 and p. 219: hedgehog). We also do this when getting into a cold bed, but birds are perhaps the most outstanding exponents of the art: their heads disappear beneath one wing, legs are pulled up close against bodies, and they crouch close together on branch or perch.

(*c*) Nature "stokes the boiler," i.e., makes the body greater in volume, so that more heat is produced. This may not occur often in human beings (though some people do put on a pound or two in wintertime); it is, however, strikingly evident in polar regions, where nature must resort to drastic means to protect creatures against death by freezing. Methods (*b*) and (*c*) are here combined: the animals' surface area is decreased and volume increased as much as possible. The compactness, therefore, is made as great as possible—the exact opposite of what is done in modern building construction (cf. p. 230).

The polar hare and polar fox are not only more rounded and less rangy in appearance than their fellows in less extreme climates: they are also bigger, more bulky. There are no snakes in snowbound arctic wastes; no birds with elongated necks and spindly legs like the ostrich, but instead his tubby cousin the penguin. When we look at penguins or sea lions or whales, we have an immediate impression of smooth, well-filled, compact bulk, i.e., of maximum heat-producing volume contained beneath minimum heat-losing surface. A tiny humming bird would freeze piteously to death in the arctic, simply because it is so small: its heat-producing volume is too restricted, and its surface area too large (cf. p. 19). A similar fate would overtake the butterfly with its great fluttering wings, or the spindly daddy longlegs, but the compact and relatively bulky bedbug would continue its loathsome existence.

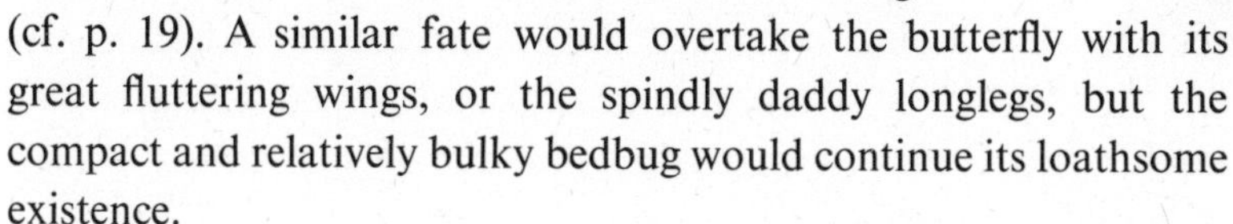

This ratio of volume to surface area also plays a decisive part on washing day, and in every case where moisture and evaporation occur. When Mrs. Smith pegs out her washing on the line, she well knows that the more surface she exposes to the breeze, the more quickly will the clothes dry. Since compactness decreases with size, i.e., the surface area from which moisture can be evaporated increases at the expense of the volume, minute creatures can live only in a moisture-laden environment. Tiny bacilli, which thrive in the cells of living creatures, are an example of this, and if such hospitality were not available to them, they would die. Many types of seed, on the other hand, can remain alive, even though they have lost most of their moisture.

We have now completed our brief survey of the strange balance between volume and surface area. Every body has both of these attributes, but it is the relationship between them, as we now appreciate, which is used to such valuable effect both in natural processes and in modern technology.

THE PRIMEVAL WORLD OF GEOMETRY

RELATIONSHIP BETWEEN SHAPES. An inflated basketball bladder or a beach ball can be pressed with ease into a wide variety of shapes, egg, pumpkin, sausage—yes, even a cube, if you apply simultaneous equal pressure from six directions. But could it be made into a shape like the inner tube of a tire, which is called a torus (see diagrams on p. 238)? Once you have managed to manipulate the ball into a long cylindrical sausage, closed at both ends, you would then have to slit open the ends, bend the cylinder into a ring, and stick the ends together with adhesive. But this would be a really impossible job, because the slitting would release the air inside, and the whole thing would collapse.

Why is it that the ball cannot be reshaped into a torus? They both have much the same qualities, i.e., one single surface, rounded in all directions, but there must be some essential difference in the spatial arrangement, or "connectivity," of their particles.

CONNECTIVITY. We shall use this word to refer to the essential character of a given surface, which remains unaltered even though the shape changes, and which can be altered only by tearing the surface. With this in mind, we can plunge into the dark, primeval world of geometry, for the connectivity of a surface has nothing to do with a single, static shape or with fixed measurements. Shapes and surfaces which now claim our attention are flexible, and, by a constant metamorphosis, can assume, as jellyfish do, a whole range of forms. But we shall not consider any process of changing shape which involves tearing the surfaces and remodeling.

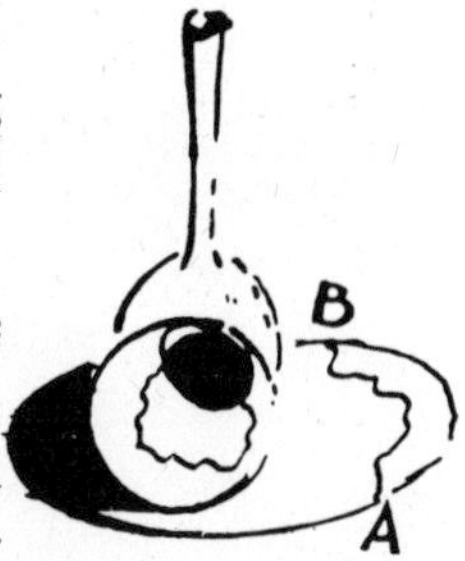

A further example may help you to see what we have in mind. If a basketball bladder is deflated, it can be laid flat on a table, and arranged in a circle, composed of a lower sheet of rubber covered over at every point by a second sheet. Since, in the magic primeval world of geometry, strange metamorphoses are possible, we will point out that a wine bottle or decanter could be similarly collapsed and laid flat. All these things share one basic quality: the same connectivity, and, in the primeval world of geometry at least, each can be transformed into the same shape as the others.

A pumped-up basketball, however, is different, and it has not the same connectivity as that of its deflated bladder or of a decanter; also it is different again from a torus. Its connectivity is the same as that of an egg, a pumpkin, or a cube.

THE GENUS OF A SURFACE. Despite our assumption of complete flexibility of substance, we cannot change a given shape into any other, but only into one which has the same "blood group," i.e., connectivity.

How can we find out that type of connectivity a surface has? Like children who take a toy apart to find out how it works, we must destroy the surface by cutting it up in order to discover its connectivity. We count the number of types of "harmless" closed cuts, which start and finish at the same point but do not cut the surface into two pieces. The maximum number r of such cuts fixes the type of connectivity and is termed the "genus" of the surface.

The smallest number of closed cuts required to separate the surface into two pieces is one more than the number of harmless closed cuts ($k = r + 1$) and is called the connectivity k of the surface. Let us now consider the surfaces already mentioned in terms of these new concepts.

Surfaces without edges, e.g., sphere and torus: Any closed cut on a sphere will divide its surface into two parts, and therefore no such cut can be reckoned as harmless. The genus is zero, and it is termed "simply connected"; its connectivity is 1. The torus allows two harmless cuts, one round its circular section, and a second one that splits open the entire ring (diagrams *a* and *b*). A third closed cut of any kind whatever would thus divide the torus into two separate pieces. Its genus r is therefore 2, and its connectivity k is 3.

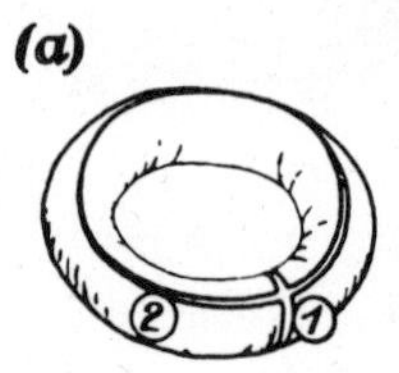

It must be assumed that the cuts are made simultaneously, because otherwise any cuts after the first would be made on a different type of surface. In the above example, for instance, the first cut would change the torus into a surface with edges, a long, hollow tube, which a second closed cut would divide into two parts, thus giving the torus a completely false genus of 1.

Surfaces with edges: Let us consider (*a*) a flat disk of negligible thickness, and a sphere with a circular hole cut in its surface, both with one curved edge; (*b*) a flat disk with a circular hole at its center (think of a thin washer): this has two curved edges.

With all three of these the first cut made is not of the same type as those considered so far, which began and finished at the same point. Here the cut begins at *A* on one edge and ends on the other edge, in the case of the washer, or at a different point *B* on the same edge in the other cases. The diagrams here illustrate this, Case *a* showing the cut through the disk with one curved edge, and, Case *b*, through the disk with two edges. This type of cut is termed a cross cut (*q*), and can be regarded as following an unbroken line from start to finish, just as do those of the closed type, if we included the edge, or edges, or parts thereof with the cut itself. The arrows on the diagrams make this clear. In *a* we start at *A*, cut across to *B*, and return to *A* round the edge of the disk. In *b* we start at *A*, continue right round the inner edge and then across to *B*, from *B* right round the outer edge, and then back to *A*.

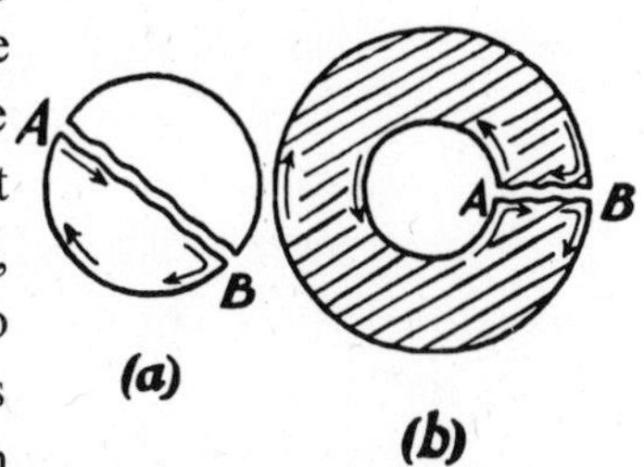

(*a*) (*b*)

A second cut, beginning and ending at an edge of the cross cut, would be itself a cross cut; this moreover applies to all kinds of surfaces with edges. It is therefore not possible with such surfaces to make a harmless closed cut of any kind.

It is clear then that such a thing as a harmless closed cut, starting and finishing at the same point, as was possible with the torus, is impossible with edged surfaces.

With these facts in mind, let us return to the task of determining the essential relationship between different shapes. With a disk a single harmless cross cut is impossible ($r = 0$); with a ring or washer one such is possible ($r = 1$); for a sphere with a hole in it, again none is possible ($r = 0$). Their respective orders of connectivity are 1, 2, 1; thus a circle has the same connectivity as a holed sphere, and also, by the way, as a completely closed sphere: all three are of the same genus zero.

As mentioned earlier, the shape of the holed sphere can be changed into a circle, but this is impossible with a closed sphere. Since all three shapes have the same genus, there must be some other factor which limits this change of shape. The rule can be expressed thus: change from one shape to another is possible only if both have the same genus (r), together with the same number of edges (e). Thus a holed sphere and a bottle can both be reshaped as circles, because all three have zero genus and one curved edge. The closed sphere is different, because, although its genus is zero, it has no edge. Thus the essential fundamental characteristics of a surface are the number of its edges and the number of harmless cuts possible (from the latter are derived both genus and order of connectivity). But there is yet another quality, not yet mentioned, and that is, for want of a better word, the number of "sides": there are one-sided and two-sided surfaces (cf. the twisted belt, p. 75). Change of shape is possible only between two surfaces if both have the same number of sides.

The truth emerges—stranger indeed than fiction—that the qualities listed above (number of edges e, genus r and order k of connectivity, and number of sides s) all remain invariant with change of shape, always provided that the surface is not torn in the process. Thus, a ball ($r = 0$, $e = 0$, $s = 2$) will never make a bottle (0, 1, 2), nor yet a torus (2, 0, 2); a twisted belt (0, 2, 1) will never become untwisted (0, 2, 2).

Thus you may see, even in the darkness of the primeval world of geometry where shapes and dimensions cease to have a constant meaning, that just when you begin to despair of discriminating between them, the analyzing intellect steps in, creating order amid the confused welter of shapes, discovering clear mathematical relationships among them, though none seemed previously to exist.

These hidden qualities do, however, have considerable application in our own familiar, everyday world. Do you know:

The story about the neighboring provinces? A king had five sons, and he said to them, "If you wish to divide my kingdom between you after my death, you must take an oath that you will divide it only in the following way. Each province must adjoin each of the other four, along a proper frontier, and not merely at one point. This will insure that each of you will be able to visit any of his brothers by his own private road, which will not pass through any land belonging to a third; nor will any of these roads cross over another road belonging to any other brother. If you cannot agree to this, then my kingdom must remain undivided."

The sons took their oath to obey, but when the old king died the land remained undivided, for nobody could find a way of fulfilling his conditions. It could be done with four (see diagram *a*), but not with five parts. As soon as a division into five provinces was planned, there would be one brother with land not bordering on one of the others, and so having to cross another's territory or private road to visit him. Maps, plans, all failed to offer a solution, and all the wise men of the court had to confess themselves beaten. So the brothers sent couriers throughout the land looking for someone who might be wiser even than the wisest.

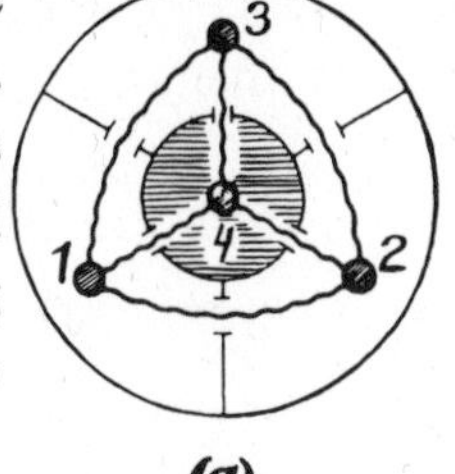

(a)

At last they found a man who claimed to have a solution, but his answer baffled them. "It can be done," he said, "but not on this earth!" To prove his point, he took a linen cloth, sketched out the five provinces (diagram *b*), and then rolled up the cloth into a tube, with states 2 and 4

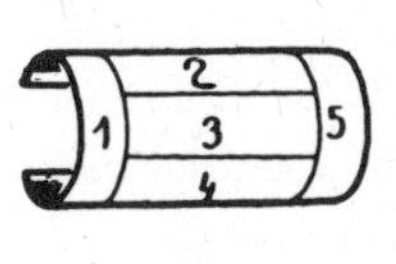

(b)

together: finally he brought the ends of the tube together (diagram *c*), thus uniting provinces 1 and 5. "There!" he said, "just what your father wished. Even had you been seven in number, it would have been possible in such a world as I have made here, and saying this, he took a second cloth, and sketched a division into seven provinces in much the same way (diagram *d*). The brothers pondered long, and then asked the wise man how it was that such a thing was possible the way he had shown, but impossible in our world. "Why, indeed!" he replied, "Just because you see our world as round, and this rolled cloth as round, that does not mean that they are the same: like human beings they are quite different in their hidden characters."

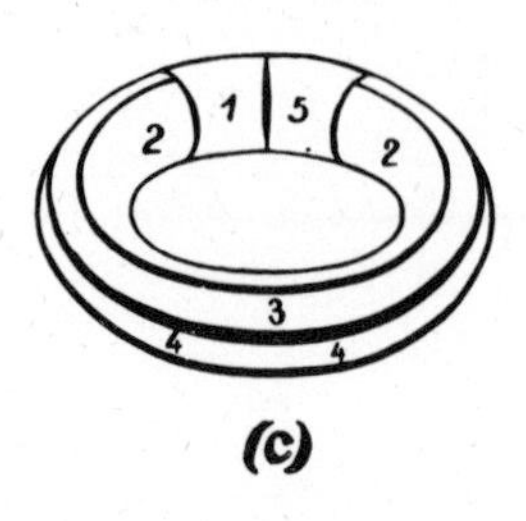

(c)

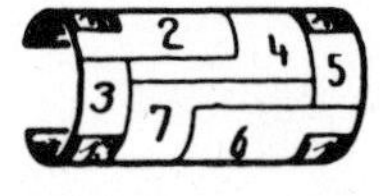

(d)

The brothers did not understand this last remark, but now they understood what their father's wish had been, and left the kingdom undivided.

You can see why only four adjacent provinces with direct access one to another are possible by looking again at diagram *a* on p. 241. Points 1, 2, 3 form a triangle, and Point 4 lies inside it. If now you take a Point 5 anywhere outside the triangle, any path between 4 and 5 crosses any path between two other points. If you fix the Point 5 inside the triangle, e.g., in the smaller triangle, 1, 2, 4, then Point 3 becomes an outside point, and any path between 5 and 3 must cross over paths between other points. This problem of not crossing other paths is basically the same as that of avoiding crossing other territories.

The world of geometry is explored by what is called topology, or geometry of position, for in it there is no dependence on measurements and shapes, but only on the relative positions of points, lines, and surfaces. The same idea was encountered in the matter of the squashed hat on p. 216.

THE FOURTH DIMENSION

The spirit world, which is supposed to manifest itself through table rappings and other supernatural phenomena, is often—and most unscientifically—referred to as being "in the fourth dimension." How do we come by this expression? It certainly has a mathematical sound, since four is a number, and dimension imples measurement.

We shall consider the volume of a room as measured in cubic yards, i.e., in cubes, all with edges one yard in length. We can imagine the room packed solid with these, like a child's blocks packed in a box. The room has three dimensions, its length x, breadth y, and height z. From these three dimensions the volume of the room can be calculated. Let us call this quality of volume "three-dimensional." We can think of each unit cube as a constituent unit cell of volume, marked Z-3. Two measurements (x, y) establish a plane figure, which has area but no volume; we shall describe this as two-dimensional, and the square marked Z-2 shows a constituent unit cell of area. Carrying this train of thought still further, one measurement x determines "one-dimensional" quality, and the line marked Z-1 represents a constituent unit. A point would therefore be of zero dimensions.

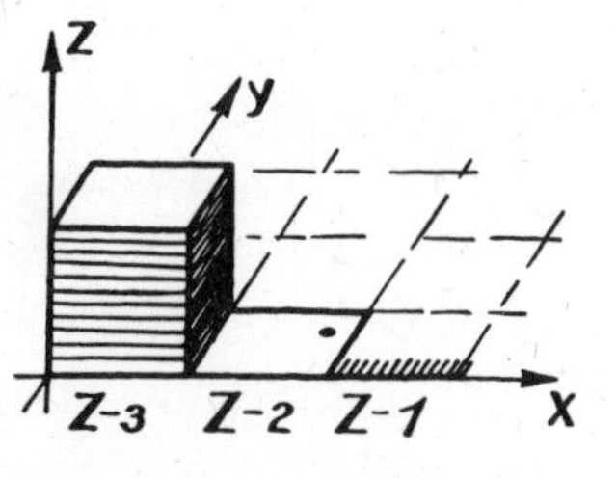

In a similar way we can rise above three-dimensional space to a higher order. Four measurements, x, y, z, w, would establish a four-dimensional space, with constituent unit cell Z-4; five measurements establish a five-dimensional space, and so on.

Viewed in this way, these spaces of a higher dimensional order seem nothing more than an ingenious and imaginative extension of our more familiar mathematical concepts of spatial arrangement, and this is indeed what they are.

It is true that we cannot actually visualize these higher orders, for our physical perception of spatial arrangement is limited to three dimensions, but we can nevertheless comprehend them. For example, we can consider how a four-dimensional unit cell *Z*-4 could be created. If the unit square *Z*-2 is bounded by four straight lines, the unit cube *Z*-3 by 6 *Z*-2 units, then the unit *Z*-4 will be bounded by 8 unit cubes. We cannot of course visualize this arrangement, but we can think about it. There has even been produced a two-dimensional sketch as an aid to comprehension. In it we see a small cube, hanging by eight threads between its own corners and the corresponding corners of a much larger cube enclosing it. If we think of each of the six "thread pyramids" (e.g., 1265/1′2′6′5′) thus formed as a perspective drawing of a cube, then we have in our minds an arrangement of eight cubes, with a total of sixteen corners, directly adjoining one another, with no spaces in between. This fulfills the idea of a four-dimensional unit cell, bounded by eight three-dimensional cubes, in the same way as a three-dimensional unit cell is bounded by six two-dimensional squares. This is not to say, however, that the four-dimensional figure would look like this; the sketch is nothing more than an aid to help us follow up the geometrical abstractions involved.

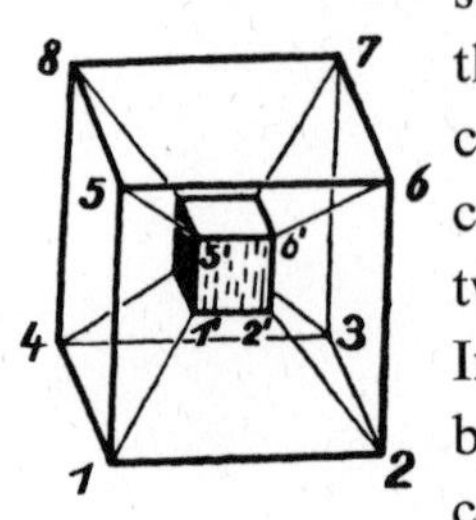

As far as algebra is concerned this movement into spaces of higher dimensions is much simpler, for here we are not hampered by our inability to visualize. A triplet of numbers (e.g., 4, 3, 5) means a particular point in a three-dimensional frame of reference; a quadruplet of numbers would therefore specify a point referred to a four-dimensional frame. If, in a two-dimensional diagram, the equation $x^2 + y^2 = r^2$ represents a circle, then in a three-dimensional frame of reference $x^2 + y^2 + z^2 = r^2$ represents a sphere, and in a four-dimensional frame of reference $x^2 + y^2 + z^2 + w^2 = r^2$ represents a "hyper-sphere." Indeed, there is nothing to prevent us from going on like this, to give the symbolic representation of the analogue of a sphere in 17-dimensional space, and to discuss its relationships with other geometrical concepts in that particular space.

THE SPIRIT WORLD. If all these multi-dimensional spaces are purely mathematical concepts, produced by the exercise of a fundamental practice in mathematics, generalization, how is it that the so-called fourth dimension has become associated with the realm of ghosts and spirits? Perhaps it is because a ghost is supposed to be capable of many things which are beyond the powers of mortal men: it can suddenly materialize in a sealed room, and just as quickly disappear; it can remove an article from a closed box without opening it, to name only two supernatural antics.

It is possible to conceive of these phenomena as being associated with a further dimension which we ourselves cannot visualize. We humans inhabit a three-dimensional world: let us now step down dimensionally and imagine another world of two dimensions only, of surfaces without depth, bounded by a single, flat space. Within this space exist two-dimensional creatures and objects which can move about in that plane only—a gold coin, for instance. In order to keep it safe, a square is placed round it, like a fence (see diagram on p. 243). This will prevent any two-dimensional creature from getting at it, unless a gap is made in the fence. There is no possibility of going over or under the fence, for this would mean moving out of the space in which all two-dimensional existence is confined. (This means, incidentally, that this two-dimensional world could have no bridges or tunnels, nor could its denizens even tie a shoelace!) But you and I, as inhabitants of a three-dimensional world, could steal upon the scene like ghosts, and lift out the coin without disturbing the square, for we approach through the third dimension—depth. All that the two-dimensional owner of the coin would see would be a hand suddenly appearing to grasp the coin, and in a flash it would be gone again!

This example suggests that a space of any dimensional order (say, n dimensions) is likely to be vulnerable to "invasion" from space of the next higher order, $(n + 1)$ dimensions. In this way a box or room in our three-dimensional world, which as far as we can see, is completely closed, even locked and sealed, might be entered from the fourth dimension without any seal or lock being broken. For this reason some spiritualists claim that the spirit world has four dimensions, and that the spirits of the departed can thus enter our world, and walk through walls, grope in sealed boxes, read books without opening them, and so on. It is even claimed by some that surgical operations can be performed upon the living without incision by those who exist "in the world beyond," utilizing attributes conferred by the fourth dimension, which we can neither see nor fully comprehend.

It is not the business of mathematics, however, to pursue such speculations concerning the spirit world; mathematically speaking, the fourth dimension is only one of the many possible extensions of our basic ideas about space and spatial relationships. A mathematician is no ghost-hunter: he is far too busy trying to explore and comprehend the strange configurations which may exist in spaces of higher dimensions.

Chapter 11

LIFE AND DEATH BY MATHEMATICAL ANALYSIS

To insure or not to insure? "If I die prematurely . . . ?" asks John Smith. "Then your dependents receive the sum of $3000," replies the insurance agent. "But the chances are that I might not even have paid in half of that sum, when I die. No company can pay out more money than it receives, if it wants to remain solvent!" The insurance man assures Smith that his company often pays out on this basis, and still manages to flourish. "But suppose all your clients were to die prematurely?" insists John Smith. "Then we should indeed go bankrupt: but they don't all do this." "But that is not to say that such a thing could never happen. Death depends entirely on the will of God: are you going to tell me that God is in the pay of your insurance company?"

John Smith, as you will have guessed, is thinking of taking out a life-insurance policy. He is just forty years of age, and the insurance agent has quoted to him a fixed monthly rate of payment (premium), payable over a twenty-year term. In return, at the age of sixty, he will receive $3000, but if he were to die before reaching sixty, his dependants will receive the same amount. It is this latter provision, which could turn out (financially) so advantageous to his family, that makes John Smith so suspicious. Surely nobody gives money away like that.

At last the insurance agent invites him to consult the local branch manager, and this worthy gentleman, with all the facts and figures at his disposal, explains how it is possible for the company to make offers of this kind.

We are going to listen in on this explanation, and the first thing that John Smith hears about is the statistical Mortality Table: this is the basis of all insurance contracts. The layman would regard it as a confusing mass of figures, but the more we study it, the more we are impressed, for its evidence reveals the working of an inexorable law, by which the very thread of our lives is controlled. It follows the lives of 100,000 people, recording, decade by decade and year by year, the numbers of those who survive, together with their respective ages, and the number of deaths. A specimen section of the table for the years 1924-1926 is shown on the next page. Column 1 gives the age x in years; column 2 the number $L(x)$ of survivors at age x; column 3 the number $D(x)$ of deceased persons whose deaths occurred at age x; column 4 shows the so-called probability of death, expressed as q per thousand. From the figures recorded we can see that, out of 100,000 babies in the first year of life, 11,538 died and therefore 88,462 lived on to reach one year of age. Out of these, 1432 died within the next year, leaving 87,030 to reach their second birthday. This shows a sharp decrease in mortality in the second year of life. Farther down the table we note that 71,006 people reached the age of fifty; almost 61,000 of these reached sixty, and at age sixty-six, with only 50,769 still living, half the original 100,000 had died. From this point onward the number of deaths increased more rapidly: 41,906 reached the age of 70, 16,066 reached 80; only 1559 reached 90, and only 20 people lived on to see their hundredth birthday. At the end of the hundredth year of life, all were dead. (The column showing figures for probability of death will be discussed on p. 254.)

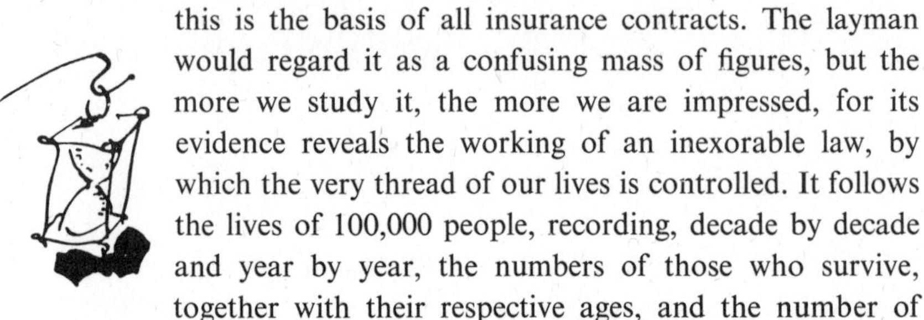

MORTALITY TABLE 1924-1926 (*simplified*)

Age x in years	*Number of living persons L (x) of age x*	*Number of deceased persons D (x) between ages x and x + 1*	*Probability of death, q per thousand*
0	100,000	11,538	115
1	88,462	1432	16
2	87,030	553	6
3	86,477	350	4
4	86,127	272	3
5	85,855	208	2
6	85,647	170	2
7	85,477	147	2
8	85,330	135	2
9	85,197	127	1
10	85,070	120	1
11	84,950	113	1
⋮	⋮	⋮	⋮
20	83,268	356	4
21	82,912	373	4
⋮	⋮	⋮	⋮
30	79,726	322	4
31	79,404	324	4
⋮	⋮	⋮	⋮
40	76,313	408	5
41	75,905	432	6
⋮	⋮	⋮	⋮
50	71,006	732	10
51	70,274	777	11
58	63,495	1263	20
59	62,232	1349	22
60	60,883	1439	24
61	59,444	1530	26
66	50,769	2064	41
⋮	⋮	⋮	⋮
70	41,906	2424	58
71	39,472	2524	64
75	28,998	2723	94
76	26,275	2686	102
⋮	⋮	⋮	⋮
80	16,066	2281	142
81	13,785	2121	154
84	7941	1570	198
⋮	⋮	⋮	⋮
90	1559	455	285
91	1144	343	300
⋮	⋮	⋮	⋮
99	35	15	421
100	20	20	1000

THE GRAPH OF MORTALITY. It will help us to visualize these rates of mortality varying from age to age if we draw a graph based on the figures given (see p. 251). On this the horizontal axis shows the age in years (x from 0 to 100); the vertical axis (at left) shows the number of survivors ($L\ [x]$ from 0 to 100,000, the scale being marked in thousands). The graph is plotted as follows:

We read from the table, for $x = 10$, the figure $L\ (10) = 85{,}070$. At the point $x = 10$ on the horizontal scale we measure a vertical line of length 85(000) and mark its upper end by a point. Similarly we mark points showing the numbers of survivors corresponding to the various values of x from 0 to 100. If the points are now joined with a smooth curve, we obtain the graph of mortality, $OCDC'$ 100, which curves in strange fashion right across the rectangle bordered by the two axes.

After dropping away steeply in the first year, it curves more gradually until somewhere near the fiftieth year of life, when it again begins to fall away sharply, resuming a gradual slope only from about the ninetieth year, until it meets the horizontal axis at year 100. If we draw, for example, the perpendicular AB at age 30, it will cut the curve at C and divide the 79,000 survivors (AC) from the 21,000 so far deceased (BC). Thus we see that the curve divided the lower area, representing the survivors, from the upper, which represents the deceased. Both these areas together constitute the rectangle formed by the two axes.

Here are a few more interesting points about the curve. When will half of the original 100,000 have died? If we draw a horizontal line through scale mark 50 on the vertical axis to meet the curve at D, and from this point drop a perpendicular to the horizontal axis, it will cut this scale at 66. After 66 years, therefore, half of the original 100,000 will be dead. The probability of any one of these people being in either category at age 66 is "even" (1 — 1), or, as we might say, the expectation of life of people age 0 years is 66 years.

By a similar graphical method, we can estimate the expectation of life of a person 30 years old. At the point 30 on the age scale, we erect the perpendicular AC, to meet the curve at C (79,000).

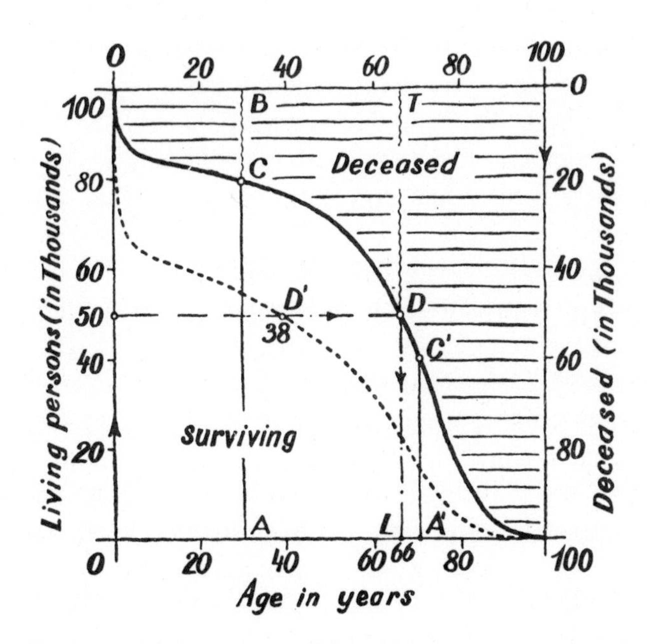

Halving this (let us call it 40,000 for convenience), we now draw through the scale point 40,000 on the vertical axis a horizontal line to cut the curve at C', and from this point drop a perpendicular which crosses the age scale at 71. Thus, in (71–30) years half of all the original people age 30 will have died, and therefore at age 30 the expectation of life is an even chance of 41 years.

THE STRUGGLE BETWEEN LIFE AND DEATH. The graph above shows also, very vividly, the bitter struggle waged by man against death in the fifty years prior to the 1920s, for we have added a dotted curve ($0D'100$), which represents the corresponding figures for the year 1880. This curves its way right across the area which represents the number of survivors in 1924-1926. The area representing the persons who died in 1880 occupies more than half of the complete area of the diagram, instead of, as in 1924-1926, less than half. The enormous infant mortality rate, current in 1880, causes the curve to drop almost vertically right down to 75,000 in the first year of life (note this death rate: 25 % for the first year of life!). The drop then eases off, falling to 65,000 at age five, and later cuts the horizontal line through 50,000 on the vertical scale at the point representing 38 years. This shows that the expectation of life of a new-born child in 1880 was only 38 years, a contrast with 66 in 1924-1926!

If two different periods of time are compared in this way, a graph, such as the one we have been considering, takes on the significance of a battlefield, with the armies of the living and the dead standing on opposing sides. The living fight to keep back the curving front line, as far and for as long as possible, from the frontier of the horizontal axis, on which is marked the age in years. Ultimately, of course, death must triumph, for not one of the 100,000 can escape, but the living fight to hold out for as long as possible. We see in our diagrams the success achieved in in the fifty years or so since 1880: the "territory" won for the living is that between the two curves of morality. Clearly, the bitterest attack was directed on the high infant mortality rate, where death struck earliest and most heavily. After age 90 is reached, death quickly breaks through to the age frontier, for then there is no point in fighting on, and death comes more as a friend than an adversary.

MORTALITY IN VARIOUS AGE GROUPS. If we use the graphical method to show the number of deaths in a given period, which occurs within the various age groups (see p. 254), we can see more readily the relative incidence of mortality as between the age groups. Thus, for 1924-1926, the still high rate of mortality in the first year of life (11,500 deaths); the much less lamentable figure of 120 at age 10 approximately; the rise in incidence between 10 and 20 years of age (about 350 at age 20); the slight lessening to about 320 around the mid-30s; and then the steep rise at age 75 to as many as 2700 deaths. The rapid reduction in the death rate thereafter does not denote a relative improvement in the fortunes of the living: it merely means that fewer die because there are far fewer left alive.

Those interested in figures may note the so-called mean expectation of life $e(x)$ of a person age x years, which gives a better indication of the mortality rate in a given population than the probable expectation of life, mentioned on p. 251. How great is the mean expectation for a person age 60 years? In order to understand fully what we mean by the term "mean expectation," let us take a small group of people age 60, say, 100 in number. Let us suppose that they die as follows:

At	age	60,	100	are	living,	and	45	die	before	reaching	61
"	"	61,	55	"	"	"	30	"	"	"	62
"	"	62,	25	"	"	"	15	"	"	"	63
"	"	63,	10	"	"	"	10	"	"	"	64
"	"	64,	0	"	"	"	0	"	"	"	65.

All have died before reaching their 64th birthday. How many years have been enjoyed by all these people before their deaths? From their 60th birthday the figures are 55 + 25 + 10, a total of 90 years, while the total number of deceased persons is 100. If we assume that the mean time of death during any particular year is at the middle (for some will die earlier, some later in the year), then each person has on an average another half year of life, and therefore for all the 100, another 50 years. The whole group, therefore, enjoys altogether 90 + 50 = 140 years after their 60th birthday. From this we see that any one of these persons has a mean expectation of 1.4 years after reaching the age of 60. (This is, of course, only according to the figures of our hypothetical example.)

In a similar way, the mean expectation for any age group can be calculated from the figures given in the mortality table. As the mean expectation is based on the actual mortality figures for all the age groups, it provides a useful measure for the variations in mortality rates which may occur from year to year. For example, we may compare the mean expectations for two different periods as follows:

	Age in years			
	0	15	45	65
Mean expectation of life for				
1870/80	36	42	21	10
1950	66 (!)	55	28	13

(The relative figures for new-born children, given in column 1, are indeed startling.)

PROBABILITY VALUES FOR LIFE AND DEATH. If, out of 100,000 persons, 11,538 die in the first year of life, the ratio $q = D : L$ (D, number deceased; L, number living) is 11,538 : 100,000 = .115 or 115 per thousand. This ratio $q(x)$ for a given age group is called the "death probability" for that age group. What does it signify? Of 100 new-born babies, about 12 will die before completing their first year of life, but the remaining 88 have a good chance of reaching the age of one year: in other words, the "life probability" of a new-born baby is .88. The life and death probabilities, for a given age group x, are connected by the following relation:

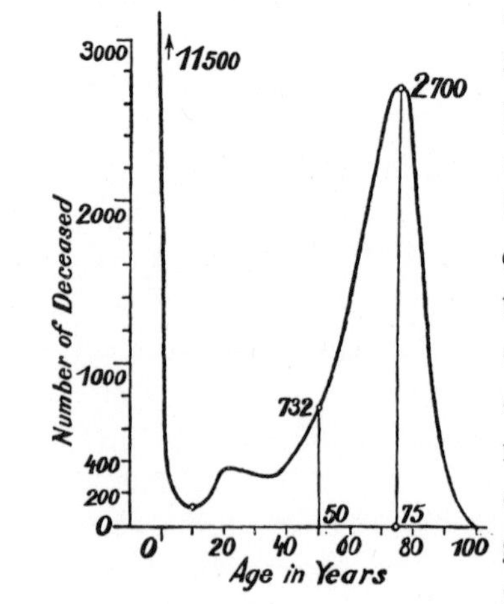

$$p(x) + q(x) = 1.$$

Similarly, the death probability for a person age 30, taken from the mortality table, is 322 : 79,726, or about 4 per thousand; the probability of not dying before age 31, i.e., the life probability $p\,(30)$, is $1 - q\,(30)$ or .966. Not until the age of 50 is reached does the death probability reach 1 %; at age 58 it is 2 %, and thereafter it rises more rapidly. For instance, at 70 it is about 6 %, at 76, 10 %, at 84, 20 % (cf. mortality table on p. 249, column 4; for theory of mathematical probability, p. 155).

If John Smith were now age 50 (for which $q = 1\,\%$), the chances would be 99 : 1 that he would live through his 51st year also, but this does not mean to say that he will definitely do so. Nobody can guarantee this: he might be run over tomorrow by a car. In view of this, the seemingly joyful thought that he stands a 99 % chance of living through the next year is small comfort. According to the principles of mathematical probability we only know that, out of a total of about 70,000 people age 50 (cf. mortality table, p. 249), 700 will die before reaching 51. This law holds good for large numbers, but it gives no guarantee to individuals (cf. p. 165).

Apart from the theoretical considerations, the mortality table still provides the basis on which insurance companies frame their terms for life insurance.

WHAT IS INSURANCE? Insurance is a method by which the individual can be safeguarded, by providing him with the money he needs in an emergency, from reserves collected from a large number of people. Fire, robbery, accident, sickness, inability to work resulting in loss of income, death—all these misfortunes might seriously affect the material well-being of an individual or his dependents. In order to ease such situations an insurance company unites its many clients into a kind of society, and the premiums collected are drawn upon to help any of the "members" in case of need. In a similar way, a building society helps people to buy houses by uniting them into a group of investors and borrowers.

John Smith is familiar with this idea from his associations at the tennis club. When recently a popular fellow member lost his best racquet the others chipped in to buy him a new one: the need of the individual was thus supplied by all the others, and nobody was out much money.

But this was just a small matter. What puzzles John Smith is how an insurance company is prepared to insure him against a car accident, which has not yet happened, and the costs of which are therefore completely unknown. How can indeterminate expenses be shared among the company's other clients? Calmly, however, the insurance agent offers him cover against car accidents, worth say $10,000, for a monthly premium of $3 only! How can the company make such offers, with potential liabilities which are not yet known? The reason is that they base their calculations on two known facts. First there is the obvious truism: "The total payments made by the company over a given period must never exceed the total premiums received from all clients during that period."

The second point is that the insurance cover offered has been based on a thorough statistical investigation into the probability of occurrence of the mishap in question, i.e., car accident, etc. After a consideration of the incidence of such events among the large numbers of motorists on the roads (a sort of mortality table for motorists), the company feels prepared to take a calculated risk, which is usually subject to certain conditions, that the same accident will not happen to too many of their clients. Accordingly, they insure individuals against the appropriate hazard, whatever it might be, and rest reasonably assured that they will only have to pay out in a limited number of cases. The over-all profits could exceed losses, and they invariably do.

Let us take a simple example: John Smith is insured against

accidents while driving his car. Statistical investigations show that out of 20,000 motorists, 400 serious accidents occur each year, and each costs the insurance company on average \$1500. Accordingly, the company states, bearing in mind their policy of liabilities not exceeding assets:

"If all those 20,000 motorists insure with us, we shall have to pay out each year 400 × \$1500 = \$600,000. This sum must be collected from the 20,000 motorists in premiums. The total premiums must therefore be \$600,000, which, shared among 20,000 subscribers, means \$30 each. Add to this about 20% for our administrative costs, profits, etc., this makes the total annual premium \$36, or \$3 monthly."

Of course, the company cannot foretell whether the coming year will turn out in conformity with the statistical evidence of previous years. If the number of accidents falls below the norm, the profits of the company will be correspondingly greater, while if more accidents occur than were expected, profits are reduced. But averaging over several years losses would tend to be canceled by profits, giving a fairly uniform over-all profit for the company. If other circumstances were to change, for example a marked increase in road traffic with resultant increase in the accident rate, the insurance company would then cover itself by increasing premiums.

LIFE INSURANCE brings in similar considerations on the part of the company. However, the situation here is much more complicated than in car-accident insurance, and therefore rather more interesting.

John Smith, you will remember, is 40 years old and proposing to insure his life for \$10,000 over a twenty-year term. At the age of 60 he will receive, if still living, \$3000 but if he dies before that time his widow will receive \$3000 at the time of his death. This is the most common form of policy, because it provides a safeguard against the untimely death of the policy holder, or a nice little nest egg at the end of the term of insurance.

The company calculates the total premium payable on such a policy in two separate parts:

(*a*) The insurance premium needed to provide the lump sum in the event of survival to the end of the term.

(*b*) The premium payable to provide a similar sum in the event of death before the end of the term of insurance.

The calculation in respect of survival is as follows (if you wish, you can omit this and continue from the middle of p. 260):

Mr. Smith is just 40 years of age. According to the mortality table (cf. p. 249), out of 76,313 people aged 40, only 60,883 live to be 60. Assuming that all 76,313 insure with us, we shall have to pay out the following sum to all those who survive in twenty years' time:

$$60{,}883 \times \$3000 = \$182{,}649{,}000.$$

This sum must be subscribed by the clients themselves in their premiums, and therefore the total premium payable by each client is \$182,649,000/76,313, i.e., \$2400.

So far, however, we have ignored the fact that John Smith's premiums earn interest. If all premiums paid were banked, they would work for their living, earning interest at, say, 3 % per annum. (If, on the other hand, the insurance company were to do a little investing, to earn a higher rate than 3 %, say, 10 %, the difference would go to swell the company's profits.) If John Smith's premiums earn interest at 3 % per annum, his actual premium payable would amount to \$2400, less the interest earned at 3 % per annum. (If John Smith were to pay the entire premium on taking out his policy, instead of paying by annual installments, the premium would be reduced by interest to \$1330, and this is in fact his intention.)

N.B. This figure of $1330 is actually a reduced premium, for John Smith would have to invest about $1660 to gain $3000 after twenty years at a rate of interest of 3 % per annum. Remember that we are assessing for the moment only the premium payable for a sum maturing at 60 years of age, and ignoring the clause which gives John Smith's dependents $3000 in the event of his death before reaching 60. German insurance companies make this reduction in premium of $330 in accordance with their practice of issuing "investment only" policies, for with these the policy lapses in the event of death before the end of its term, and the money paid in is forfeited, entirely or in part. This type of policy is rarely issued, for clearly it would attract only such people as bachelors without dependents, who might be prepared to risk the loss of premiums against the chance of gaining an extra $330 on the successful completion of the term of the policy.

ASSESSMENT OF THE PREMIUM PAYABLE IN RESPECT TO THE DEATH-CLAUSE. It is possible that John Smith might die at any time during the twenty-year term of his policy. If, as we assumed earlier, all 76,313 people at age 40 were insured with the company, the total premiums received would have to be sufficient to cover all payments of $3000 to the beneficiaires of those dying before reaching 60. These are estimated in column 3 of the mortality table as follows:

Those dying between 40 and 41 — 408
" " " 41 and 42 — 432
. . . .
" " " 59 and 60 — 1349

The total number of deaths amounts to 14,081, and in each case the beneficiary receives $3000, so that the company's total liability is $42,000,000. Accordingly, to cover this, each policy holder must pay a premium of approximately $550. As it is unlikely, however, that all would die at the same time, the company would not have to pay out the full sum at once, but only a small part of this. The usual practice is that the total assets are deposited in the bank, earning compound interest at, say, 3%, and only the sums needed for payments are drawn out from time to time. The benefit of the interest earned is passed on to policy holders in the form of reduced premiums: in effect they would be asked to contribute only about 77% of $42,000,000, which is approximately $32,000,000 i.e., $425 instead of $550 per policy holder.

We can now assess the combined premium payable by John Smith if he takes out a policy of the type which he has in mind.

Premium to yield $3000 on reaching 60	$1330
Premium to yield $3000 in the event of death before reaching 60	$425
Total	$1755

With this explanation of the workings of insurance, John Smith's suspicions are allayed. It is true that the company cannot tell him how long he is going to remain on earth, but they are able to offer him useful terms, by which he can gain profitable security for his dependants in the event of his untimely death, or else a nice little nest egg to cheer his old age. Remember the principles on which all this is based: the law of probability as exemplified by the mortality table, and the practice of balancing assets and liabilities within a system, whereby the insurance of the many helps to provide for the misfortunes of the few. This is indeed a worthy example of mathematical knowledge applied to the welfare of mankind.

THE SIGNIFICANCE OF STATISTICS. Let us now turn from our study of the practical use of insurance and the calculations upon which policies are based, in order that we may look at the strange "bird's eye view" of life provided by the mortality table.

What is most impressive is the strange amalgam, which the table presents, between the fates of individuals and the law which binds them all. A man dies in extreme old age after a life crowded with incident: his death seems to us just and proper in the ordering of human affairs. But many times also we come across cases where fate has struck suddenly and blindly, taking a young man full of ambitions and plans for his life, or a child not yet out of the cradle. Is there—can there be—any law which governs such seemingly haphazard events?

If we look beyond the individual fates of men, and survey the vital statistics of 100,000 or more, then suddenly we see before us the law in accordance with which we all go to our deaths. The results of this law are revealed to us by the mortality table and its graphical representations, which we have already considered. Each one of us, no matter how or when we shall eventually die, will stand in a huge concourse with many others, as a figure in some mortality table or as a point on a graph.

This is the great revelation of statistical analysis: the fact that the great crowd, the large number, will exhibit a certain character or pattern of behavior, which is not manifested by the units of which the crowd is made. Even death strikes in accordance with a plan, though to us the choice of victims may seem quite haphazard.

The idea is perhaps not unfamiliar to us in our everyday lives. "You cannot see the wood for the trees": in terms of statistics this is to say that the underlying law is obscured by contemplation of many individual instances. Or again, "No individual player is outstanding, but the team always wins its games": statistically the group has qualities quite different from those of its constituent parts. The fact that one man might outlive all his children, when he might have been expected to die before any of them, is only a clear indication that individual instances can contravene the law which rules the multitude, without however making that law invalid.

The law governing death is one of the most fundamental of reality. The task of statistics is to investigate this and other laws of fundamental significance, and to do this it must be applied to every sphere of knowledge and activity, in industry, commerce, biology, medicine, physics, surveying the trend of behavior of large samples of chosen specimens. Nowadays, statistical method is universally used to predict the likelihood of individual behavior by a study of the combined effect in a large sample. Often no other method is practicable: it is not possible to measure the speed of a single molecule or atom of a gas, but it is possible to prepare a diagram showing the distribution of speeds for all the particles within a given volume of that gas.

Let us now proceed to a further point: all statistical results are expressed in terms of numbers. Instead of a person or object or process, we use a number. In the mortality table there is no mention of names, characters, abilities, family backgrounds, or any other personal features—all is reduced to a bald numerical statement of deaths occurring within a given period. Only in this way can the working of the underlying law be examined.

Nowadays many of us dislike the depersonalizing influence of statistical method. We have the idea that it is not we ourselves who matter, but only our numbers in the bureaucratic card index. Numerical indexing, or, often, the "punched card" system, is widely used for such surveys as a census of population. What we fear is that those appointed to govern on our behalf will cease to regard us as living people with feelings of our own. The tax authorities, for instance, may cease to realize our true problems, and may be guided only by numerical abstractions of income, code number, and such. In similar fashion, we deplore the mad chase after bigger and better records in sport, manufacture, and many other fields.

In its true and positive significance, however, all this numerical categorizing is only a means toward the attainment of new and deeper insight into problems which affect mankind. It is rather wonderful that this profound recognition was first stated at the dawn of our western civilization by the Greek philosopher Pythagoras, who said, "Number is the nature of all things." As long as we remember that number is a means toward achieving understanding, and not an end in itself, we shall not fall a prey to false bureaucracy.

With the best of intentions many wrong conclusions can be drawn from statistics. A workman builds a wall in 10 hours, and receives $20 for his labor. This is a proper use for figures, to represent a job of work carried out, but these figures could be manipulated statistically to suggest that 10 workmen could build a similar wall in one hour. But to go beyond the bounds of practical possibility, and suggest that 100 workmen could build it in six minutes, or 1000 workmen in 36 seconds (each being paid a little more than 2 cents for his work), would be to draw a completely false and ridiculous conclusion from the original statement; this is a clear case of abuse of statistics.

How far is it possible to use statistical information without drawing wrong conclusions? It is difficult to answer this question in general terms, because it involves having an appreciation of practical limitations, which vary according to the particular situation under consideration. This appreciation is the difficult art of realizing how far a useful idea may be carried out in practice without exceeding its usefulness. Statistics can reveal the presence of unexpected and fundamental laws, which can be harnessed for the good of mankind; they can also, without being faulty in themselves, be sadly misinterpreted, and give rise to extravagant calculations which have no application in practice. In this respect, the well-known claim that you can prove anything by statistics is not without a grain of truth.

Not every "unreal" calculation, however, is completely meaningless. For instance, if a mechanic working for $3.00 an hour produces 600 piston rings in an hour on his machine, the labor cost per ring will be one half of a penny. This amount is not "really" used to calculate the worker's salary each week, but it is a useful figure for the accountants when they assess production costs.

A STEP INTO INFINITY

"If you wish to penetrate infinity, pursue the finite as far as you can" (Goethe). The infinite lies within us and around us, and there are many paths leading to it. We feel its existence in the music of Beethoven and other great composers, and it is what we mean when we talk of eternity. When we think of God, we think of Him as being somehow beyond the limits of our mortal world. Infinity is the realm of the soul, but when we try to comprehend its nature fully we find ourselves sliding insecurely on the slippery ice of philosophical speculation, for we cannot skate on the ice of infinity, wearing only the clumsy skates of our finite world. Mathematics has proved this: it was the stubborn determination to resolve certain intractable illogicalities in mathematics that led to the study of the concept of infinity, and this in its turn produced an enormous but totally unexpected enrichment of our knowledge. Indeed, it might be said that the greatest single contribution of Western culture to mathematical knowledge has been in the systematic comprehension of infinity, and its utilization for calculating purposes.

IS INFINITY A NUMBER? There arc two roads to infinity—the road "outward" and the road "inward"—the one to the infinitely large, the other to the infinitely small. Counting 1, 2, 3, and on, the outward road, we realize that there can be no last integer, for the next can always be reached by adding one. In the same way, counting "inward," i.e., 1, 1/2, 1/3, etc., it is clear that there is no smallest fraction. These examples illustrate what is meant by the deceptive terms "infinitely large" and "infinitely small": there is in fact no limit to the range of numbers, no top or bottom rungs on the numerical ladder! It might well be said that this is an elusive sort of answer—it is like jumping on the head of your own shadow: you never manage to catch it, for it has always moved on a little farther to elude you. But at least the hazy clouds of mystery surrounding the idea of infinity have been dispelled. Infinity is not a number in the sense of being a definite position on the numerical ladder. A realization of this helps to clear up many contradictions which arise from a misunderstanding of infinity as a number. Consider, for instance, these examples.

A straight line 5 in. in length contains an infinite number of points, and if we add 3 or 5 points there will still be in either case an infinite number. In figures, therefore, $3 + \infty = 5 + \infty$. Hence ∞ can be subtracted from each side of the equation, leaving us with the paradoxical statement that $3 = 5$.

Or a straight line a has an infinite number of points, and so the square a^2 will contain a number of points measured by "an infinite number multiplied by an infinite number." In symbols, $\infty = \infty^2$. Divide both sides of this equation by ∞. The ridiculous result is that $1 = \infty$!

No mathematician would attempt to frame equations of this kind, because infinity is *not* a number: we cannot do calculations with infinity as we do with finite numbers.

The symbol ∞ is the Roman symbol for thousand (CIↃ), adapted slightly and first used by the English mathematician John Wallis in the seventeenth century, to represent infinity.

Often, both roads to infinity appear in the same problem. Draw inside a circle a series of regular figures with 6, 12, 24 . . . etc. as the number of sides. The perimeters of these figures draw closer and closer to the circumference of the circle, as the number of sides increases. The perimeter p is measured by the product of the number of sides n and the length of one side a, i.e., $p = na$. If the number of sides is increased without limit (in symbols $n \to \infty$), then the length of each side decreases also without limit ($a \to 0$). If the "infinitely large" and "infinitely small" values were considered as valid numbers to calculate with, we should have the ridiculous statement $p = 0 \times \infty$, and nobody can do anything with that! It is like saying that a finite value, the perimeter, is measured by the product of nothing and the infinite. The correct way of expressing the line of thought, allowing no symbols and no equation, is as follows:

The perimeter of a regular polygon approximates more and more closely to the circumference of its circumscribing circle, when the number of sides is increased without limit, with a corresponding limitless reduction of the length of each side. This is a perfectly comprehensible statement in which no hazy or confusing use has been made of the word infinity.

The two roads which lead to infinity are vividly portrayed in many anecdotes and folk tales. There is one story of a small bird which flies once every thousand years to sharpen its beak on a strange mountain which consists of one huge diamond. When the whole of the mountain has been worn away, one second of eternity will have passed. (This might be represented in freakish symbolic form as follows: $1/0 = \infty$, where 1 represents the diamond mountain, 0 the single act of beak-sharpening, and ∞ the number of sharpenings.)

In geometrical diagrams, too, there are the two roads to infinity: a straight line can be extended farther and farther outward, to infinity, and within the line is an infinite array of points. But even here we encounter ideas which defy our imagination.

THE ILLUSIVE CONCEPT. We are unable to grasp the concept of perpetual continuity, which is here involved. How many points are there in a 1 in. section of a straight line? An infinite number. And on 2 in.? Again an infinite number. But will there be twice as many? Certainly, this is what we might expect, if—and this is the crux of the matter—they can be counted at all. They cannot of course be counted, but it can be shown that actually there are not twice as many points on the 2 in. section as on the other, but the same number: that is, an infinite number! Draw two parallel lines *AB* and *A'B'*, one below the other as shown, and *A'B'* twice as long as *AB*. Now join *A'A* and *B'B* and extend them to cross at *S*. Think of *SAA'* as a ray of light from the source *S* passing over *AB* to *SBB'*. Every point *P* on *AB*, through which the ray passes, will have a corresponding point *P'* on *A'B'*, and conversely to every point on *A'B'* corresponds one and only one point on *AB*. When the ray of light reaches the final position *SBB'*, it has passed over every point on *AB* and an equal number of points on *A'B'*. This argument would hold good, even if the lines *SAA'* and *SBB'* were extended an infinite distance to enclose a line of infinite length: this line also would have the same number—an infinite number—of points on it!

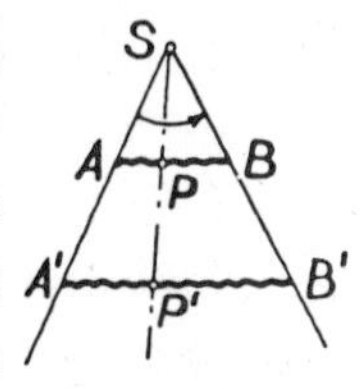

SOME VARIATIONS ON THE SAME THEME. If the line *AB* is bent at *C*, a ray of light emanating from *S* would pass through all points on its length, and through all the corresponding points on the straight line of infinite length which lies at infinity. If, moreover, the straight line *AB* is curved into a circle with *S* as center, the revolving ray of light would show that the circumferences of all circles with a common center at *S*, no matter what their radii might be, would still have the same number—an infinite number—of points on them!

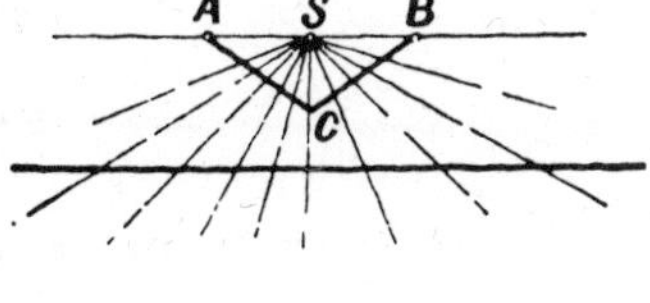

In these examples the idea of a totality ceases to have any meaning. Our powers of visualization also seem to be paralyzed, for as we usually visualize a straight line we think of it as rather like a string of pearls, with points separate and distinct from one another, but placed side by side and touching, each point followed by a next. According to this concept we assume, naturally enough, that a longer line has more points in it than a shorter one, but our demonstrations have shown that such is not the case: the points of the line must therefore be differently constituted, not one after another but continuous, connected throughout in space without interval or break. This is a difficult concept, which defies our abilities of visualization. Philosophers have for long concerned themselves with this novel concept, to which they give the name "continuum."

Mathematical thought can help us somewhat to clarify our ideas about continuum. As shown in the top diagram on p. 267, there is a "one-to-one correspondence" between the points on AB and those on $A'B'$. If a similar type of correspondence can be observed between the constituent points of two separate infinite sets, then these are called "corresponding sets," as for example the sets of points which make up the lines AB and $A'B'$. This term is more suitable than any other which might suggest the idea of a (finite) total number, for it is this very misconception which gives rise to confusion and misunderstanding in our minds.

It has been established that one-to-one correspondence exists between the points on one side of a square and those distributed on its surface area; also that there is one-to-one correspondence between points on one edge of a cube and those enclosed within its volume. It is therefore true to state that the set of points on a line corresponds to the set distributed on a plane surface, or even contained within a cube. All three sets, in space of one, two, or three dimensions, illustrate the quality of continuity.

The infinite sequence of the integers 1, 2, 3, etc. does not possess this quality. If it had the same continuity, the points on a line could be counted by being placed in one-to-one correspondence with the integers, and there would be a final point. Obviously this is not possible. However, if the even integers are extracted from the sequence of the natural numbers, thus removing "half" of them, they can be regarded as the 1st, 2nd, 3rd, etc. even numbers, and we have immediate evidence of one-to-one correspondence with the sequence of all integers. The infinite set of even numbers can therefore be said to correspond to the infinite set of natural numbers, and both sets will extend to infinity. From this it can be seen that the mathematical concept of continuity demolishes the illogicality suggested by the idea of total number, according to which the half (i.e., the set of even numbers) would seem to be as numerous as the whole (i.e., the set of all the integers)!

This one-to-one correspondence between the unbounded set of natural numbers and the unbounded set of even numbers is a characteristic of their infinite nature, for there is no such correspondence between finite sets of, say, 100 dried peas and a selection from them of 10 peas. It is quite impossible to say of two such sets that the constituents of one in any way correspond to those of the other.

Remember that we have said that it is not possible to enumerate the constituents of a continuous set of points. We shall now try to explain how it is possible to understand the concept of continuity. It is done by thinking in terms of what can be enumerated. If every possible number could be represented by a point on a straight line, much as is done with whole numbers on the scales put on the axes of graphs, the line would be filled with a continuous series of points.

Now consider the question, how many numbers are there in the interval from .5 to 1? The answer is, of course, an infinite number. If the interval is shortened, from .5 to .6, there is still an infinite number of intermediate points, and similarly with a still shorter interval. We conclude therefore that, however short the interval may be, it still contains an infinite number of points. As every number can be represented by a point on a line, it can be further understood that to any one point there can be no neighbor, because to any one number there is no next number, since whatever number is selected as a possible next in size, there is still an infinite number of values between the two.

In this way we can grasp the concept of continuity with our minds, and that in fact is all we can do, for it is impossible to visualize a continuous series of points, any more than we can visualize the following problems.

The points 0 and 1 are marked at the ends of a straight line. Suppose we now remove these end points so that the line has neither start nor finish, and yet it exists for we did not remove all of it, but only its ends. Such are the paradoxes of infinite sets, and here are two more examples to show how difficult, nay impossible, it is to visualize a continuum.

THE PUZZLE OF THE LARGE AND SMALL WHEELS. On the side of a large pulley wheel a smaller one is firmly fixed, both on the same axis. The ratio of their diameters, and therefore also their circumferences, is 2 : 1. Suppose we roll the large wheel along a straight edge, until it has completed one revolution. The distance rolled, AB, is equal to its circumference. In the

course of this operation the smaller wheel has also completed one revolution, and has moved a distance $A'B'$, which is equal to AB. This is impossible because it suggests that the circumference of the smaller wheel is equal to that of the larger, whereas in fact it is only half as long. Where has that other half come from?

In fact, the smaller wheel does not merely roll: it also slides. In the circumstances that we have described, the distance rolled equals the distance slid, but we do not notice the sliding because it takes place simultaneously with the rotating, and however short the distance rolled by the larger wheel, the smaller one will still roll *and* slide to keep up with it.

Certain ideas associated with this arrangement of large and small wheels give rise to even more intriguing phenomena:

When the radius of the smaller wheel is zero, it does not roll at all, but only slides. Now if the smaller wheel rolls instead of the larger ($A'B'$ being the line rolled on), then the length rolled out must shrink from the track AB of the big wheel to the $A'B'$ of the smaller, and to get round in time all points on the circumference of the larger wheel must move faster; to use motorists' phraseology, the larger wheel is subjected to "wheel spin." In the limiting case, with the radius of the small wheel zero, the larger does *not* move forward at all, but simply rotates at a standstill, like a car wheel in loose sand.

Let us now consider the relationship between the two wheels from a different point of view, which will help us to understand what happens. Fixed in the middle of a large equilateral triangle ABC is a smaller equilateral triangle $A'B'C'$ (diagram *a*, below). If the large triangle is now tipped over twice to the right, using first B and then C as pivots, then it has covered altogether the distance $ABCA$, equal to its own perimeter. The small triangle, however, has covered only a part of its rolling distance $A'B'C'A'$: the parts it actually covers, $A'B'$, $B'C'$, $C'A'$, are interrupted by spaces $B'B$, $C'C$. These spaces are rather like the expansion gaps between the ends of rails on a railway track. Now keep the perimeter the same length, but double the number of corners; in other words, consider a hexagon $ABCDEF$ with a smaller concentric hexagon $A'B'C'D'E'F'$, whose sides are half those of

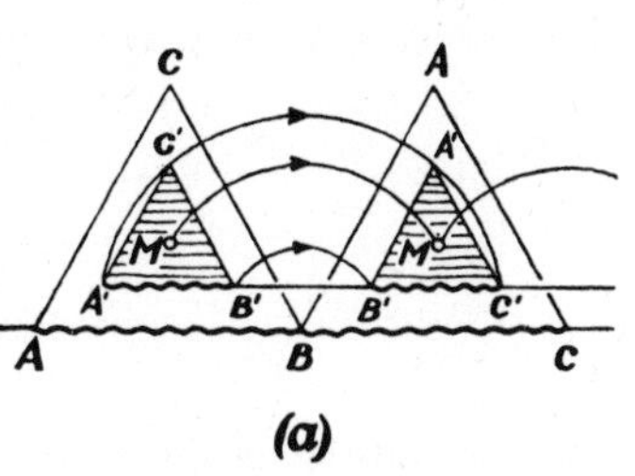

(a)

the larger (diagram *b*). Let us now roll the larger hexagon on its successive corners, starting with *B*, so that its whole perimeter is measured out along the straight line *ABC . . . A*. Considering the successive positions of the hexagon after each of its six "topples," there appears between the sides of the smaller hexagon a series of six gaps, like the expansion gaps between rails. The "gaps" are smaller than they were in the case of the triangle, while the arc *MM* is flatter than it was in that former example (diagram *a*). Gaps and sides together make up a length equal to the perimeter of the larger hexagon.

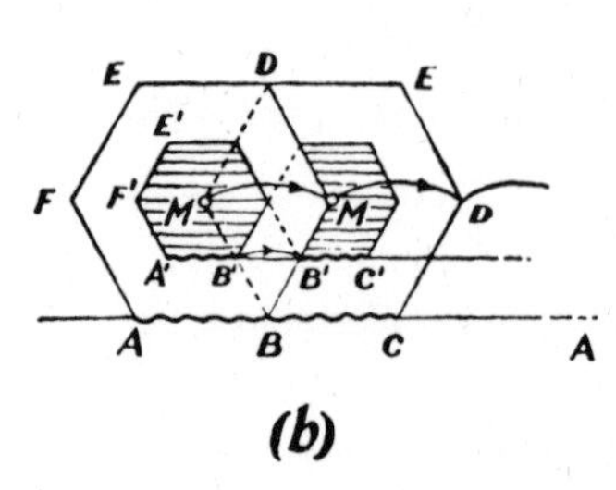

(b)

It is now clear what happens as the number of corners (and therefore sides) is progressively doubled. When the perimeter of the large polygon is rolled out on the line *A . . . A*, the gaps and sides of the smaller polygon make up a length equal to the perimeter of the larger, and the arcs described by the centers grow steadily flatter.

What happens in the limiting case, when the polygon has become a circle? The side of the polygon has shrunk to a single point, the point of contact of the circle with the ground. The side of the smaller polygon has also shrunk to a point, and the gap likewise, while the path of the center is straightened out. The path rolled out by the small circle is as before incomplete, and is supplemented by the "gap points," with a continuous succession of infinitesimal rolls and slides. As points have no magnitude, the distance *A′B′C′A′* consists of "gap points" and "covered points" in continuity! And we well know by now that it is pointless to attempt to visualize this situation!

ACHILLES' RACE WITH THE TORTOISE. This curious paradox, stated by the Greek philosopher Zeno of Elea some 2500 years ago, makes the startling claim that, if the fleet-footed Achilles were to give a slow, ponderous tortoise a head start, he would be quite unable to overtake it! It is possible to give some mathematical justification of this strange assertion, if we invoke the aid of the continuum. Let us suppose that Achilles can run twelve times as fast as the tortoise, which is given a start of 5 mi. The race begins with Achilles starting from A_0 and the tortoise from T_1, 5 mi. away. We can argue that Achilles cannot overtake the tortoise, for while he runs from A_0 to A_1, the tortoise creeps forward from T_1 to T_2, thus maintaining a lead, albeit less than 5 mi. In fact, the lead is now 5/12 mi. So the race continues, and when Achilles has run from A_1 to A_2, the tortoise still keeps his lead, much smaller now ($5/12^2 = 5/144$), but a lead none the less. Subsequently the lead diminishes further, from 5/144 to 5/1728 and then to 5/20,736

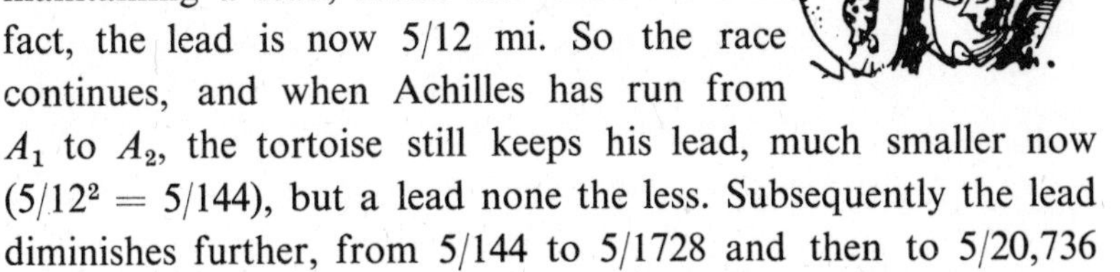

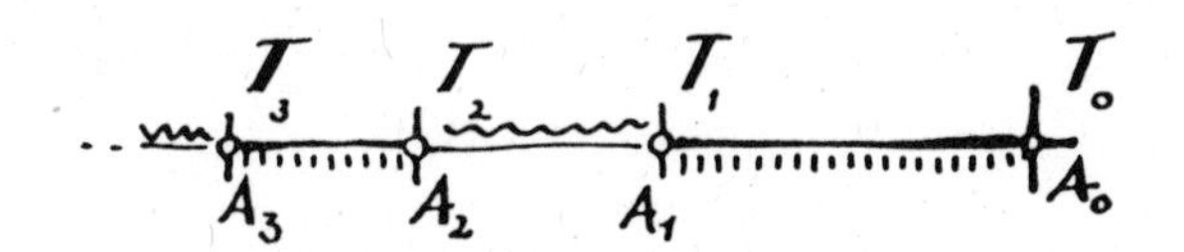

and so on, but it never completely disappears. If we could imagine a course of infinite length, containing therefore an infinite number of stretches, the tortoise's lead would certainly be reduced to an infinitesimal size, but it would still be a lead—or so one might suppose! In actual fact, this reasoning is quite erroneous: we can observe a race of this kind at any time, by watching the hands of a clock. If the minute hand (fleet-footed Achilles) were to set off in pursuit of the hour hand (that ponderous tortoise), their respective starting positions being as for one o'clock, the minute hand soon overtakes its rival at precisely 5 and 5/11 minutes past. You can check this of course with your own watch, and it can also be proved by calculations, as will be seen on p. 276.

Why should Zeno attempt to convince us of something that is patently false? Was it to set us thinking? Actually, his purpose was to expose the contradiction, ever present in our world, between "that which is and that which seems to be." Zeno had a theory, much supported in his day, that the true nature of the world resided in that which was at rest: movement was to him a snare and a delusion. Putting this another way, only things at rest are real and capable of comprehension; movement cannot be comprehended, so it simply does not exist. We can understand that according to the argument Achilles can never overtake the tortoise: that he does in fact do so was proof enough to Zeno, not that our logical powers are at fault, but that movement is deceptive and illusory!

The ordinary man may well find it difficult to follow such curious complexities of thought. Zeno is, of course, touching on the difficult ideas of continuum and infinity, which mathematicians have been able to explain satisfactorily (at any rate for their own purposes) only in modern times. It is these ideas which we are now trying to explain, and in order to do this we will consider another example.

A market place is a square with side 100 yards. In order to cross it from *A* to *C*, the quickest route is along the diagonal *AC* (in yards $100\sqrt{2} = 141.4$), but there is another route round the sides via *B*, 200 yards in length, and so nearly 60 yards farther than by the diagonal route.

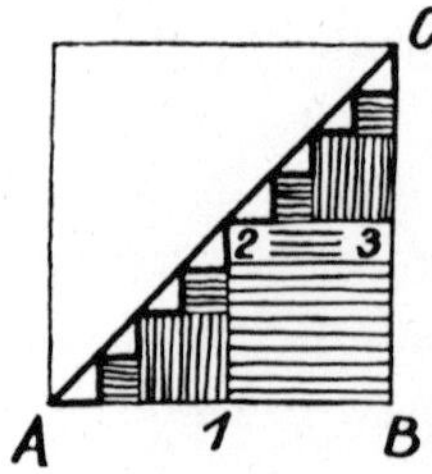

C
2
3
A
1
B

Nevertheless, we can "prove" that both routes must be of the same length. If you follow the zigzag course *A*123*C*, like a section of a flight of stairs, the distance covered is 200 yards. If the number of steps is increased, and the size of step decreased in proportion, the total distance still remains at 200 yards. But an infinite number of infinitesimally small steps would be no different from the diagonal, 141.4 yards in length, and yet the distance would still be 200 yards. Which is right: 200 or 141 yards?

You may well wonder why we should plunge into such unnecessary difficulties over a matter that is so completely obvious, and can be checked by measurement.

Obvious it may be to our eyes, which are limited by our restricted environment, but the dark, remote, transitional world, where our powers of visualization forsake us, is where the change from zigzag line to straight line takes place, and it is here that we are quite unable to resolve the contradiction. In actual fact our powers of visualization have led us astray. However small and numerous the zigzags may be, such a course still retains its step-like nature, and would never be a straight line.

Nevertheless, the final step across the dividing line between finite and infinite is obscured in our minds. Let us try to promote a clearer understanding by the use of numbers.

In the sequence of fractions, $f = 1, \frac{1}{2}, \frac{1}{3}, \frac{1}{4} \ldots$, the greater the denominator, the smaller the fraction becomes. We can express it in this way: as the denominator approaches infinity, the value of f approaches 0. The number 0 thus becomes the "retaining wall" or "limit" for the infinite sequence of fractions. The fractions are all ranged on one side of this wall, and there is an infinite number of them. For instance, even between the values 0 and 1/1,000,000 lies an infinite number of fractions, all with denominators greater than 1,000,000. It is impossible to specify any fraction which lies closer to 0 than all others, and which will not allow the interpolation of other smaller fractions between itself and 0.

This is a fundamental truth. If for any infinite sequence there is specified a similar "retaining wall," it is termed the limiting value, or more simply the limit. Thus, the limit of the above sequence of fractions is 0. So it is that this new concept of limiting value becomes associated with the idea of an infinite (i.e., never-ending) series of numbers, enabling us to think quite clearly in terms of a limit or transitional point, dividing the finite from the infinite. Can there be two limits to an infinite sequence, one at either end, or only one?

Before we attempt to answer this question, let us consider an example where no limit is possible, and that is the case of the sequence of natural numbers 1, 2, 3, 4, etc. We cannot specify here any number which limits the sequence on one side, and acts as a retaining wall. On either side of any number in the sequence lies an infinite number of terms (we are assuming of course the inclusion of negative numbers in the sequence). The same is true of the zigzag path mentioned earlier: the sums of the steps, however numerous they may be, form the sequence of equal values, 200, 200, 200, etc.: they are not limited by the number 141.4 as is the diagonal. Thus the diagonal does not represent the transition into the finite of the infinite series of zigzag lines, as our powers of visualization seem to suggest.

Let us now return to the race between the two hands of the clock. We shall tabulate first the values of the decreasing lead, held by the hour hand, as it moves round in competition with the faster minute hand (cf. the tortoise's lead, p. 273). Secondly, we will tabulate the cumulative sum of these values.

Section of course	*Lead*	*Cumulative total*
1st	5/12 = 0.416666	0.416666
2nd	5/144 = 0.034722	0.451388
3rd	5/1728 = 0.002893	0.454281
4th	5/20,736 = 0.000241	0.454522
	etc.	

It can be established by simple arithmetic that the endless numerical sequence in the last column of this table approaches closer and closer to the limiting value 0.454545 = 5/11. This is the finite "retaining wall" of this infinite sequence, and this is why the minute hand catches up with the hour hand, as soon as the latter has moved 5/11th of a minute past its starting point. Hence we can see how the concept of limiting value disproves the conclusion that Achilles can never catch the tortoise.

CALCULATIONS INVOLVING INFINITY. The limiting value of the sequence tabulated above is called either the "limiting sum" of the sequence in Column 2 or, as it is sometimes expressed, "the sum to infinity" of the sequence. This type of sum is by definition quite different from our usual notion of what is meant by the word.

Mathematicians have worked out a whole range of types of limiting values, and the results are extensively used in working out the "derivative" and "integral" of a function. They have thereby gained unexpectedly new insight into the structure of curves, and their gradients, and areas formed by them. The use of limiting values has enabled mathematicians to tame the concept of infinity and apply it in many useful ways. By its aid, for instance, can be calculated the length of curved lines, however complicated their paths, and also the areas of surfaces bounded by curves. In earlier times this could be done only in a very few special instances.

The mathematicians of the ancient world used much the same method in calculating the circumference of a circle, although they did not understand the process quite as clearly as we do today. In calculating the circumference of a circle with a known diameter the problem is approached via an infinite sequence of regular polygons, which either circumscribe or are contained within the circle. Their perimeters form two infinite sequences which approach from both sides a certain limiting value, which is the circumference of the circle. It is a curious fact, illuminated for us by our analysis of infinity, that this finite measurement can be determined only by a calculation involving infinity.

Although the determination of limiting values involves purely numerical processes, the study of geometry has also given rise to new and profound ideas, as a result of introducing the concept of infinity. We will examine just one illustration of this.

THE RING OF INFINITY. So far we have considered only roads which lead to infinity, but we shall now consider a path which leads back from infinity into the finite. Round a point S, which

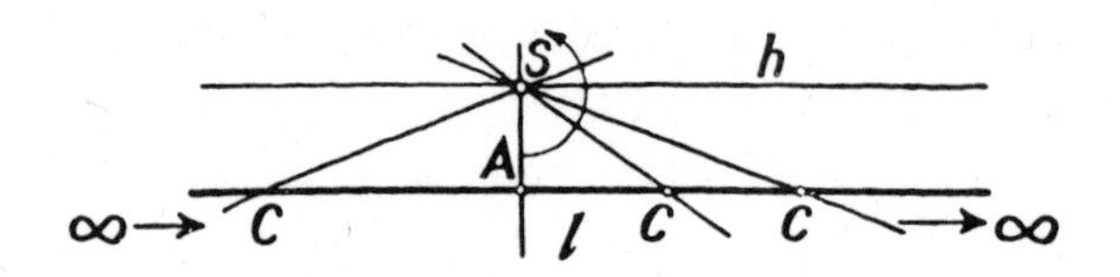

lies outside a straight line l, a second straight line h is revolved in a counter-clockwise direction. Eventually it cuts the line l at a point C which, as h continues to revolve, moves farther and farther along the line l. When h is once more parallel to l, the point C has moved off to infinity, but if h continues to revolve C reappears from the left. It is as if this point has in fact traveled round in a complete circle—the ring of infinity!

Pursuing this idea further, there is a one-to-one correspondence between each position of the line h and of the point C, and vice versa. C is at the intersection of lines l and h, and if h is parallel to l the correspondence must still hold: parallel straight lines will intersect at points at infinity!

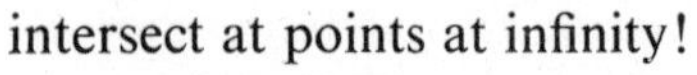

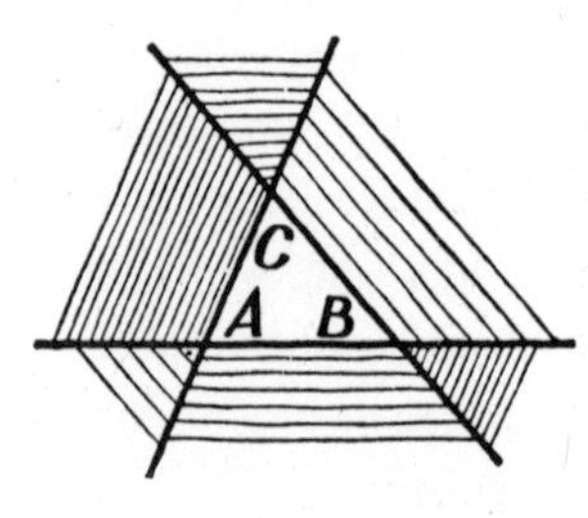

A straight line, if extended both ways to infinity, has, as we might say, only one vanishing point, i.e., the point at infinity. This being so, we can see how the six areas formed by the three lines, which are the sides of a triangle, should not be considered as six distinct areas, but only three, since the twin ends of each of the three original lines will coincide if extended to infinity. This gives only four distinct areas, counting the interior of the original triangle, and not seven, as one would at first suppose. You can check this with the aid of the diagram at the bottom of p. 278, and a little imagination: extend the line *AB* both ways to infinity; *A* and *B* will move round the ring of infinity to meet one another at *C*, where once more they emerge into the finite, and the same is true of *CA* (*B*) and *CB* (*A*). The different kinds of shading help to indicate the areas in each case.

The different sections of a cone are in the same way connected by the ring of infinity. The point *A′* of the circle begins to move along the extension of the diameter *AA′*, and as long as *A′* remains in the finite, an ellipse is formed; but when *A′* reaches infinity, the section is a parabola, and when *A′* returns to the finite, coming from the left, it is a hyperbola. The same effect would be produced by stretching an ellipse out to infinity and back again.

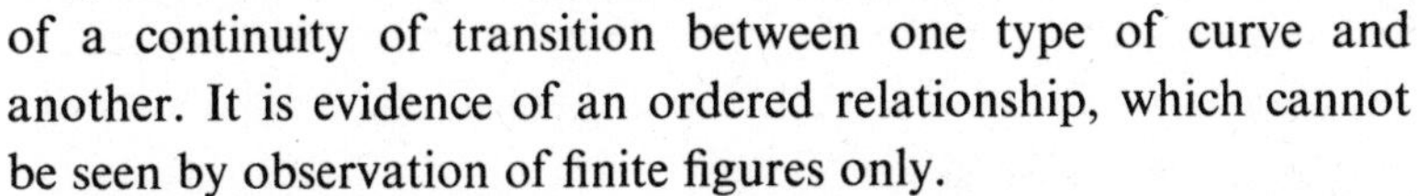

The insight which we gain here by introducing the concept of infinity to geometrical diagrams enables us to appreciate the existence of a continuity of transition between one type of curve and another. It is evidence of an ordered relationship, which cannot be seen by observation of finite figures only.

In conclusion let us marvel that the human intellect has been able to comprehend this profound interrelation, which is due entirely to our ability to tame and make useful application of that strange concept of the infinite. It is indeed a most worthy testimonial to man's intellectual endeavors, his striving ever to throw aside the false logic based on emotion and crack-brained speculation, so that he may arrive at the truth which is the nourishment of the free mind.

EPILOGUE: THE SIGNIFICANCE OF MATHEMATICS

So ends our expedition into the broad land of Mathematics. We have not seen everything there is to see, but as a walk in the country helps us to breathe in the fresh air, marvel at the sky above, and sense the spirit and the forces which pervade all nature, on our trip also you may have had similar experience. You have had explained to you how the mathematician thinks, what he thinks about, and how he enlists the aid of mathematics, without ever exhausting its rich potential.

You have also seen something of many individual problems, and how they are resolved by mathematics, and you will surely have recognized the presence of the two fundamental concepts of number and form. But still, looking back on it all, you will ask, "What is mathematics?"

It is the study of order, and is therefore a direct expression of the organizing powers of man. Many fundamental concepts of our minds are almost intuitive, for instance "one," "many," "number," "whole," "part," "circle," "square," "straight line," etc. To see each of these in their original simplicity, and investigate the limitless interweaving of their relationships: these are the great intellectual exercises of mathematics. Creatively the intellect uses all fundamental concepts to give form and clarity to all that is apparently without form or explanation, to all that sea of confused observations and feelings that is constantly striving to swamp the mind and spirit of mankind.

The "idea" of the circle was not derived by man from actual observations, such as the circular shape of flowers; on the contrary, his organizing intellect recognized all round things as possessing the fundamental shape of the circle. Where else, if not from the realm of human intellect, would the circle have gained its prime significance as a complete and perfect line, with every part controlled from one central point? This perfect interrelation of center and circumference was brilliantly exemplified by the ancient Greek theater, in which the audience was seated in circular tiers around the players, who could thus command the full attention of everyone.

It should not surprise us to encounter mathematics in every branch of human activity, in industry and commerce, in learning and art. By its aid the mariner fixes his position at sea, the merchant calculates his profit, and the engineer builds his machines. But its true significance does not lie in practical use as most people believe. How many prime numbers are there? Here is a question that won't help you to earn a penny, nor will the answer: an infinite number. Though without practical value, the solution of this problem made its discoverer Euclid immortal (p. 58).

Would you consider the wonderful rose window in Strasbourg Cathedral useful or practical? Of course not, and here we have a perfect analogy to help our understanding of the deeper significance of mathematics. Both are manifestations of the questing human spirit, which seeks to create form and order where none previously existed, and which seeks to penetrate yet higher and more elaborate realms of form through understanding.

The Greek word *mathematike* originally meant "(the art of) teachable knowledge." Teachable implies "that which is organized," and so the Greek word had in fact the meaning which we here ascribe to it. Nevertheless, our word "mathematics" has somehow remained an alien, its real meaning neither understood nor appreciated by most laymen. It has acquired something of the musty smell of the schoolroom, making people think that in order to understand its nature they must study a branch of knowledge completely divorced from real life. Yet mathematics results from a natural tendency of the human mind, which has helped to make us what we are. How many women there are who profess a hatred of "cold, calculating mathematics," and yet bring a delicate sensitivity to their arrangements of a table or a vase of flowers! How well they understand the importance of symmetry, the balancing of shapes and the beauty of varied proportions. How many women are skilled in devising ornamental designs, which involve the most abstract mathematical patterns? Yet they would be astonished if their activities were called mathematical. Such is the effect of the word, and yet we have no other to take its place. If you contend that all these feminine activities are purely artistic, you still cannot deny that one of the basic concerns of art is with form or shape, and thus there is bound to be a strong link with mathematics. In the rose window of Strasbourg, what can be attributed to art, and what to mathematical thought? Can the two elements be separated?

If mathematics stems directly from a natural tendency in human beings, how is it that there is such widespread revulsion against it? It is because, as in music, and far more than in any other subject, intuition must be carefully controlled and trained: true appreciation is entirely a matter of careful teaching. Geography and history might easily be self-taught: playing the cello or learning mathematics can rarely be done that way.

Man has a natural talent for detecting order in his world and and this helps us to understand why mathematics is independent of both people and time. Modern man has been able to develop and elaborate the ideas of the ancient Greeks. The Arabs sounded chords of thought which have reverberated down the centuries to us. We must thank India for our number symbols and the simple calculating techniques.

At one time, in the eighteenth century, mathematics constituted an intellectual link between all the nations of Europe, for after all the spirit of Western humanism was, and still is in large part, a mathematical spirit. Its good side is manifest in the building of cathedrals and bridges, the bad side in the forging of cannon and all the insane architecture of mass destruction.

For alongside the noble significance of mathematics—"Number is the nature of all things" (Pythagoras), which means that all shapes are made comprehensible by their relationship through number to other shapes, the tree by the relation between trunk and crown, the temple by the relation between its various parts—alongside this noble significance exists the execration of number, which seeks not order but subjection, with questionnaire and card index, with the measuring of every human endeavor against the yardstick of money (greatest! quickest! cheapest!), with the obdurate, inhuman machinations of bureaucracy. These typify the satanic aspects of number, and are opposed by its noble aims.

It is the sublime spirit in man, from which mathematics arose, that makes it as impossible to deny a mathematical truth, as it is to deny a dictate of the conscience. It is completely unassailable, and from its very truth issues forth its beauty. There is an old saying, "Beauty is the shining light of truth." Viewed in this exalted sense mathematics becomes "a reflection of the Spirit of God. Men have a part in it because man was fashioned by God in His own image" (Kepler).

Index